COURSE I

mSpace Volume 1

Printed in the U.S.A.

ISBN 978-0-545-84852-7

3 4 5 6 7 8 9 10 14 23 22 21 20 19 18 17 16

490429

Program Overview

MATH 180 features high-interest themes, stories, and careers.

Multiplicative Thinking

Buzz Worthy

CAREER CLUSTER
Marketing and Advertising

Social Climbers Artists, inventors, and entrepreneurs use social media to turn their visions and business ideas into reality.

The Distributive Property

Designing Your World

CAREER CLUSTER
Art and Design

Paint the Town Artists use detailed grids and a lot of help to take on a larger-than-life project in the favelas of Rio de Janeiro, Brazil.

Division

On a Mission

CAREER CLUSTER
Community and Public Service

Global Soap One man is on a mission to prevent illness by putting a bar of recycled soap in every child's hand.

Fraction Concepts

Be My Guest

CAREER CLUSTER
Hospitality and Tourism

Making the Cut A group of high school chefs use discipline and careful measurements to take their culinary skills to the next level.

Fraction Relationships

Doctor's Orders

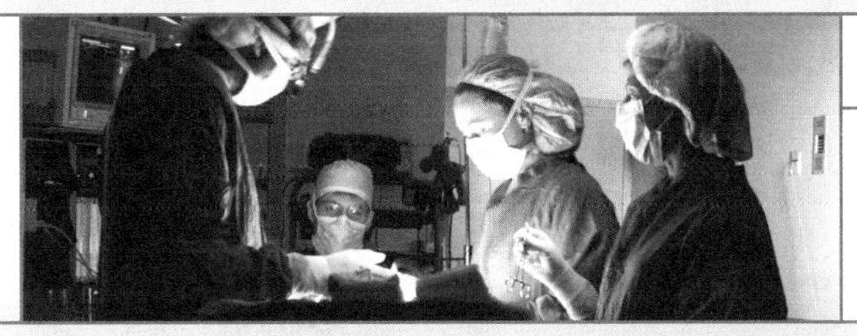

CAREER CLUSTER
Health and Medicine

Have a Heart Every day is a race against time for transplant doctors, their patients, and families.

Fraction Multiplication and Division

Out of This World

CAREER CLUSTER
Science and Engineering

Destination: Mars Landing a rover on Mars is just the beginning of NASA's big plans for exploring the Red Planet.

Decimals and Place Value

How Does It Work?

CAREER CLUSTER
Computers and Technology

Against the Clock It takes a sophisticated combination of precise timing and technology to measure the speed of an Olympic champion.

Decimal Operations

You're the Boss

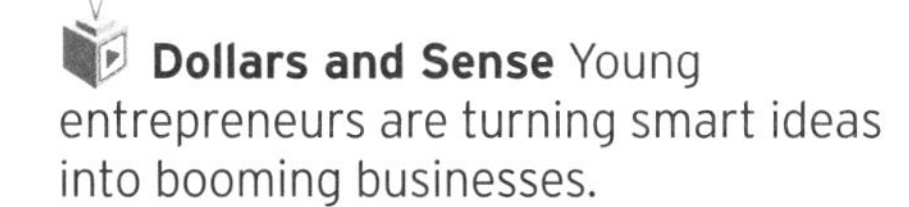

CAREER CLUSTER
Business and Management

Dollars and Sense Young entrepreneurs are turning smart ideas into booming businesses.

Both Sides of Zero

Final Frontier

CAREER CLUSTER
Environmental Science

Living Below Zero Antarctica's extreme temperatures and landscape are a daily challenge for the researchers and scientists who work there.

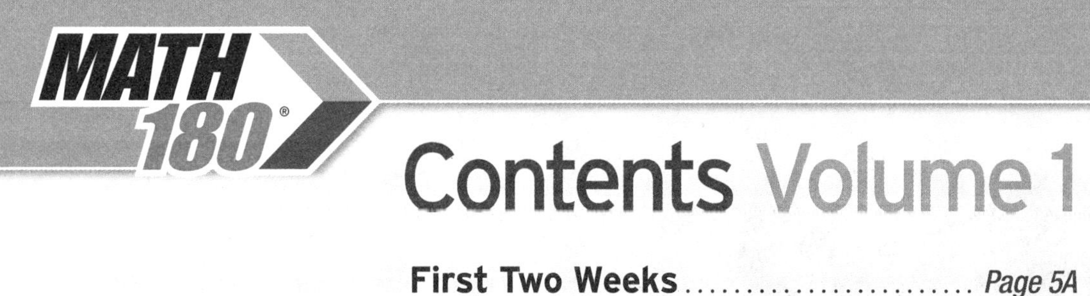

Contents Volume 1

Take the Mindset Scan

THIS IS NOT A TEST!
It is an opinion survey about your beliefs, goals, and thoughts on intelligence.

Some people believe that you are born with or without certain skills. Others believe that you can become better at anything through hard work and effort. Let's find out what you think.

> **Decide how much you agree or disagree with each statement. Circle and write your answer.**

RATING SCALE | Choose a number on the left to agree or on the right to disagree.

	Statement	Agree a lot	Agree	Agree a little	Disagree a little	Disagree	Disagree a lot	PROFILE NUMBER
A	No matter how much intelligence you have, you can always change it a good deal.	6	5	4	3	2	1	
B	You can learn new things, but you cannot really change your basic level of intelligence.	1	2	3	4	5	6	
C	I like my work best when it makes me think hard.	6	5	4	3	2	1	
D	I like my work best when I can do it really well without too much trouble.	1	2	3	4	5	6	
E	I like work that I'll learn from even if I make a lot of mistakes.	6	5	4	3	2	1	
F	I like my work best when I can do it perfectly without any mistakes.	1	2	3	4	5	6	
G	When something is hard, it just makes me want to work more on it, not less.	6	5	4	3	2	1	
H	To tell the truth, when I work hard, it makes me feel as though I'm not very smart.	1	2	3	4	5	6	

> **Add up all the profile numbers and write the total.**

TOTAL

Determine Your Mindset

› **If your profile number falls into this range:**

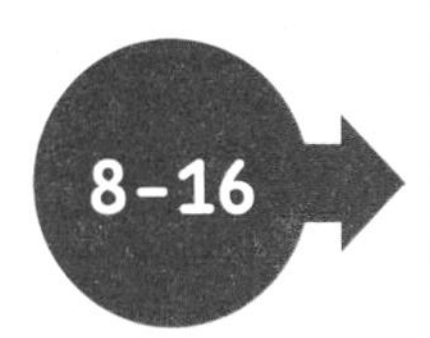

You strongly believe that your intelligence is fixed—it doesn't change much. If you can't perform perfectly, you would rather not do something. You think smart people don't have to work hard.

You think that your intelligence doesn't change much. You prefer not to make mistakes if you can help it, and you also don't really like to put in a lot of work. You think learning should be easy.

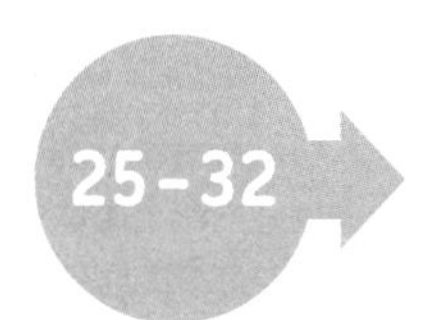

You are unsure about whether you can change your intelligence. You care about your performance and you also want to learn, but you don't really want to have to work too hard for it.

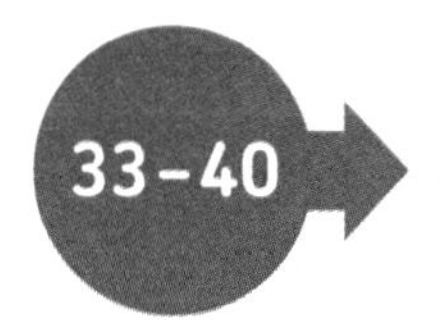

You believe that you can increase your intelligence. You care about learning and you're willing to work hard. You want to do well, but you think it's more important to learn than to always perform well.

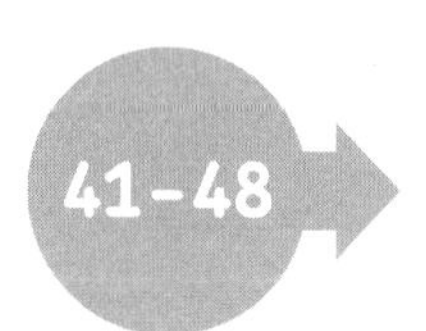

You really feel sure that you can increase your intelligence by learning and you like a challenge. You believe that the best way to learn is to work hard, and you don't mind making mistakes while you do it.

Compare Two Mindsets

› **Fill in both definitions and answer the questions below.**

FIXED Mindset

means that ______________________

GROWTH Mindset

means that ______________________

Reflection Questions

Ⓐ Which survey question surprised you?

I was surprised by the question about ______________________

because ______________________

Ⓑ What would you like to learn about mindsets?

I would like to learn about ______________________

because ______________________

Interest Inventory

> Complete the sentences for yourself and two classmates.

	Me	Classmate 1	Classmate 2
Name			
Outside of school I like to . . .			
One special talent I or someone in my family has is . . .			
My favorite website is . . .			
One thing that makes me happy is . . .			

Favorite Numbers

> Record three classmates' names and favorite numbers on the shirts. Explain their choices.

DAY 4

Using Your Brain

Use a Growth Mindset to complete these sentences.

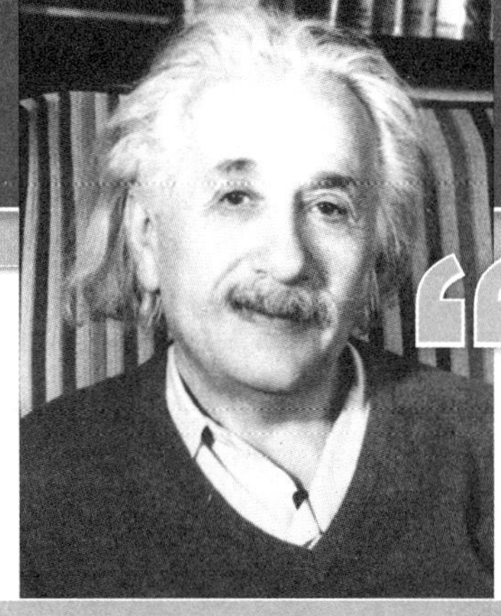

"Anyone who has never made a mistake has never tried anything new."

Albert Einstein
Nobel Prize–winning scientist and mathematician

	When math is challenging I should... *(check one)*		I know this because...
1	☐ Avoid the challenge	☐ Take on the challenge	
2	☐ Give up easily	☐ Keep trying	
3	☐ Put in little effort	☐ Put in my full effort	
4	☐ Not ask my teacher for extra help and support	☐ Ask my teacher for extra help and support	
5	☐ Ignore comments from my teachers	☐ Learn from comments from my teachers	
6	☐ Get upset by the success of others	☐ Learn from the success of others	

Reflection Questions

Ⓐ How can you use a Growth Mindset when you study math?

I can use a Growth Mindset by ______________________________

____

____

____

____

____

Ⓑ What will you do the next time you face challenges in math class?

I will meet challenges in math by ______________________________

____

____

____

____

____

DAY 5

I'll Tell You

> Fill in the text messages below with two facts and one opinion about yourself.

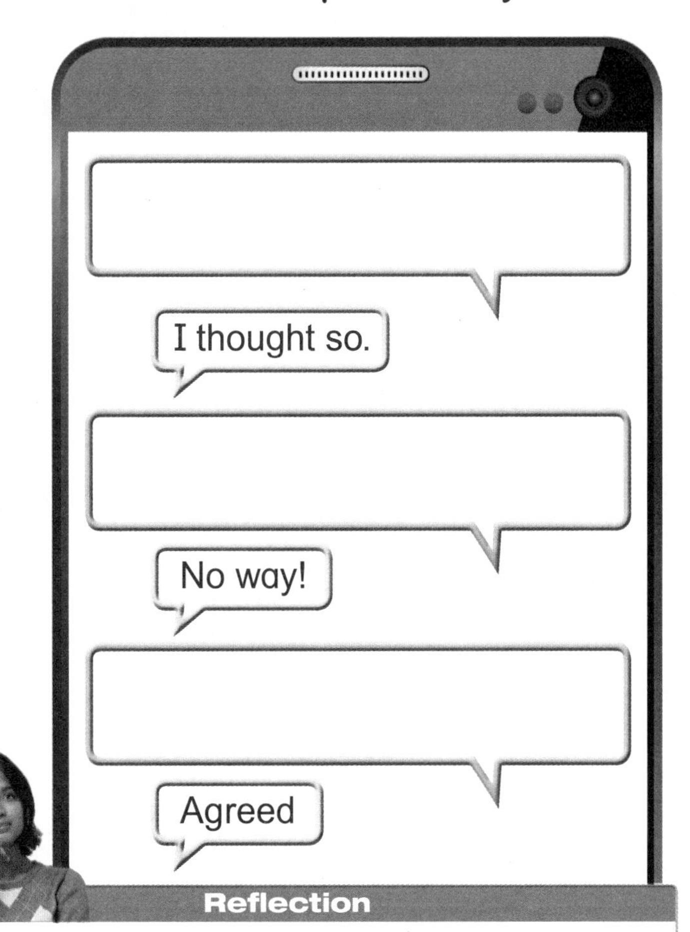

Reflection

Name two interesting or surprising things you learned about your classmates.

____

____

____

DAY 6

MATH 180 Software K-W-L

> Fill in the first two columns on Day 6, and the third column on Day 10.

What I Know	What I Want to Know	What I Learned
LEARN ZONE/FAST TRACK		
EXPLORE ZONE		
SUCCESS ZONE		
BRAIN ARCADE		

"I'm hungry for knowledge. The whole thing is to learn every day, to get brighter and brighter. That's what this world is about."

Jay-Z
Rapper, producer, entrepreneur

Setting Goals

> Fill in the table to describe three goals. Include an amount of time you will spend achieving each goal.

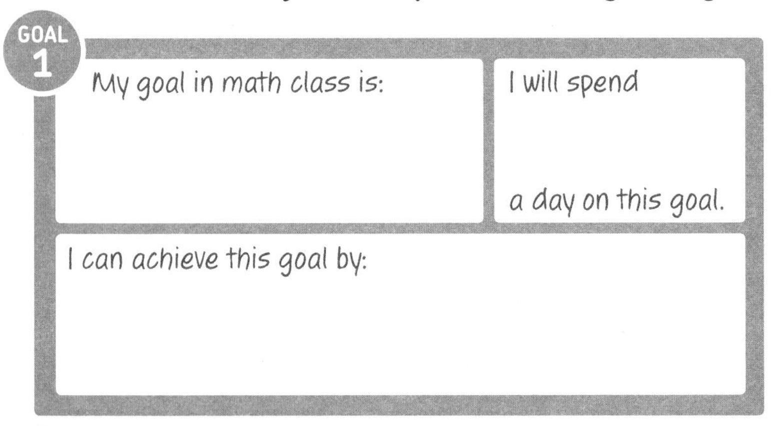

GOAL 1

My goal in math class is:

I will spend

a day on this goal.

I can achieve this goal by:

GOAL 2

My goal in school is:

I will spend

a day on this goal.

I can achieve this goal by:

GOAL 3

My goal outside of school is:

I will spend

a day on this goal.

I can achieve this goal by:

Thinking About the Future

> List your career goals, and then the goals of two classmates.

	Self	Interview 1	Interview 2
1 Name:			
2 What jobs or careers interest you?			
3 Why do these jobs or careers interest you?			
4 Do you know adults in this career?			
5 What must you accomplish before you can reach this goal?			

Reflection Questions

Ⓐ How are the career goals in the chart similar to one another?

Ⓑ How are the career goals different from each other?

Mission Statements

The purpose of a mission statement is to explain the purpose or goal of an organization, company, or person.

American Red Cross

Prevents and alleviates human suffering in the face of emergencies by mobilizing the power of volunteers and the generosity of donors.

Inspiring Americans to protect wildlife for our children's future.

facebook

Give people the power to share and make the world more open and connected.

Reflection

Using what you learned about Growth Mindset, write your own mission statement. It should show the kind of person and student you strive to be.

My mission is to ______________________

____

____

____

____

I have to work, for my soul.

Jennifer Lopez
Singer and actress

How can you apply your mission statement...

Outside of school

In school

In this class

What Is Success?

› **Define success and failure in your own words. Then answer the reflection questions.**

> *Do the thing you cannot do. Fail at it. Try again. Do better the second time.*
>
> Oprah Winfrey
> Television host
> and entrepreneur

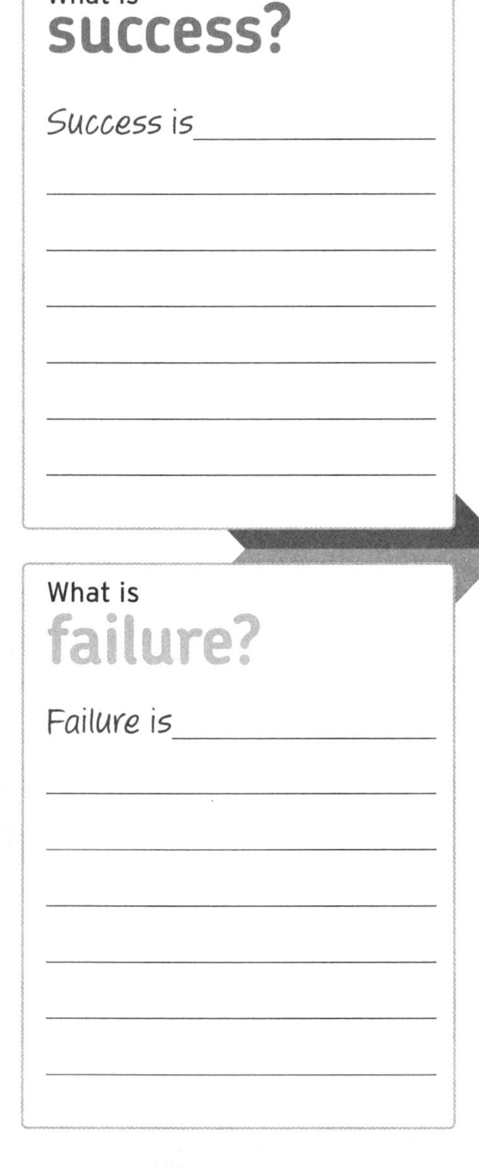

What is
success?

Success is ______________________

____

What is
failure?

Failure is ______________________

____

Reflection Questions

Ⓐ How will you succeed in *MATH 180*?

I will succeed in MATH 180 by ______________________

____

Ⓑ If you make a mistake on a math problem, what will you do next?

If I make a mistake, I will ______________________

____

Ⓒ How will you know that you are successful in math?

I will know that I am successful in math when ______________________

____

Ⓓ How can you keep a Growth Mindset as you study math?

I can keep a Growth Mindset by ______________________

____

BLOCK 1

Multiplicative Thinking

Buzz Worthy

VOCABULARY

- Associative Property of Multiplication
- Commutative Property
- equal groups
- equation
- factor
- multiple of 10
- product
- variable

Social Climbers

How do you use social media?

In this Anchor Video, artists and inventors use social media to turn their visions and businesses into reality.

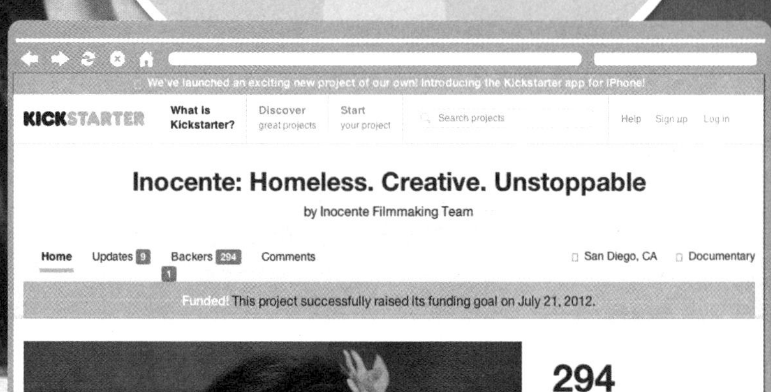

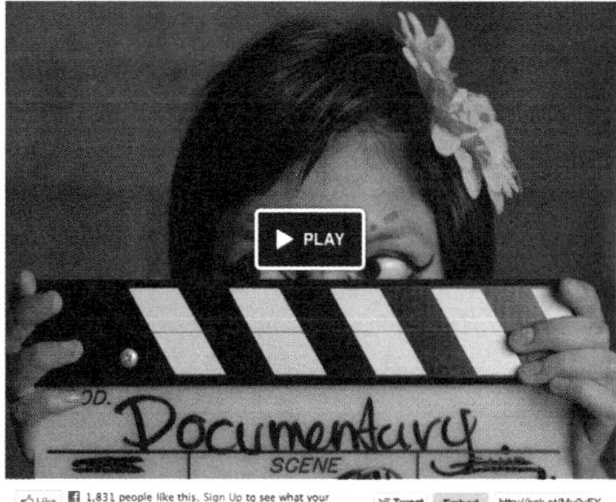

Documentary

Math in Digital Media

In this Block, you will explore how math is used in digital media, marketing, and advertising.

Companies hire

Advertisers

to create media ads for their products. A **30-second** TV commercial during the Superbowl costs more than **$4 million**.

Are you an expert in a topic?

Bloggers

post their experiences for readers to respond. Bloggers can make money by receiving a **flat fee** per post or a **percentage** per page click or per site visit.

APP

Developers

create content for smart phones, tablets, and computers. They need to keep up their skills in this fast-paced career. Experts **calculate** that technology capacity **doubles** every two to three years.

SOUND

Designers

are experts in acoustics, or the science of sound. They use the **properties** of sound waves in digital media, including the alert dings you hear on social media sites.

MARKET RESEARCH

Analysts

collect information that helps companies better understand people's buying habits. This field is expected to increase **41%** in the next decade.

Equal Groups in Multiplication

LESSON 1

Block Preview

> Think about the Anchor Video and answer this question.

If you started your own Internet company, what would it be?

> Explain your thinking.

If I started my own Internet company, it would ______________

____

____

____

LESSON 2

Number Strings

> Add this set of expressions mentally.

$14 + 14$
$13 + 13$
$14 + 13$
$14 + 15$

> Pick one of the expressions and explain how you solved it.

I solved ________ + ________ by

____

____

____

LESSON 3

Find the Pattern

> Write a number in the circle using the rule.

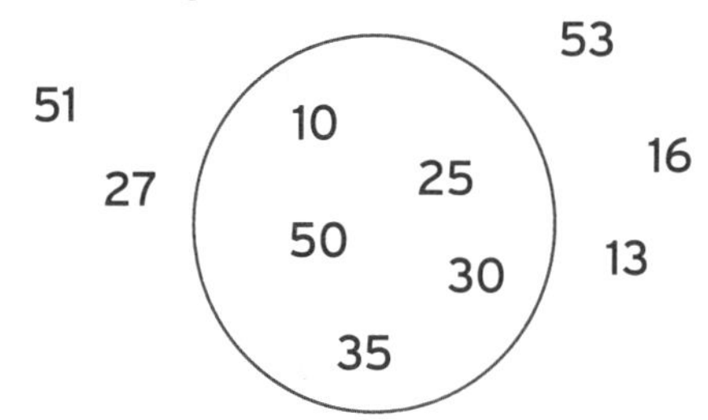

> Why does the number you wrote belong in the circle?

I wrote ________ in the circle because ______________

____

____

LESSON 4

Tell Me All That You Can

> About 12:

- ______________________
- ______________________
- ______________________
- ______________________
- ______________________
- ______________________

> Six multiplication equations equal 12. Write as many as you can.

_____ × _____ = 12
_____ × _____ = 12
_____ × _____ = 12
_____ × _____ = 12
_____ × _____ = 12
_____ × _____ = 12

LESSON 5

Which Does Not Belong?

> These numbers form a multiplication pattern. Circle the number that does not belong.

6, 12, 18, 25, 30, 36

> How do you know which number does not belong?

I know ________ *does not belong because* ______________________

____

The correct number is ________.

Sum It Up!

> In this Topic, you learned that multiplication is about finding the total number of objects in equal groups.

I can use an array model to show 3 × 5.

Then I count by 5s or add to find the total.
5, 10, 15
5 + 5 + 5 = 15

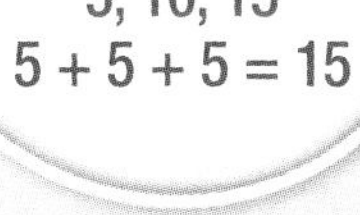

Identify Equal Groups

> WORKED EXAMPLE

STEP 1 **Model equal groups with tiles.**

4 Equal Groups of 5

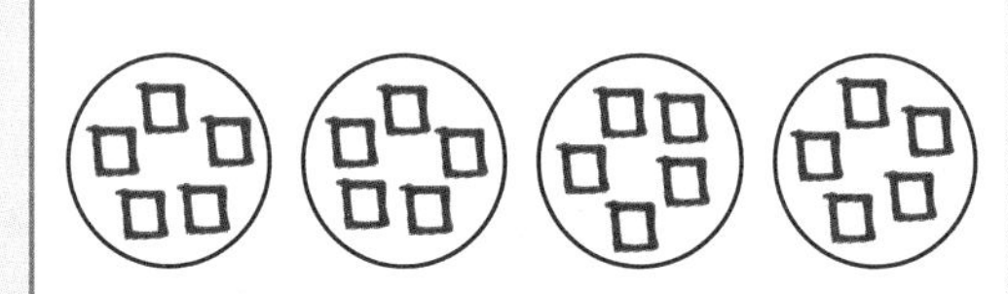

STEP 2 **Count to find the total.**

Count by 5s: 5 10 15 20

STEP 3 **Add to find the total.**

Addition Equation: $(5 + 5) + (5 + 5)$

$10 + 10 = 20$

STEP 4 **Write a multiplication equation.**

Multiplication Equation: $4 \times 5 = 20$

> TRY IT

1

STEP 1 **Model equal groups with tiles.**

3 Equal Groups of 6

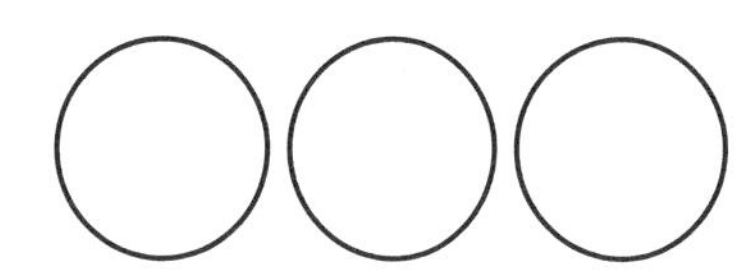

STEP 2 **Count to find the total.**

Count by 6s: ______________________

STEP 3 **Add to find the total.**

Addition Equation:

STEP 4 **Write a multiplication equation.**

Multiplication Equation:

____

> PRACTICE

2

STEP 1 **Model equal groups with tiles.**

4 Equal Groups of 7

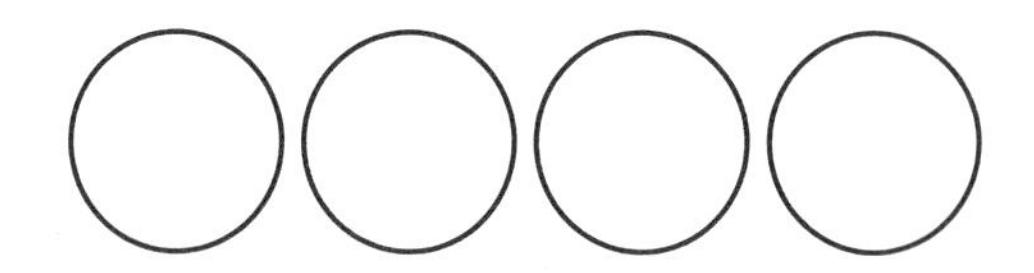

STEP 2 **Count to find the total.**

Count by 7s: ______________________

STEP 3 **Add to find the total.**

Addition Equation:

STEP 4 **Write a multiplication equation.**

Multiplication Equation:

____

multiply *(v)* to determine the total number of objects in equal groups

> PRACTICE

3 5 Equal Groups of 4

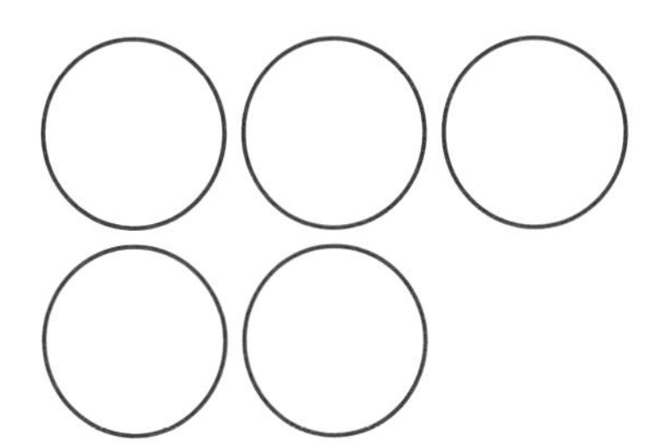

Count by 4s: ____________________

Addition Equation:

Multiplication Equation:

____

4 6 Equal Groups of 5

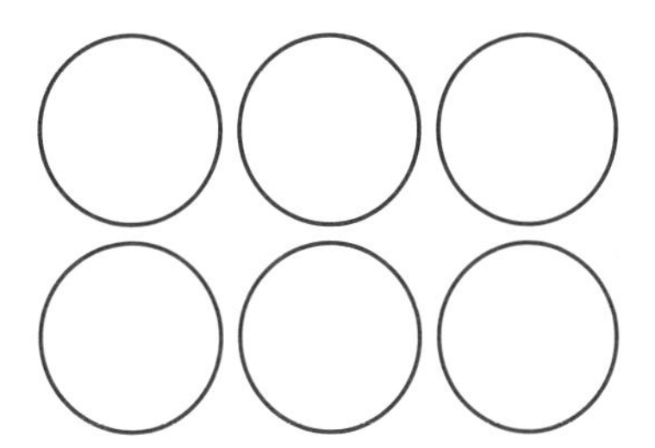

Count by 5s: ____________________

Addition Equation:

Multiplication Equation:

____

5 4 Equal Groups of 5

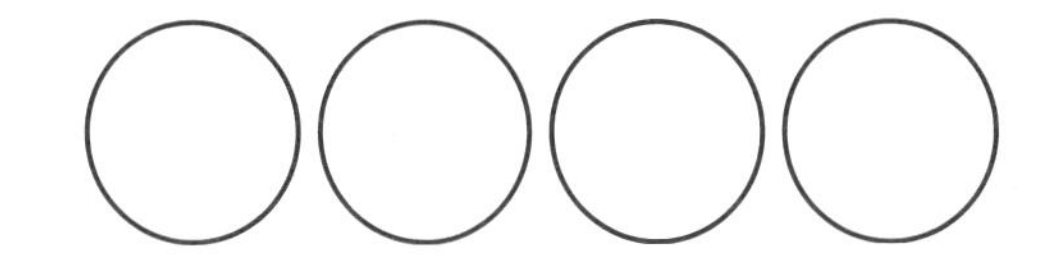

Count by 5s: ____________________

Addition Equation:

Multiplication Equation:

____

6 2 Equal Groups of 8

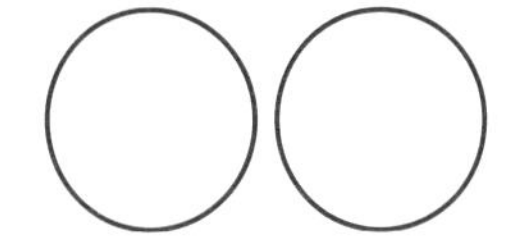

Count by 8s: ____________________

Addition Equation:

Multiplication Equation:

____

EXIT Ticket

BLOCK 1

> **Model and find the total number in 3 equal groups of 4.**

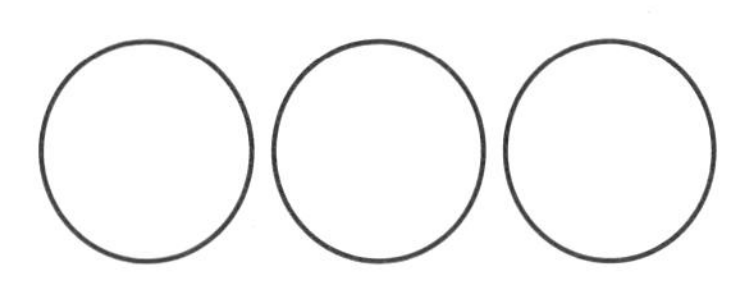

Count by 4s: ____________________

Addition Equation:

Multiplication Equation:

____

> **What are two ways you can read the equation $3 \times 4 = 12$?**

____

____

TOPIC 3

TOPIC 2

TOPIC 1

These are the same steps you'd take to find out how many quarters there are in 3 dollars.

SCORE (0) (1) (2)

LESSON 2
CONCEPT

Interpret Products

> WORKED EXAMPLE

STEP 1 **Model equal groups with an array.**

4 Equal Groups of 6

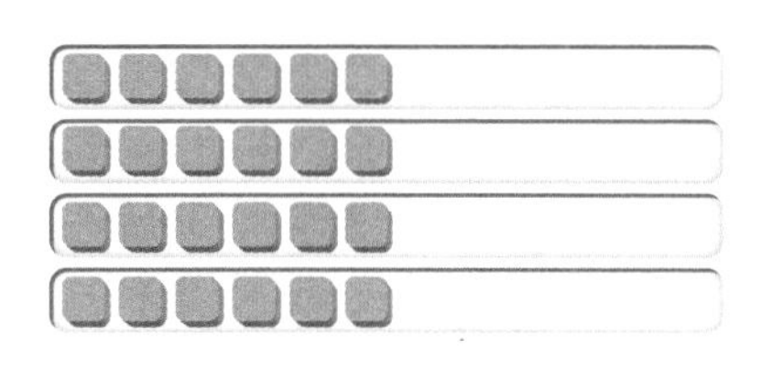

STEP 2 **Count to find the total.**

Count by 6s: 6, 12, 18, 24

STEP 3 **Add to find the total.**

$(6 + 6) + (6 + 6)$

$12 + 12 = 24$

STEP 4 **Write a multiplication equation.**

Multiplication Equation: $4 \times 6 = 24$

> TRY IT

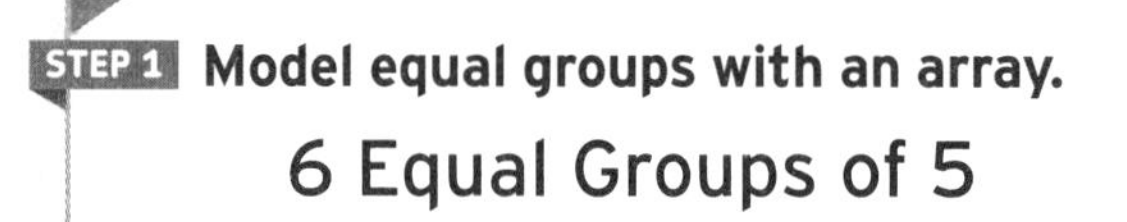

1

STEP 1 **Model equal groups with an array.**

6 Equal Groups of 5

STEP 2 **Count to find the total.**

Count by 5s: ______________________

STEP 3 **Add to find the total.**

Addition Equation:

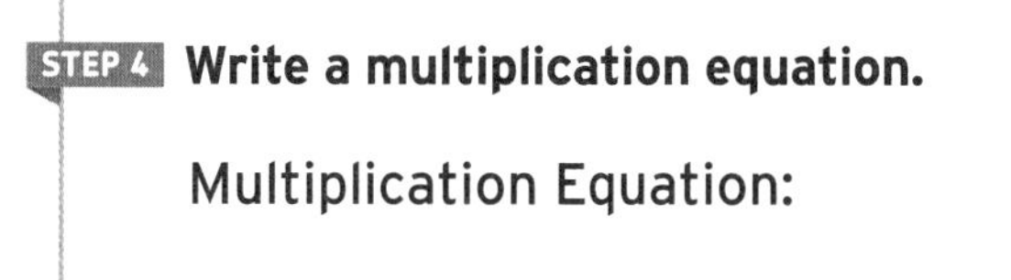

STEP 4 **Write a multiplication equation.**

Multiplication Equation:

____

> PRACTICE

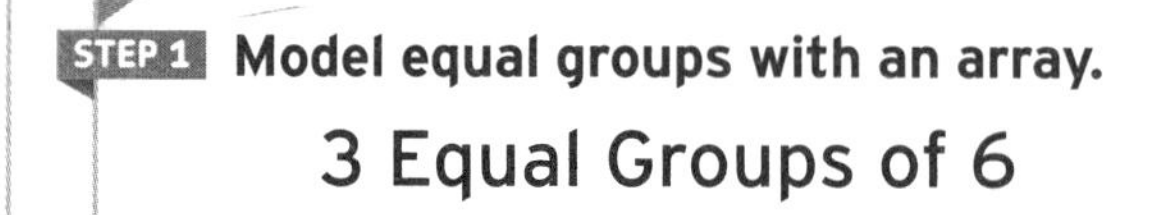

2

STEP 1 **Model equal groups with an array.**

3 Equal Groups of 6

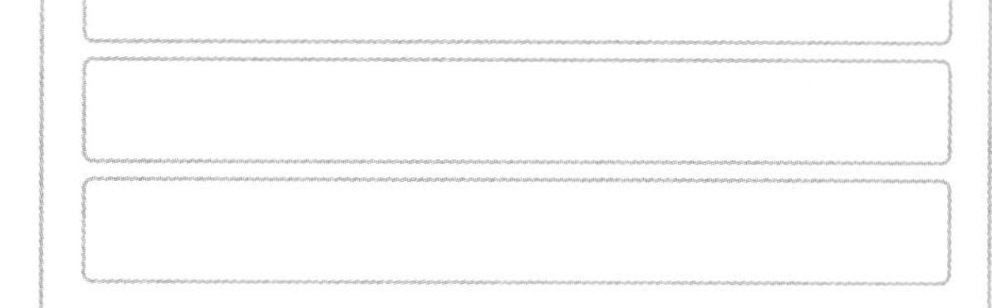

STEP 2 **Count to find the total.**

Count by 6s: ______________________

STEP 3 **Add to find the total.**

Addition Equation:

STEP 4 **Write a multiplication equation.**

Multiplication Equation:

____

factor *(n)* the number you multiply to find a product

product *(n)* the result of multiplication

> PRACTICE

3

4 Equal Groups of 4

Count by 4s: ______

Addition Equation:

Multiplication Equation:

______

4

5 Equal Groups of 4

Count by 4s: ______

Addition Equation:

Multiplication Equation:

______

EXIT **Ticket**

> **Use the array to model and find the total number in 4 equal groups of 3.**

Count by 3s: ______

Addition Equation:

Multiplication Equation:

______

> **How does modeling with an array help you find the total number of things in groups?**

Modeling with an array helps me find the total number by

______

______

______

SCORE (0) (1) (2)

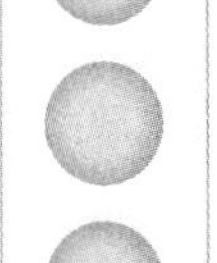

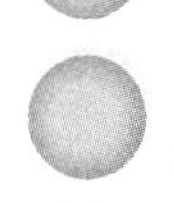

TOPIC 1

Apply the Commutative Property

WORKED EXAMPLE

STEP 1 **Represent the expression with an area model.**

5 × 7

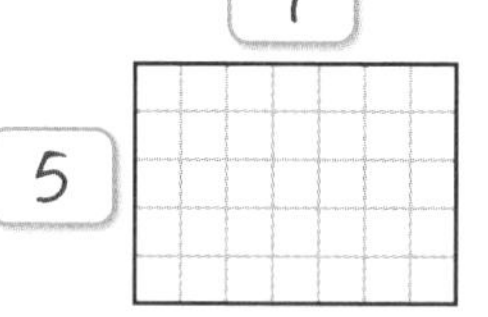

STEP 2 **Add or count to find the product.**

Count by 7s: 7, 14, 21, 28, 35

Addition Equation: (7 + 7) + (7 + 7) + 7
14 + 14 + 7 = 35

Multiplication Equation: 5 × 7 = 35

STEP 3 **Rotate the area model.**

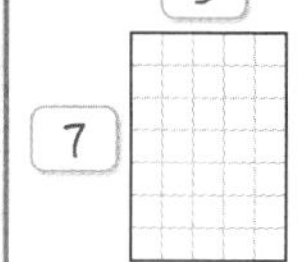

Count by 5s: 5, 10, 15, 20, 25, 30, 35

Addition Equation:
(5 + 5) + (5 + 5) + (5 + 5) + 5
10 + 10 + 10 + 5 = 35

Multiplication Equation: 7 × 5 = 35

STEP 4 **Write a multiplication equation.**

5 × 7 = 7 × 5

TRY IT

1

STEP 1 **Represent the expression with an area model.**

3 × 8

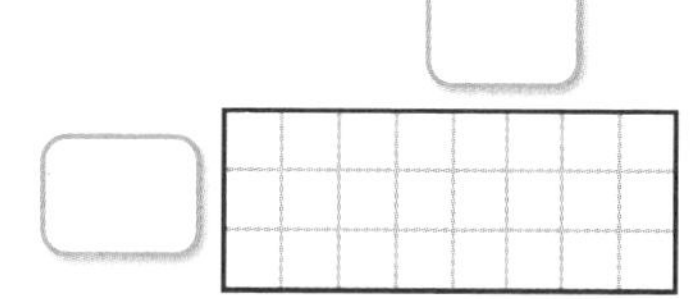

STEP 2 **Add or count to find the product.**

Count by 8s: ____________

Addition Equation:

Multiplication Equation: ____________

STEP 3 **Rotate the area model.**

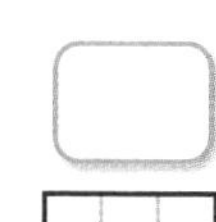

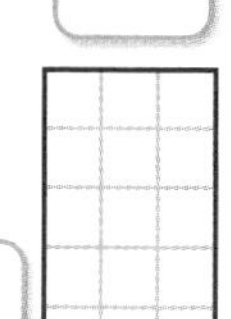

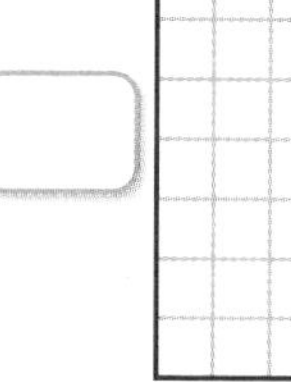

Count by 3s:

____

Addition Equation:

Multiplication Equation:

____

STEP 4 **Write a multiplication equation.**

____ × ____ = ____ × ____

PRACTICE

2

STEP 1 **Represent the expression with an area model.**

4 × 6

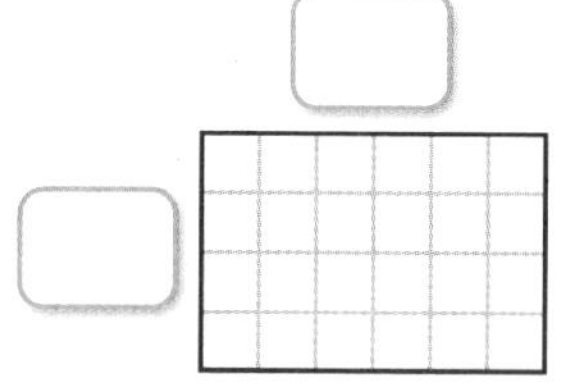

STEP 2 **Add or count to find the product.**

Count by 6s: ____________

Addition Equation:

Multiplication Equation: ____________

STEP 3 **Rotate the area model.**

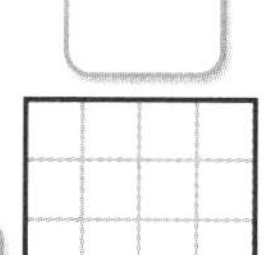

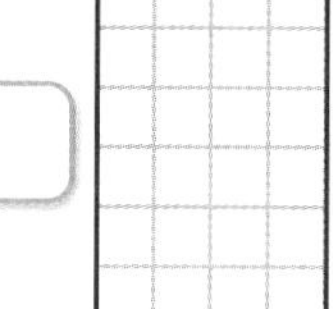

Count by 4s:

____

Addition Equation:

Multiplication Equation:

____

STEP 4 **Write a multiplication equation.**

____ × ____ = ____ × ____

area model *(n)* a rectangle with equal rows of squares, similar to an array

Commutative Property *(n)* changing the order of the factors does not change the product

> PRACTICE

3 3×6

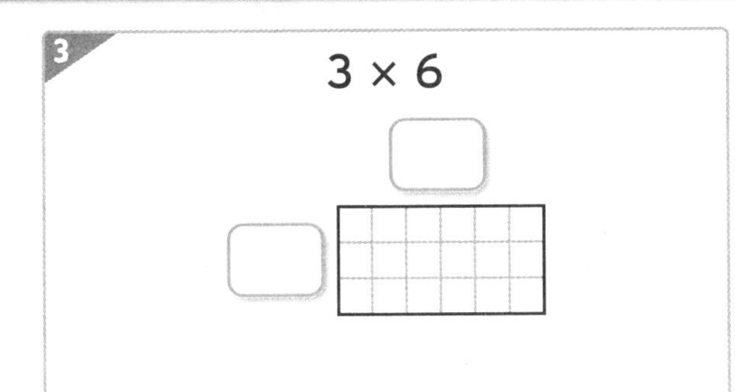

Count by ____s: ______________________

Addition Equation:

Multiplication Equation: ______________

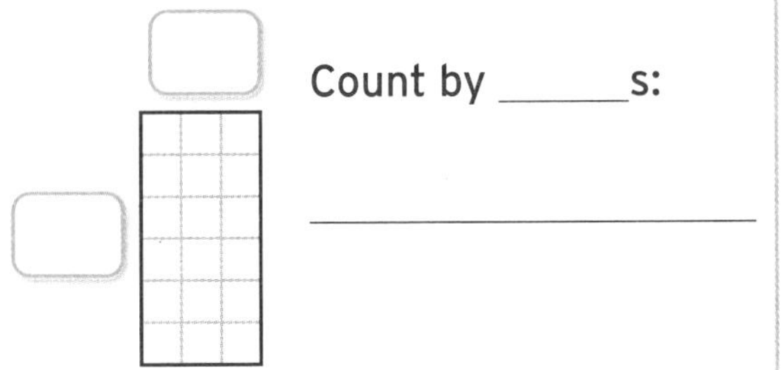

Count by ______s:

____

Addition Equation:

Multiplication Equation:

____

______ × ______ = ______ × ______

4 6×7

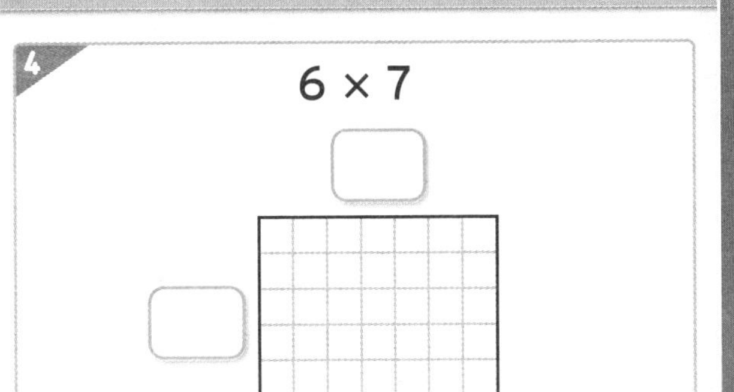

Count by ____s: ______________________

Addition Equation:

Multiplication Equation: ______________

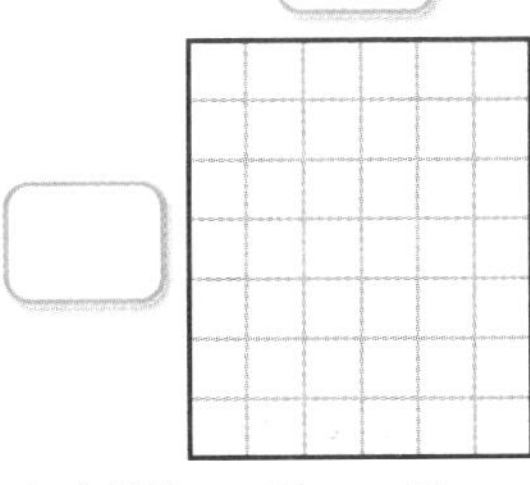

Count by ______s:

____

Addition Equation:

Multiplication Equation:

____

______ × ______ = ______ × ______

EXIT Ticket

BLOCK 1

> **Find the product.**

9×4

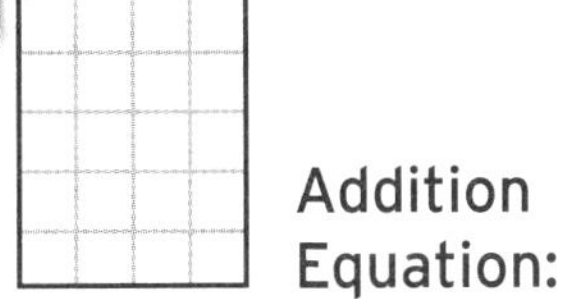

Count by ______s:

____

Addition Equation:

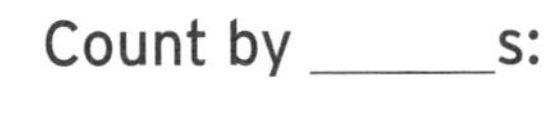

Multiplication Equation:

____

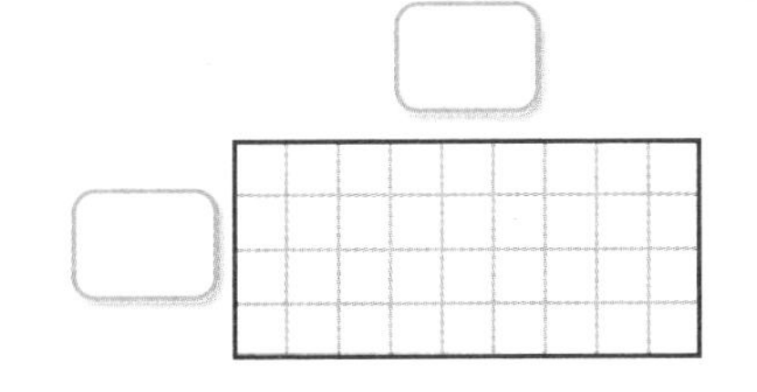

Count by ______s: ______________

Addition Equation:

Multiplication Equation:

____

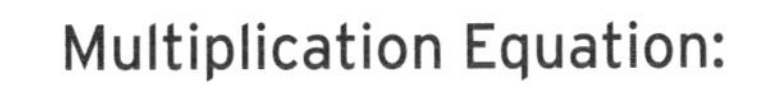

______ × ______ = ______ × ______

SCORE (0) (1) (2)

TOPIC 3

TOPIC 2

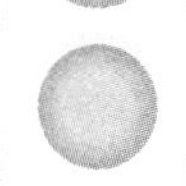

TOPIC 1

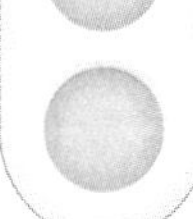

Reinforce Multiplication Facts

RULES

Tic-Tac-Go (Level 1)

What You Need

- *mSpace* pages 16–19
- counters

How to Play

- Players move only one counter after the first turn.
- Players may place a counter on top of another counter.
- Use Player A's *mSpace* page for the first game and Player B's page for the second.

How to Win

- The winner is the first player to complete a path from edge to edge.
- Paths can be made by marking squares from top to bottom or side to side.

> HOW TO PLAY

STEP 1 Player A places counters on two factors.

24	2	3	36	15
20	10	18	12	9
4	12	6	5	25
16	8	16	30	1

1 2 3 4 5 (6)

STEP 2 Player A marks an X on the product. Record the equation.

24	2	3	36	15
20	10	~~18~~ X	12	9
4	12	6	5	25
16	8	16	30	1

1 2 3 4 5 (6)

PLAYER A

Equations
3 x 6 = 18

STEP 3 Player B moves one counter to another factor.

24	2	3	36	15
20	10	~~18~~ X	12	9
4	12	6	5	25
16	8	16	30	1

1 2 3 4 (5) 6

STEP 4 Player B marks an O on the product. Record the equation.

24	2	3	36	(15)
20	10	~~18~~ X	12	9
4	12	6	5	25
16	8	16	30	1

1 2 3 4 (5) 6

PLAYER B

Equations
3 x 5 = 15

RECORDING SHEET

Tic-Tac-Go (Level 1)

Decide who is Player A and who is Player B. Record your equations in the appropriate table.

24	2	3	36	15
20	10	18	12	9
4	12	6	5	25
16	8	16	30	1

1 2 3 4 5 6

PLAYER A

Equations

PLAYER B

Equations

Check the winner:	
_____ Player A	_____ Player B

RECORDING SHEET

Tic-Tac-Go (Level 1)

> Decide who is Player A and who is Player B. Record your equations in the appropriate table.

24	2	3	36	15
20	10	18	12	9
4	12	6	5	25
16	8	16	30	1

1 2 3 4 5 6

PLAYER A

Equations

PLAYER B

Equations

Check the winner:	
_____ Player A	_____ Player B

> Optional: Use this space for calculations.

EXIT Ticket

BLOCK 1

> **Answer this question.**

You are the X. What would be your next move?

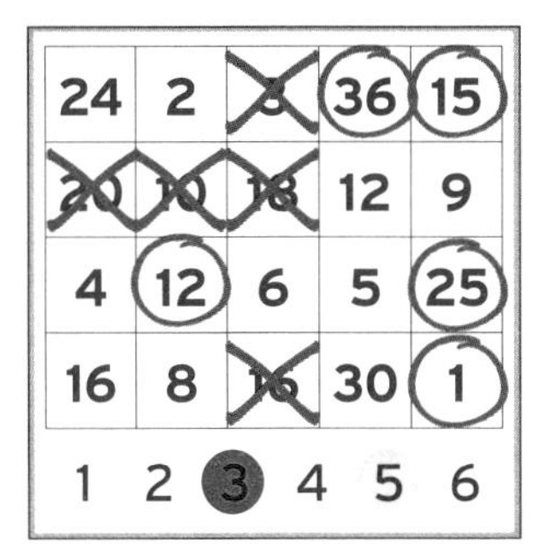

I would move the ______________ *counter to* ______ *because* ______
____

SCORE ⓪ ① ②

CAREER EXPLORATION

> **Bloggers hope to reach as many people as possible on their sites.**

How might a blog post go viral, or multiply, across all forms of social media?

TOPIC 3

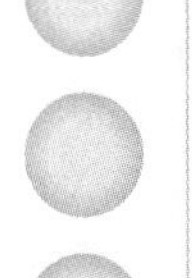

TOPIC 2

TOPIC 1

Explain Multiplication Patterns

BLOCK 1

> WORKED EXAMPLE

STEP 1 **Find the rule.**

INPUT	EQUATIONS	OUTPUT
1		2
2		4
3		6
4		8
5		10

Output = 2 × Input

STEP 2 **Express the rule with a variable.**

Output = 2 × n

Output = 2n

STEP 3 **Complete the missing outputs.**

INPUT	EQUATIONS	OUTPUT
1		2
2		4
3		6
4		8
5	5 x 2 = 10	10
10	10 x 2 = 20	20
12	12 x 2 = 24	24

STEP 4 **Apply the rule using a different input.**

If the input is 50, then the output is 100.

> TRY IT

1

STEP 1 **Find the rule.**

INPUT	EQUATIONS	OUTPUT
1		3
2		6
3		9
4		12
5		

Output = _____ × Input

STEP 2 **Express the rule with a variable.**

Output = _____ × _____

Output = _____

STEP 3 **Complete the missing outputs.**

INPUT	EQUATIONS	OUTPUT
1		3
2		6
3		9
4		12
5		
10		
12		

STEP 4 **Apply the rule using a different input.**

If the input is 100, then the output is _____.

> PRACTICE

2

STEP 1 **Find the rule.**

INPUT	EQUATIONS	OUTPUT
1		5
2		10
3		15
4		20
5		

Output = _____ × Input

STEP 2 **Express the rule with a variable.**

Output = _____ × _____

Output = _____

STEP 3 **Complete the missing outputs.**

INPUT	EQUATIONS	OUTPUT
1		5
2		10
3		15
4		20
5		
10		
12		

STEP 4 **Apply the rule using a different input.**

If the input is 100, then the output is _____.

> PRACTICE

3

STEP 1 **Find the rule.**

INPUT	EQUATIONS	OUTPUT
1		7
2		14
3		21
4		28
5		

Output = _____ × Input

STEP 2 **Express the rule with a variable.**

Output = _____ × _____

Output = _____

STEP 3 **Complete the missing outputs.**

INPUT	EQUATIONS	OUTPUT
1		7
2		14
3		21
4		28
5		
10		
12		

STEP 4 **Apply the rule using a different input.**

If the input is 100, then the output is _____.

4

STEP 1 **Find the rule.**

INPUT	EQUATIONS	OUTPUT
1		9
2		18
3		27
4		36
5		

Output = _____ × Input

STEP 2 **Express the rule with a variable.**

Output = _____ × _____

Output = _____

STEP 3 **Complete the missing outputs.**

INPUT	EQUATIONS	OUTPUT
1		9
2		18
3		27
4		36
5		
10		
12		

STEP 4 **Apply the rule using a different input.**

If the input is 100, then the output is _____.

EXIT Ticket

BLOCK 1

TOPIC 3

TOPIC 2

TOPIC 1

> **Complete this function table.**

INPUT	EQUATIONS	OUTPUT
1		4
2		8
3		12
4		
		20
6		

> **Identify the rule and complete the sentence frames.**

For every input n, the value of the output is _________.

If the input is 50, then the output is _________.

Which multiplication pattern can you identify in this function table?

SCORE ⓪ ① ②

Facts and Factors

LESSON 1

Number Strings

> **Add this set of expressions mentally.**

80 + 5
78 + 2 + 3
78 + 5
78 + 15
78 + 17

> **How does knowing 78 + 2 + 3 help you solve 78 + 5?**

Knowing 78 + 2 + 3 helped me solve 78 + 5 because ________

____

____

____

LESSON 2

Brain Teaser

> **Solve this riddle.**

The product of two factors is 24. The difference between the two factors is 10.

What are the two factors?

_____ and _____

> **What steps did you take to solve this problem?**

The first step I took was ________

____

Then I ________

____

LESSON 3

Which Does Not Belong?

> **Use this list of numbers to create factor pairs for the same product. Circle the number that does not belong.**

Factors: 3, 10, 1, 6, 2, 4, 15, 30, 5

Factor Pairs:
- ________ and ________
- ________ and ________
- ________ and ________
- ________ and ________

> **How did you decide which number does not belong?**

I decided which number does not belong by ________

____

____

LESSON 4

Build It

› Build as many expressions as you can by writing factors in the blanks below.

____ × ____ × ____ = 36

- ________
- ________
- ________
- ________
- ________
- ________
- ________
- ________

› How would you know if you found all of the possible solutions?

I would know if I found all of the possible solutions because ______

____

____

____

LESSON 5

Missing Numbers

› Write the missing factors in the multiplication equations.

1 × ____ = 8

2 × ____ = 16

3 × ____ = 24

4 × ____ = 32

5 × ____ = 40

› What pattern is formed by the products of the equations?

The pattern formed is ________

____

____

____

Sum It Up!

› In this Topic, you learned to name factors and factor pairs of a number. You also learned to name missing factors.

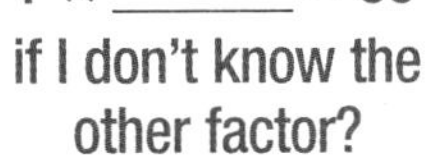

How can I solve 7 × ____ = 56 if I don't know the other factor?

When I solve for a missing factor, I start with a fact that I know.

7 × 7 = 49

If I add another group of 7 to 49, I get 56.

So, 7 × 8 = 56.

The missing factor is 8.

Multiply 1-Digit Factors

> WORKED EXAMPLE

STEP 1 Split one factor.

8×7

5 + 2

STEP 2 Split the rectangle.

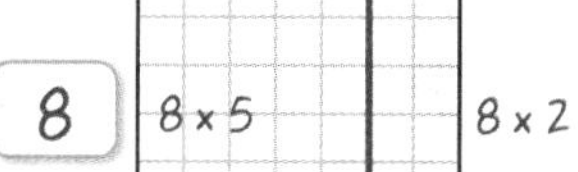

STEP 3 Find the product for each smaller rectangle.

Equation 1 → 8 x 5 = 40
Equation 2 → 8 x 2 = 16

STEP 4 Add the products.

40 + 16 = 56
8 × 7 = 56

> TRY IT

1

STEP 1 Split one factor.

9×6

_____ + _____

STEP 2 Split the rectangle.

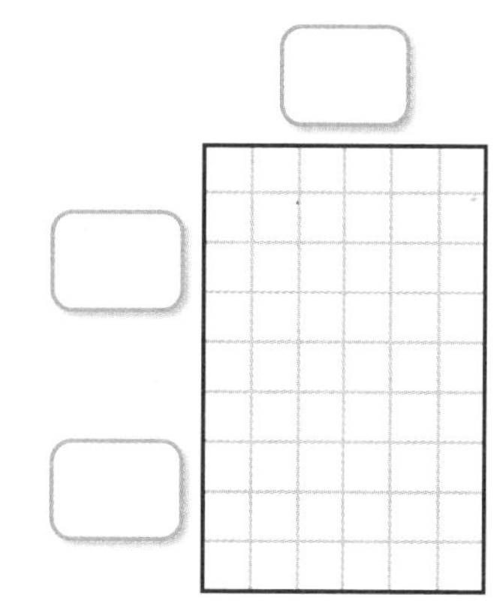

STEP 3 Find the product for each smaller rectangle.

Equation 1 → __________

Equation 2 → __________

STEP 4 Add the products.

_____ + _____ = _____

_____ × _____ = _____

> PRACTICE

2

STEP 1 Split one factor.

8×8

_____ + _____

STEP 2 Split the rectangle.

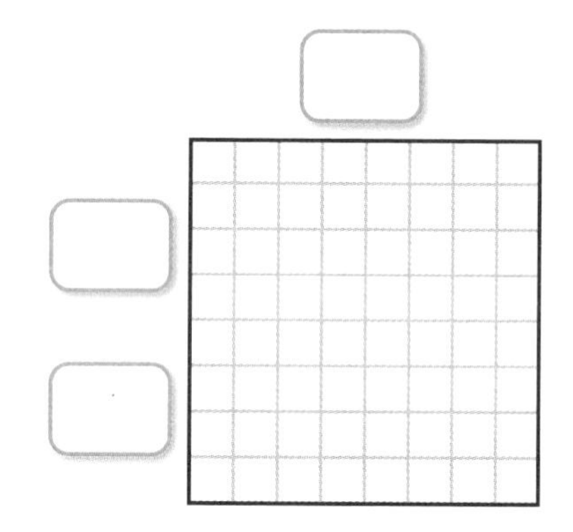

STEP 3 Find the product for each smaller rectangle.

Equation 1 → __________

Equation 2 → __________

STEP 4 Add the products.

_____ + _____ = _____

_____ × _____ = _____

PRACTICE

3

6×8

_____ + _____

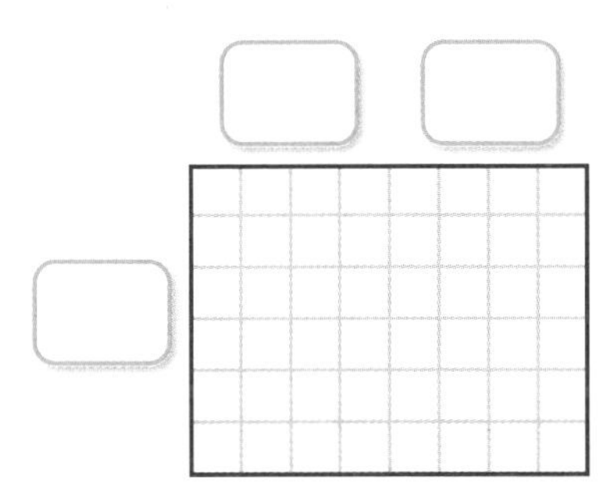

Equation 1 → __________

Equation 2 → __________

_____ + _____ = _____

_____ × _____ = _____

4

8×9

_____ + _____

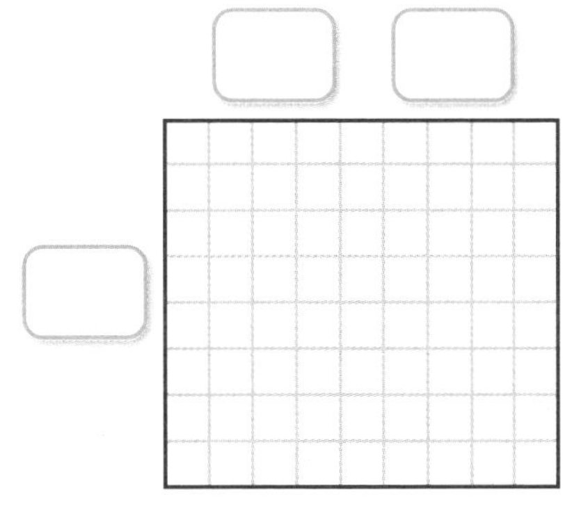

Equation 1 → __________

Equation 2 → __________

_____ + _____ = _____

_____ × _____ = _____

EXIT Ticket

BLOCK 1

TOPIC 3

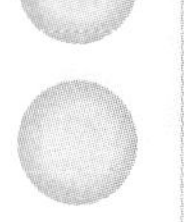
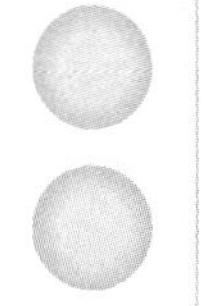

Find the product.

7×6

_____ + _____

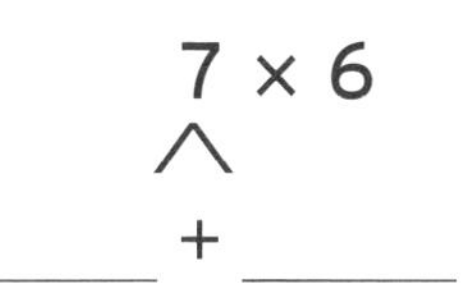
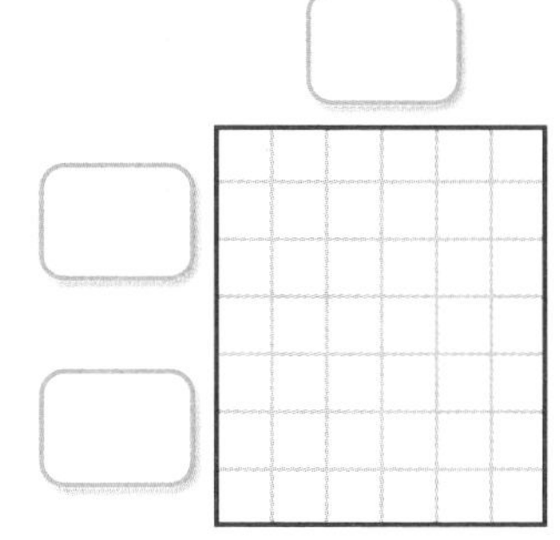

Equation 1 → __________

Equation 2 → __________

_____ + _____ = _____

_____ × _____ = _____

TOPIC 2

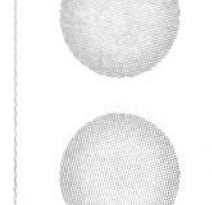
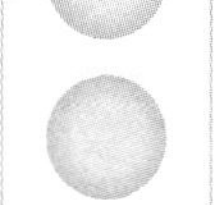

TOPIC 1

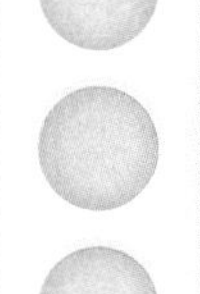

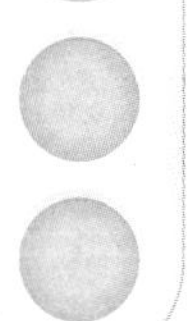

How does splitting a rectangle help you multiply?

Splitting a rectangle helps me multiply because __________

____

____

____

SCORE (0) (1) (2)

Find Factor Pairs

> WORKED EXAMPLE

STEP 1 **Use multiplication facts to find factors.**

$1 \times 30 = 30$

$3 \times 10 = 30$

$5 \times 6 = 30$

STEP 2 **Find factors of factors.**

$5 \times 6 = 30$

$5 \times 3 \times 2 = 30$

STEP 3 **Find the remaining factors.**

$(5 \times 3) \times 2 = 30$

$15 \times 2 = 30$

STEP 4 **List all factor pairs.**

Factor Pairs: 1 and 30
2 and 15
3 and 10
5 and 6

> TRY IT

1

STEP 1 **Use multiplication facts to find factors.**

Factors of 42

STEP 2 **Find factors of factors.**

STEP 3 **Find the remaining factors.**

STEP 4 **List all factor pairs.**

______ and ______

______ and ______

______ and ______

______ and ______

> PRACTICE

2

STEP 1 **Use multiplication facts to find factors.**

Factors of 36

STEP 2 **Find factors of factors.**

STEP 3 **Find the remaining factors.**

STEP 4 **List all factor pairs.**

______ and ______

______ and ______

______ and ______

______ and ______

______ and ______

factors of a number *(n)* the numbers that divide exactly, with no remainder, into a number

> PRACTICE

3

Factors of 63

______ and ______

______ and ______

______ and ______

4

Factors of 70

______ and ______

______ and ______

______ and ______

______ and ______

EXIT Ticket

BLOCK 1

TOPIC 3

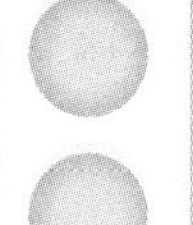

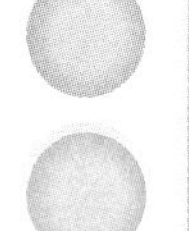

TOPIC 2

TOPIC 1

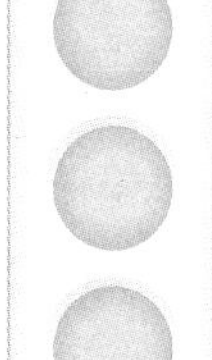

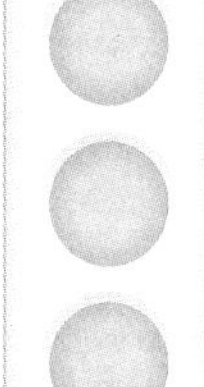

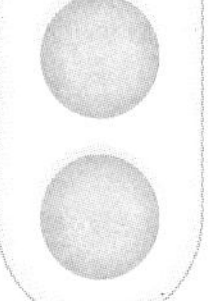

> **Find the missing factor pairs.**

This student left out two factor pairs for 24. Add the missing pairs to the list.

Factors of 24

______ and ______

2 and 12

3 and 8

______ and ______

> **Answer this question.**

If you know that 2 and 12 are factor pairs of 24, do you also need to list 12 and 2 as factor pairs? Why or why not?

I do/do not need to list 12 and 2 as factor pairs because

____

____

____

____

____

____

SCORE ⓪ ① ②

Find Missing Factors

> WORKED EXAMPLE

STEP 1 Write a missing-factor equation.

6 people went to dinner. The total bill was $54. How much did each person pay if the bill was shared equally?

Missing Factor Equation:

$\_\_\_\_ \times 6 = 54$

STEP 2 List facts you know.

$\_\_\_\_ \times 6 = 54$

$6 \times 6 = 36$

STEP 3 Add equal groups.

$36 + 6 = 42$

$7 \times 6 = 42$

$42 + 6 = 48$

$8 \times 6 = 48$

$48 + 6 = 54$

$9 \times 6 = 54$

STEP 4 Name the missing factor.

Missing Factor: 9

Each Person Paid: $9

> TRY IT

1

STEP 1 Write a missing-factor equation.

7 people went to dinner. The total bill was $42. How much did each person pay if the bill was shared equally?

Missing Factor Equation:

STEP 2 List facts you know.

STEP 3 Add equal groups.

STEP 4 Name the missing factor.

Missing Factor: ______

Each Person Paid: ______

> PRACTICE

2

STEP 1 Write a missing-factor equation.

8 people went to dinner. The total bill was $56. How much did each person pay if the bill was shared equally?

Missing Factor Equation:

STEP 2 List facts you know.

STEP 3 Add equal groups.

STEP 4 Name the missing factor.

Missing Factor: ______

Each Person Paid: ______

equation *(n)* a mathematical sentence in which the values on both sides of the equal sign are the same (equal)

> PRACTICE

3 4 people went to dinner. The total bill was $28. How much did each person pay if the bill was shared equally?

Missing Factor Equation:

Missing Factor: ______

Each Person Paid: ______

4 8 people went to dinner. The total bill was $64. How much did each person pay if the bill was shared equally?

Missing Factor Equation:

Missing Factor: ______

Each Person Paid: ______

5 $8 \times \_\_\_\_\_\_ = 72$

Missing Factor: ______

6 $\_\_\_\_\_\_ \times 7 = 63$

Missing Factor: ______

EXIT Ticket

BLOCK 1

> Solve this problem.

6 people went to dinner. The total bill was $48. How much did each person pay if the bill was shared equally?

Missing Factor Equation:

Missing Factor: ______

Each Person Paid: ______

> Answer this question.

Another night, 8 people went to dinner and spent $48. Explain how you know how much each person spent without doing calculations.

I know how much each person spent without doing any new calculations because ______

______

______

______

SCORE (0) (1) (2)

TOPIC 3

TOPIC 2

TOPIC 1

Use Reasoning With Multiplication

RULES

Tic-Tac-Go (Level 2)

What You Need

- *mSpace* pages 30–33
- counters

How to Play

- Players move only one counter after the first turn.
- Players may place a counter on top of another counter.
- Use Player A's *mSpace* page for the first game and Player B's page for the second.

How to Win

- The winner is the first player to complete a path from edge to edge.
- Paths can be made by marking squares from top to bottom or side to side.

> HOW TO PLAY

STEP 1 Player A places counters on two factors.

18	32	24	15	48
28	40	35	64	20
30	12	56	21	15
9	25	49	42	36

3 4 5 **(6)** 7 8

STEP 2 Player A marks an X on the product. Record the equation.

18	32	24	15	48
28	40	35	64	20
X 30	12	56	21	15
9	25	49	42	36

3 4 5 **(6)** 7 8

PLAYER A

Equations
5 x 6 = 30

STEP 3 Player B moves one counter to another factor.

18	32	24	15	48
28	40	35	64	20
X 30	12	56	21	15
9	25	49	42	36

3 4 5 **(6)** 7 8

STEP 4 Player B marks an O on the product. Record the equation.

18	32	24	15	O 48
28	40	35	64	20
X 30	12	56	21	15
9	25	49	42	36

3 4 5 **(6)** 7 8

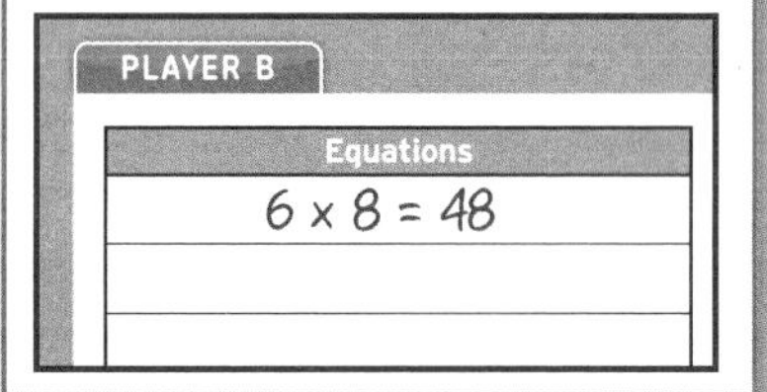
PLAYER B

Equations
6 x 8 = 48

RECORDING SHEET

Tic-Tac-Go (Level 2)

› Decide who is Player A and who is Player B.
Record your equations in the appropriate table.

18	32	24	15	48
28	40	35	64	20
30	12	56	21	15
9	25	49	42	36

3 4 5 6 7 8

PLAYER A

Equations

PLAYER B

Equations

Check the winner:	
_____ Player A	_____ Player B

RECORDING SHEET

Tic-Tac-Go (Level 2)

> Decide who is Player A and who is Player B. Record your equations in the appropriate table.

BLOCK 1

18	32	24	15	48
28	40	35	64	20
30	12	56	21	15
9	25	49	42	36

3 4 5 6 7 8

PLAYER A

Equations

PLAYER B

Equations

Check the winner:	
______ Player A	______ Player B

> **Optional: Use this space for calculations.**

EXIT Ticket

BLOCK

TOPIC 3

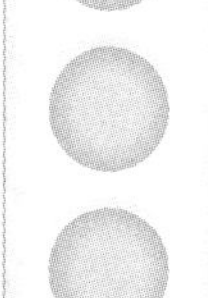

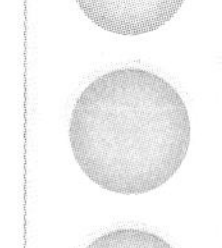

TOPIC 2

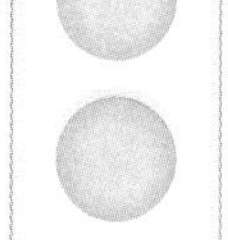

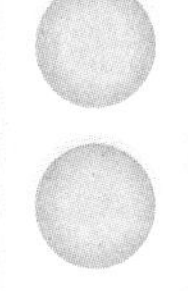

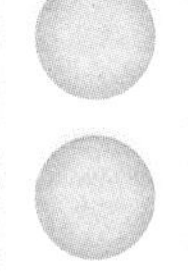

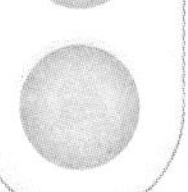

> **Answer this question.**

It is Player X's turn. What move should Player X make next?

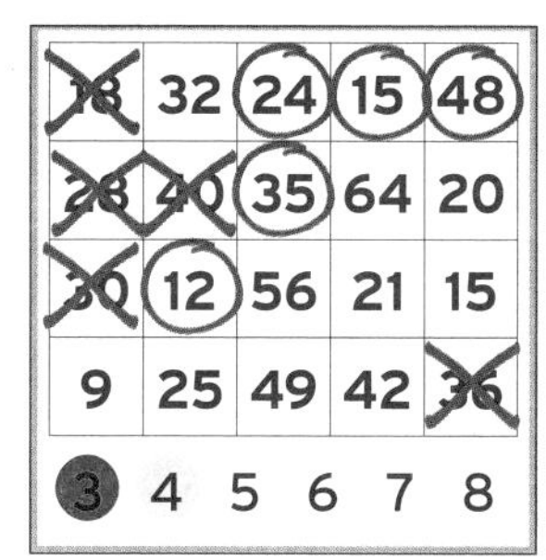

Player X should move the counter from ______ to ______

because ______________________

____

SCORE (0) (1) (2)

CAREER EXPLORATION

> **A social media editor manages the online media for a company.**

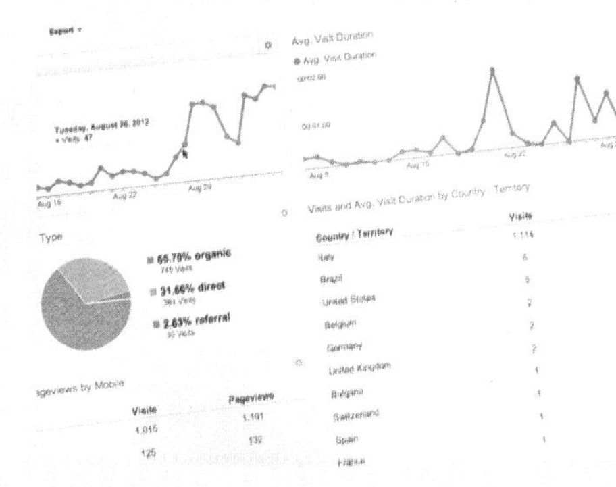

How could a social media editor use multiplication to figure the number of site hits in 1 week?

Solve Equal Groups Problems

> WORKED EXAMPLE

Read It! **Read and identify the problem.**

VIDEO GAME DESIGNER

Alesha sends emails about a video game to 4 people. She sends 2 emails to each person. How many emails does she send altogether?

PROBLEM TYPE Equal Groups Problem

Show It! **Represent the problem.**

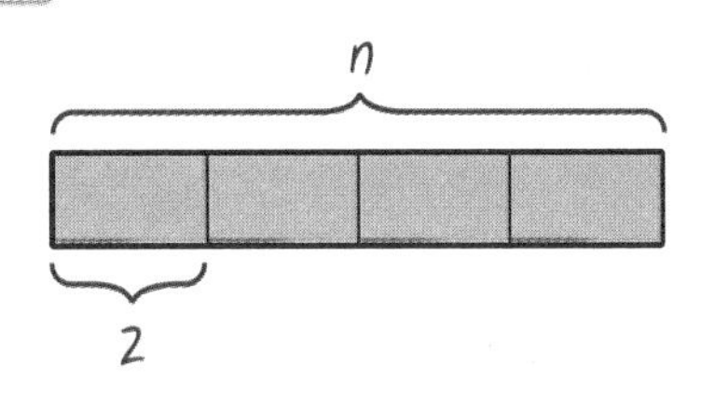

Solve It! **Solve the problem.**

$4 \times 2 = n$
$4 \times 2 = 8$
$n = 8$

Alesha sends 8 emails altogether.

Check It! **Check your work.**

> TRY IT

1

Read It! **Read and identify the problem.**

BLOGGER

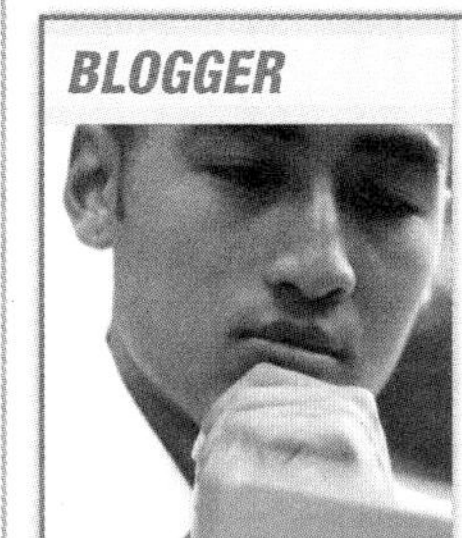

Dave's goal is to write 20 reviews on his blog each week. Last week, he wrote 3 reviews each day for 7 days. How many reviews did Dave write last week? Did he meet his goal?

PROBLEM TYPE ______

Show It! **Represent the problem.**

Solve It! **Solve the problem.**

Dave wrote ______ reviews last week.

Did he meet his goal? ______

Check It! **Check your work.**

> PRACTICE

2

Read It! **Read and identify the problem.**

SOCIAL MEDIA EDITOR

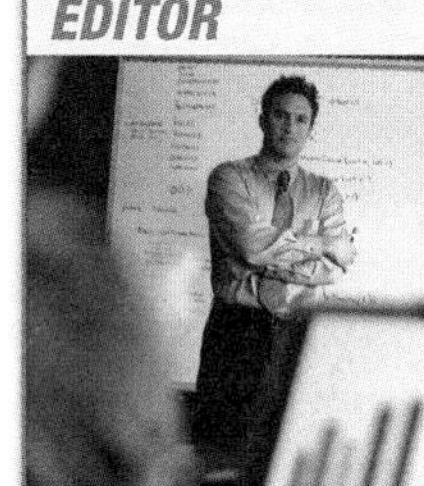

Jin's website offers free music downloads for an upcoming concert. Yesterday, 5 people downloaded 5 songs each. How many songs did they download altogether?

PROBLEM TYPE ______

Show It! **Represent the problem.**

Solve It! **Solve the problem.**

5 people downloaded ______ songs altogether.

Check It! **Check your work.**

PRACTICE

3

Sonja plans 15 interviews for her client each month. In February, she plans 4 groups of 3 interviews. Has she planned enough interviews?

PROBLEM TYPE ______

Sonja plans ______ interviews in February.

Has she planned enough interviews?

______

4

MARKETING MANAGER

Katy promotes new video games at a gaming store. She gets a bonus if she sells more than 60 video games. If 9 people each buy 6 video games, does Katy get a bonus?

PROBLEM TYPE ______

Katy sells ______ video games.

Does Katy get a bonus? ______

EXIT Ticket

BLOCK 1

Draw a bar model and solve this problem.

7 contestants on a TV show send 8 text messages each to friends asking for their votes. How many text messages did they send in all?

PROBLEM TYPE ______

The contestants sent ______ text messages altogether.

SCORE (0) (1) (2)

TOPIC 3

TOPIC 2

TOPIC 1

10 as a Factor

LESSON 1

Tell Me All That You Can

> About 10:

- ______
- ______
- ______
- ______
- ______
- ______

> Write addition or multiplication equations with 10 as an addend, sum, factor, or product.

- ______ • ______
- ______ • ______
- ______ • ______
- ______ • ______

LESSON 2

Find the Pattern

> Find the rule. Then, write a number in the circle using the rule.

Inside the circle: 50, 150, 1780, 320, 930, 30

Outside the circle: 24, 378, 1019, 94, 57

> Why does the number you wrote belong in the circle?

I wrote ______ in the circle because ______

______

______

LESSON 3

Brain Teaser

> Solve this riddle.

I am an even factor of 24.
I have only 2 factors.
Which number am I? ____

> How did you begin working on this problem?

I began working on this problem by ______

______

______

LESSON 4

Number Strings

› **Add this set of expressions mentally.**

99 + 38
98 + 47
98 + 99
99 + 99 + 5

› **Choose an expression from the list and explain how you solved it.**

I solved ______________________

by ____________________________

____

____

LESSON 5

Who's Right?

› **Talia and Jay found two different answers to the same problem.**

You have 3 playlists. Each playlist has 7 songs. How many songs do you have altogether?

Talia	Jay
$3 + 7 = 10$	$3 \times 7 = 21$

Who's right? ________

› **How do you know who is correct?**

I know ______ is correct because

____

____

____

____

Sum It Up!

› **In this Topic, you learned to multiply numbers by 10, and to multiply multiples of 10 by multiples of 10.**

How do I multiply numbers by multiples of 10?

Rename each multiple of 10 as a factor times 10. Then regroup and multiply.

$$30 \times 70$$
$$(3 \times 10) \times (7 \times 10)$$
$$(3 \times 7) \times 10 \times 10$$
$$(21 \times 10) \times 10$$
$$210 \times 10 = 2100$$

Multiply by 10

> WORKED EXAMPLE

STEP 1 **Understand multiples.**

Multiples of 4:
4 8 12 16 20 24 28 32...

Multiples of 6:
6 12 18 24 30 36 42 48...

STEP 2 **List multiples of 10.**

Multiples of 10:
10 20 30 40 50 60 70...

STEP 3 **Identify a pattern.**

EXPRESSION	NUMBER OF TENS	PRODUCT
2 × 10	2 tens	20
3 × 10	3 tens	30
4 × 10	4 tens	40
5 × 10	5 tens	50
6 × 10	6 tens	60
7 × 10	7 tens	70
8 × 10	8 tens	80
12 × 10		
20 × 10		

STEP 4 **Apply the pattern to greater factors.**

EXPRESSION	NUMBER OF TENS	PRODUCT
2 × 10	2 tens	20
3 × 10	3 tens	30
4 × 10	4 tens	40
5 × 10	5 tens	50
6 × 10	6 tens	60
7 × 10	7 tens	70
8 × 10	8 tens	80
12 × 10	12 tens	120
20 × 10	20 tens	200

> TRY IT

1

STEP 1 **Solve for a missing factor.**

$\_\_\_\_\_ \times 10 = 320$

STEP 2 **Solve for the product.**

$10 \times 17 = \_\_\_\_\_$

STEP 3 **Identify the number of 10s.**

_____ tens = 290

> PRACTICE

2

STEP 1 **Solve for a missing factor.**

$10 \times \_\_\_\_\_ = 180$

STEP 2 **Solve for the product.**

$37 \times 10 = \_\_\_\_\_$

STEP 3 **Identify the number of 10s.**

_____ tens = 650

multiple *(n)* a product of a given number and a whole number

multiple of 10 *(n)* a number that has a factor of 10

› PRACTICE

3 $7 \times$ ______ $= 70$	**4** ______ $\times 10 = 610$
5 $86 \times 10 =$ ______	**6** $135 \times 10 =$ ______
7 $830 =$ ______ tens	**8** $100 \times 10 =$ ______
9 ______ tens $= 960$	**10** ______ $\times 10 = 790$
11 $10 \times 61 =$ ______	**12** ______ tens $= 3700$
13 $830 \times 10 =$ ______	**14** $340 =$ ______ tens
15 $1080 =$ ______ tens	**16** $358 \times 10 =$ ______

EXIT Ticket

BLOCK 1

› Solve these problems.

$10 \times$ ______ $= 420$

$37 \times 10 =$ ______

$680 =$ ______ tens

› Answer this question.

Choose one problem above and explain how you solved it.

I solved ______________ by

____

____

____

____

____

Multiplying 10 times a factor moves every digit in the factor one place to the left.

TOPIC 3

TOPIC 2

SCORE ⓪ ① ②

Reason With Greater Factors

RULES

Tic-Tac-Go (Level 3)

What You Need

- *mSpace* pages 40–43
- counters

How to Play

- Players move only one counter after the first turn.
- Players may place a counter on top of another counter.
- Use Player A's *mSpace* page for the first game and Player B's page for the second.

How to Win

- The winner is the first player to complete a path from edge to edge.
- Paths can be made by marking squares from top to bottom or side to side.

> HOW TO PLAY

STEP 1 **Player A places counters on two factors and multiplies them.**

810	640	480	360	630
300	420	320	350	280
720	250	490	240	450
160	540	200	400	560

4 5 6 7 8 9

STEP 2 **Player A multiplies the product by 10 and marks an X on that number.**

810	640	480	360	630
300	420	320 (X)	350	280
720	250	490	240	450
160	540	200	400	560

4 5 6 7 8 9

PLAYER A

Equations
(4 x 8) x 10
32 x 10 = 320

STEP 3 **Player B moves one counter to another factor and multiplies them.**

810	640	480	360	630
300	420	320 (X)	350	280
720	250	490	240	450
160	540	200	400	560

4 5 6 7 8 9

STEP 4 **Player B multiplies the product by 10 and marks an O on that number.**

810	640	480	360	630
300	420	320 (X)	350	280
720 (O)	250	490	240	450
160	540	200	400	560

4 5 6 7 8 9

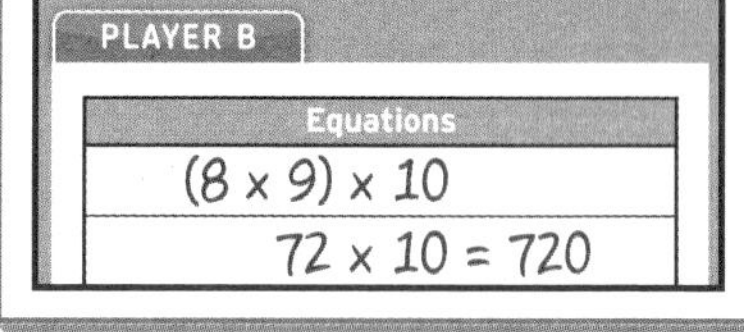
PLAYER B

Equations
(8 x 9) x 10
72 x 10 = 720

RECORDING SHEET

Tic-Tac-Go (Level 3)

> Decide who is Player A and who is Player B. Record your equations in the appropriate table.

810	640	480	360	630
300	420	320	350	280
720	250	490	240	450
160	540	200	400	560

4 5 6 7 8 9

PLAYER A

Equations

PLAYER B

Equations

Check the winner:	
_____ Player A	_____ Player B

RECORDING SHEET

Tic-Tac-Go (Level 3)

> Decide who is Player A and who is Player B.
Record your equations in the appropriate table.

810	640	480	360	630
300	420	320	350	280
720	250	490	240	450
160	540	200	400	560

4 5 6 7 8 9

PLAYER A

Equations

PLAYER B

Equations

Check the winner:	
______ Player A	______ Player B

> Optional: Use this space for calculations.

EXIT Ticket

BLOCK 1

> **Answer these questions.**

To win a round of *Tic-Tac-Go (Level 3)*, you need to mark the square with 360 inside. There are several ways to make 360. What are the possible factors you could place your counters on? How do you know?

I could place my counters on

________________ because

____

____

____

____

SCORE (0) (1) (2)

CAREER EXPLORATION

> **Market researchers use surveys to learn which products you like.**

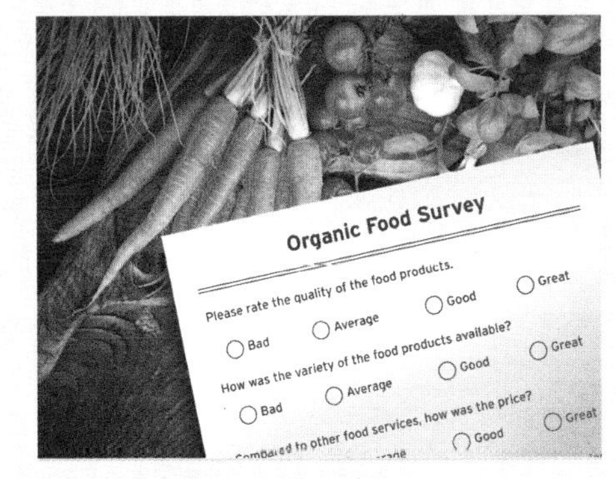

Think about the results of a market research survey. What math might a researcher use?

TOPIC 3

TOPIC 2

TOPIC 1

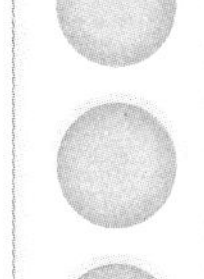

LESSON 3
CONCEPT

Multiply by Multiples of 10

> WORKED EXAMPLE

STEP 1 Rename the multiple of 10.

4×80

8 × 10

STEP 2 Apply the Associative Property.

$(4 \times 8) \times 10$

STEP 3 Find the product.

$(4 \times 8) \times 10$

$32 \times 10 = 320$

STEP 4 Write the equation.

$4 \times 80 = 320$

> TRY IT

1

STEP 1 Rename the multiple of 10.

6×40

______ × ______

STEP 2 Apply the Associative Property.

STEP 3 Find the product.

STEP 4 Write the equation.

> PRACTICE

2

STEP 1 Rename the multiple of 10.

70×4

______ × ______

STEP 2 Apply the Associative Property.

STEP 3 Find the product.

STEP 4 Write the equation.

Associative Property of Multiplication *(n)* When multiplying two or more numbers, you can group the numbers in any order and the product will be the same.

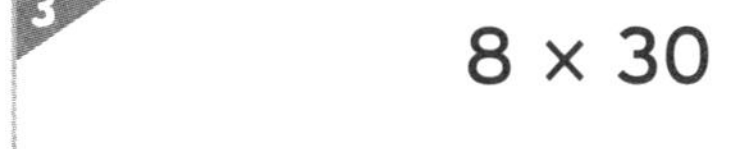

› PRACTICE

3 8×30

4 90×5

5 70×9

6 8×60

7 6×80

8 50×3

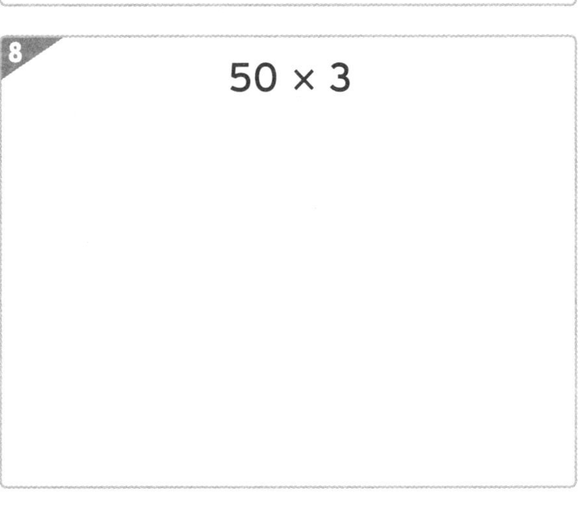

EXIT Ticket

BLOCK 1

TOPIC 3

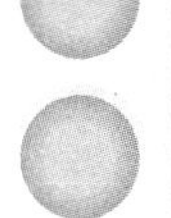

› Find the product.

9×50

TOPIC 2

› Answer this question.

You solved for the product of 90×5 in Problem 4. Why are the products for 90×5 and 9×50 the same?

The products for 90×5 and 9×50 are the same because

TOPIC 1

SCORE ⓪ ① ②

Multiply by Multiples of 10

> WORKED EXAMPLE

STEP 1 Rename the multiples of 10.

40 × 70

4 × 10 × 7 × 10

STEP 2 Rearrange the factors.

4 × 7 × 10 × 10

STEP 3 Apply the Associative Property.

(4 × 7) × 10 × 10

STEP 4 Find the product.

(28 × 10) × 10

280 × 10 = 2800

40 × 70 = 2800

> TRY IT

1

STEP 1 Rename the multiples of 10.

30 × 50

____ × ____ × ____ × ____

STEP 2 Rearrange the factors.

STEP 3 Apply the Associative Property.

STEP 4 Find the product.

> PRACTICE

2

STEP 1 Rename the multiples of 10.

80 × 40

____ × ____ × ____ × ____

STEP 2 Rearrange the factors.

STEP 3 Apply the Associative Property.

STEP 4 Find the product.

multiple of 10 *(n)* a number that has a factor of 10

› PRACTICE

3

80×30

4

50×90

5

60×70

6

50×60

7

40×80

8

30×90

EXIT Ticket

BLOCK 1

› **Find the errors and fix the math.**

$$80 \times 70$$

$$8 \times 10 \times 7 \times 10$$

$$(8 \times 7) \times 10$$

$$56 \times 10 = 560$$

$$80 \times 70 = 560$$

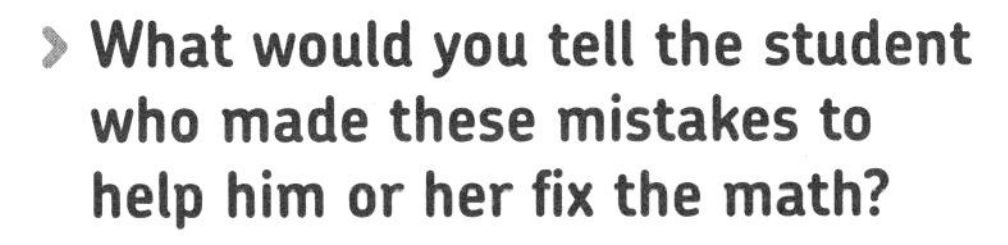

› **What would you tell the student who made these mistakes to help him or her fix the math?**

I would tell the student that

____

____

____

____

____

____

____

SCORE (0) (1) (2)

TOPIC 3

TOPIC 2

TOPIC 1

Solve Compare Problems

> WORKED EXAMPLE

Read It! **Read and identify the problem.**

VIDEO PRODUCER

Amy posts 4 online videos about a new theme park. Dan posts 3 times as many videos as Amy. How many more videos does Dan post?

PROBLEM TYPE Compare Problem

Show It! **Represent the problem.**

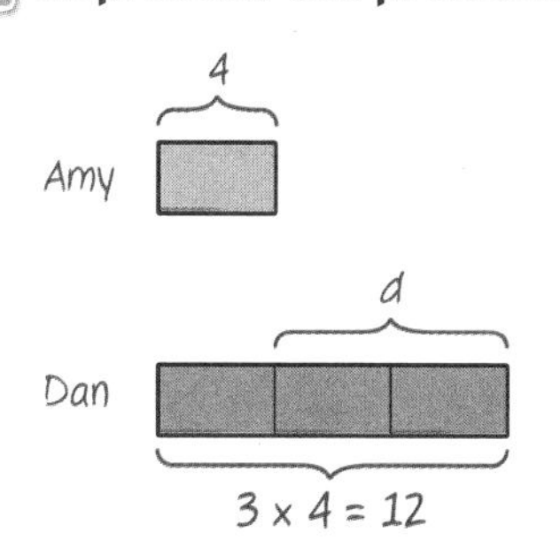

Solve It! **Solve the problem.**

$d = 2 \times 4$

$d = 8$

Dan posts 8 more videos.

Check It! **Check your work.**

> TRY IT

1

Read It! **Read and identify the problem.**

MARKETING MANAGER

An online store gives away 8 samples of peach yogurt. It gives away 4 times as many samples of honey yogurt. How many fewer peach samples does it give away?

PROBLEM TYPE ______

Show It! **Represent the problem.**

Solve It! **Solve the problem.**

The store gives away ______ fewer peach samples.

Check It! **Check your work.**

> PRACTICE

2

Read It! **Read and identify the problem.**

ADVERTISING AGENT

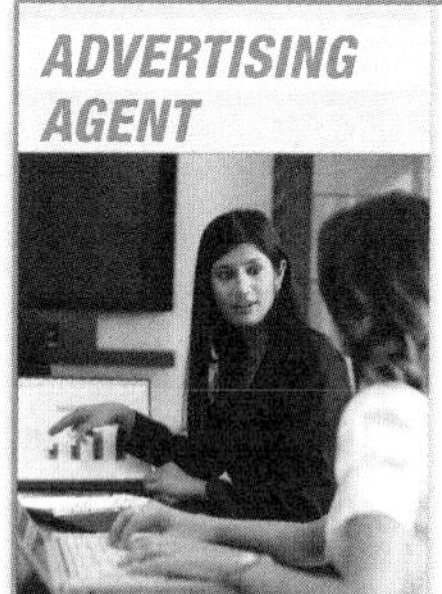

Lana buys 3 ads on a website. Omar buys 5 times as many ads on the same website. How many more ads does Omar buy?

PROBLEM TYPE ______

Show It! **Represent the problem.**

Solve It! **Solve the problem.**

Omar buys ______ more ads.

Check It! **Check your work.**

> PRACTICE

3

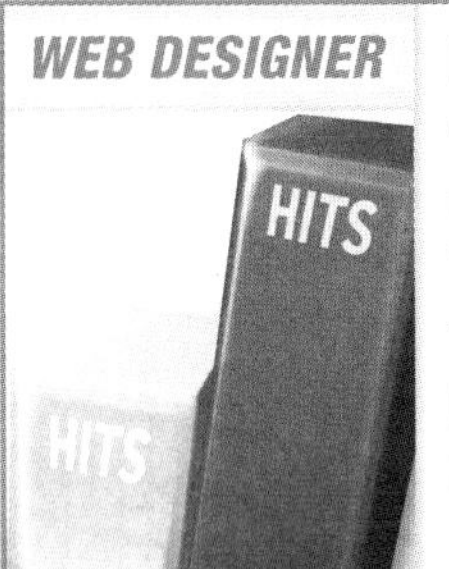

WEB DESIGNER Nadine designs two websites. Website A receives 5 hits. Website B receives 10 times as many hits. How many fewer hits does Website A receive?

PROBLEM TYPE ______________________

Website A receives ______ fewer hits.

4

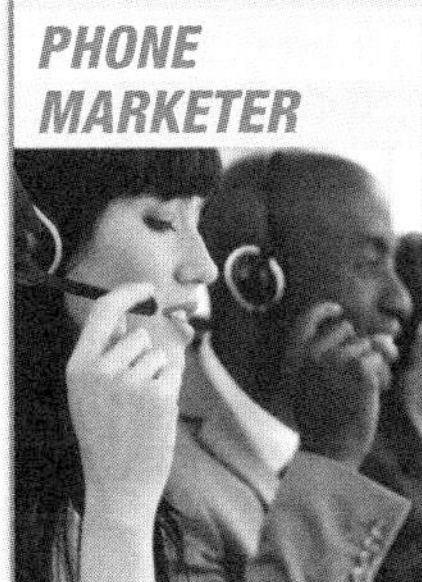

PHONE MARKETER Raj makes 90 marketing calls in a week. Fiona makes 6 times as many marketing calls. How many more marketing calls does Fiona make?

PROBLEM TYPE ______________________

Fiona makes ______ more calls than Raj.

EXIT Ticket

BLOCK 1

TOPIC 3

TOPIC 2

TOPIC 1

> **Solve this problem.**

You post two videos online. In the first hour, Video A gets 7 views. Video B gets 9 times as many views. How many more views does Video B get?

PROBLEM TYPE ______________________

Video B gets ______ more views.

SCORE ⓪ ① ②

BLOCK 1 **PERFORMANCE TASK**

> YOUR JOB
Social Media Manager

> YOUR TASK
Make a prize plan for a contest and calculate its total cost.

BLOCK 1

ANCHOR VIDEO CONNECTION

As the Anchor Video shows, giving away prizes is a great way to attract people's attention and get them talking about your website.

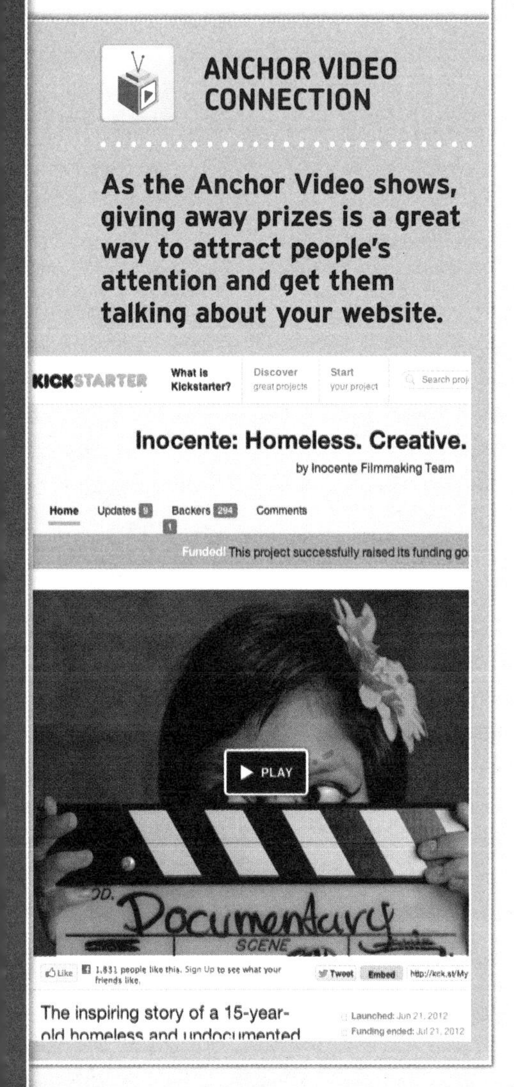

Develop a Marketing Contest

> **You are running a contest to promote a new website. Your budget for prizes is $1000. Make two prize plans, and then predict which plan will attract more entries.**

A EXPLORE

Complete the table to show the cost for different quantities of each prize. Some values are entered for you. In Apply, you will use the data in the table to create two plans.

SAMPLE PLAN

Contest Prizes		
Place	**Prize**	**Quantity**
1st	Game player	3
2nd	Headphones	4
3rd	T-shirt	4
4th	Cap	2
TOTAL		13

Tablet
$300

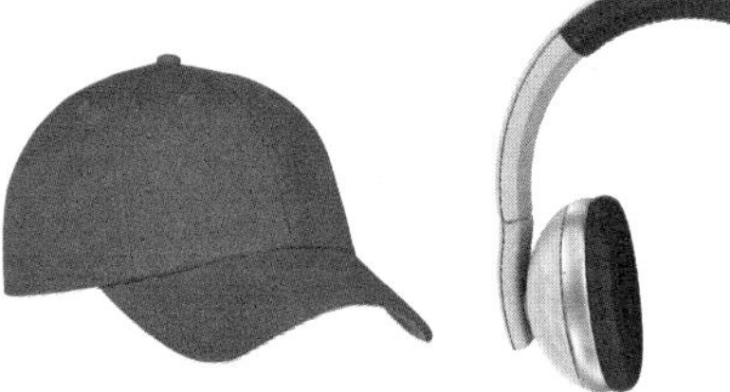

Cap
$10

Headphones
$30

T-shirt
$15

Game player
$100

Cost of Prizes (dollars)								
Prize	**1**	**2**	**3**	**4**	**5**	**6**	**7**	**8**
Cap	10	20	30					
T-shirt								
Headphones								
Game player								
Tablet								

B APPLY

For each plan, choose 4 prizes and their quantities. Your goal is to make the total cost of each plan equal $1000.

PLAN 1: CONTEST PRIZES

PLACE	PRIZE	QUANTITY	COST PER PRIZE	QUANTITY × COST PER PRIZE	COST
1st				______ × ______	
2nd				______ × ______	
3rd				______ × ______	
4th				______ × ______	
	TOTAL			TOTAL	

PLAN 2: CONTEST PRIZES

PLACE	PRIZE	QUANTITY	COST PER PRIZE	QUANTITY × COST PER PRIZE	COST
1st				______ × ______	
2nd				______ × ______	
3rd				______ × ______	
4th				______ × ______	
	TOTAL			TOTAL	

C ANALYZE

PREDICT Which plan do you think will attract more entries and gain more attention for the website? Explain why.

____

____

____

REFLECT What are the advantages and disadvantages of choosing the tablet for a first prize?

____

____

____

Evaluate

› **Rate how well you and your partner understood and completed each part of the performance task.**

Rating Scale			
None	Limited	Partial	Thorough
0	1	2	3

A Calculated the cost of different quantities of each prize.

Me 0 1 2 3

Partner 0 1 2 3

B Completed two plans for contest prizes and calculated their costs.

Me 0 1 2 3

Partner 0 1 2 3

C Answered each question accurately.

Me 0 1 2 3

Partner 0 1 2 3

EXTEND

If one of the plans costs $1025, why must a T-shirt be one of the prizes?

____

____

____

____

____

____

Scan Your Learning Strategies

Congratulations! You've completed Block 1 of *MATH 180*. For each question, fill in the circle that best describes your mindset. Then complete the sentence frames.

A CHALLENGE SEEKING

When you take on new challenges, you learn more and your brain becomes stronger and smarter.

Did you take on any challenging goals in the Success Zone during BLOCK 1?

① I did not try to do any challenging math in the Success Zone. I only tried the math problems I already knew how to do.

② I tried to do challenging math problems in the Success Zone because I had to or my teacher made me.

③ I chose to try really difficult problems, like the Wild Card, even when I didn't have to.

I (did/did not) take on challenging goals because

____

____

____

B EFFORT & PRACTICE

Practice gives your brain the exercise it needs to work at its best.

Did you commit time and effort to the Brain Arcade during BLOCK 1?

① I rarely played Brain Arcade games during this Block.

② I played Brain Arcade games only when I needed to. I practiced only a little at home, during lunch, and after school.

③ I played Brain Arcade games as much as possible. I even practiced at home, during lunch, or after school.

I spent (little/some/a lot of) time on the Brain Arcade because ______________________

____

____

C PERSISTENCE

When you keep trying to solve difficult problems, connections build up in your brain over time.

What did you do when you struggled to solve BLOCK 1 *mSpace* problems?

① I gave up on them very quickly.

② Sometimes I kept trying, or I asked a classmate or teacher for the answer.

③ I kept trying as much as possible and didn't give up. I reviewed earlier work, and I asked a classmate or teacher to help me understand the problems.

I (never/sometimes/often) gave up on math problems because ______________________

____

____

D LEARNING FROM MISTAKES AND FEEDBACK

Mistakes can be an opportunity to grow and stretch your "brain muscles."

What did you do when you made a mistake on a BLOCK 1 math problem?

① I tried to forget about it or made an excuse for it.

② I tried to keep from making the mistake again.

③ I thought about what I could have done differently and tried to improve.

I responded to my mistakes by ______________________

____

____

____

Score Your Mindset

Add up all the numbers that you selected (1, 2, or 3.) Then read the feedback in the chart.

If your total score was:	*You were in the:*
	**Fixed Mindset Zone** You were in the Fixed Mindset Zone this time. Your mindset may have held you back from doing your best.
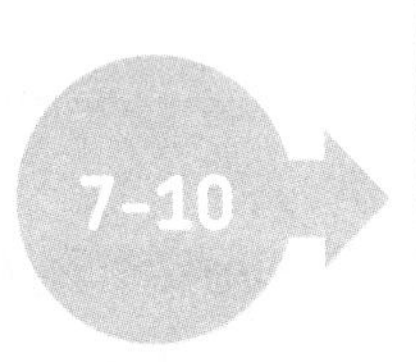	**Mixed Mindset Zone** You were in the Mixed Mindset Zone this time. You may have used some Growth Mindset thinking, but in other ways you may have held yourself back.
	**Growth Mindset Zone** You were in the Growth Mindset Zone this time. You used strategies that will help you grow your brain and get smarter.

How can you develop a Growth Mindset?

- Read the statements in the Mindset Scan again.
- Make a plan to help you choose the third statement in each category when you take a scan like this one again. Include specific goals in your plan.
- Review your plan as you study. Try to meet the goals you set for yourself.

Brain Boosting

What will you do to help your brain stay in the Growth Zone?

I will focus on:

- ☐ Challenge seeking
- ☐ Effort and practice
- ☐ Persistence
- ☐ Learning from mistakes

"Life is a lot like surfing... When you get caught in the impact zone, you've got to just get back up. Because you never know what may be over the next wave."

Bethany Hamilton, Professional surfer

What will I do?

____

Who will help me?

____

When will I do it?

____

How will this help me to grow?

____

BLOCK 2

The Distributive Property

Designing Your World

VOCABULARY

- bar model
- Distributive Property
- estimate
- expression
- factor
- partial product
- product
- variable

Paint the Town

Have you seen any murals in your neighborhood?

In this Anchor Video, a community in Brazil uses math to make one of the biggest murals in the world!

Math in Design

In this Block, you will explore how math is used in art, architecture, and design.

Industrial DESIGNERS

develop products that we use every day, like cars, toys, and the chair you're sitting on.

Game DESIGNERS

work in a **$65 billion**-per-year industry. And it's growing every year!

Have a knack for style?

Fashion DESIGNERS

create original clothing by sketching designs and selecting fabrics and patterns.

Architecture is a fast-growing field. By 2020, there will be over 140,000 jobs for

Architects

in the United States.

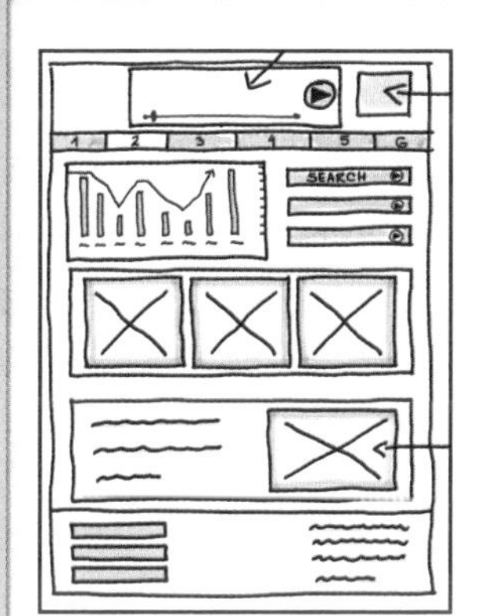

Do you like being your own boss? About **one-third** of

Web DESIGNERS

are self-employed.

Place Value in Multiplication

BLOCK 2

LESSON 1

Block Preview

> **Think about the Anchor Video and answer this question.**

If you wanted to make a large mural out of a picture, how would you do it?

> **Explain your strategy.**

I would make the mural by ______

______

______

______

______

LESSON 2

Build It

> **Create the greatest possible product by multiplying any two of these factors.**

1 3 5 9

Which two factors did you choose?
______ and ______

The greatest possible product is ______ .

> **Why did you choose these two factors?**

I chose these two factors because

______

______

______

LESSON 3

Brain Teaser

> **Solve this riddle.**

I am an odd factor of 36.
I have only 2 factors.
Which number am I? ______

> **Explain your reasoning.**

The mystery number is ______

because ______

______

______

______

LESSON 4

Tell Me All That You Can

› **About 36**

- ______
- ______
- ______
- ______

› **36 has 9 factors. How many can you name?**

The factors of 36 are:

•	•	•
•	•	•
•	•	•

LESSON 5

Who's Right?

› **Trey and Jane found two different answers to the same problem.**

Trey	Jane
$16 \times 4 = 64$	$16 \times 4 = 46$

Who's right? ______

› **How do you know who is correct?**

I know ______ is correct because ______

______

______

______

Sum It Up!

› **In this Topic, you learned how to multiply 1-digit by 2-digit numbers using place value and the Distributive Property.**

How does using the Distributive Property make multiplication easier?

You can use an area model to show and make sense of the multiplication.

5×14

BLOCK 2 > TOPIC 1

LESSON 1

CONCEPT

Multiply With a 2-Digit Factor

BLOCK 2

> WORKED EXAMPLE

STEP 1 **Split the factor greater than 10.**

7×16

10 + 6

16 is 1 ten and 6 ones.

STEP 2 **Split and label the rectangle.**

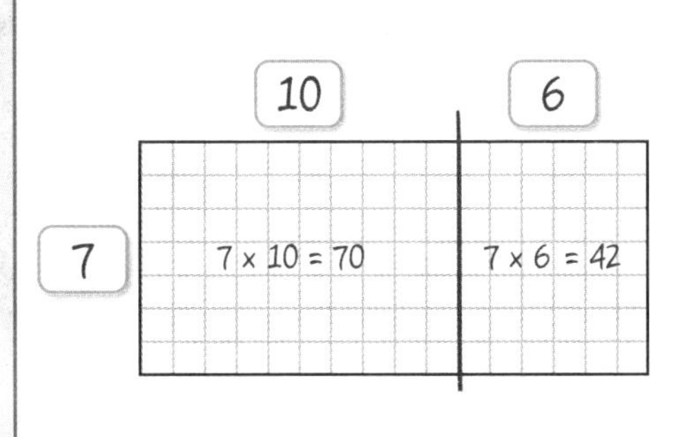

STEP 3 **Find the partial products.**

Equation 1 → 7 x 10 = 70

Equation 2 → 7 x 6 = 42

STEP 4 **Add the partial products.**

70 + 42 = 112

7 × 16 = 112

> TRY IT

1

STEP 1 **Split the factor greater than 10.**

14×6

______ + ______

______ is ______ ten and ______ ones.

STEP 2 **Split and label the rectangle.**

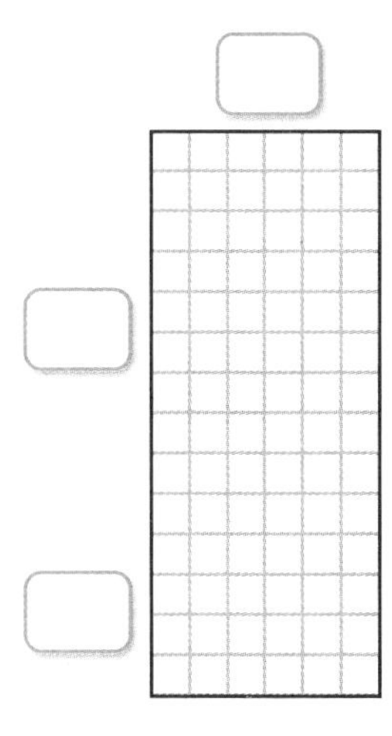

STEP 3 **Find the partial products.**

Equation 1 → ______________

Equation 2 → ______________

STEP 4 **Add the partial products.**

______ + ______ = ______

$14 \times 6 =$ ______

> PRACTICE

2

STEP 1 **Split the factor greater than 10.**

8×15

______ + ______

______ is ______ ten and ______ ones.

STEP 2 **Split and label the rectangle.**

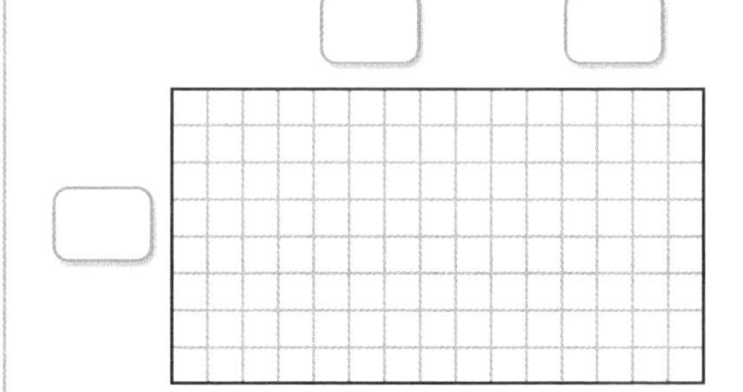

STEP 3 **Find the partial products.**

Equation 1 → ______________

Equation 2 → ______________

STEP 4 **Add the partial products.**

______ + ______ = ______

$8 \times 15 =$ ______

partial products *(n)* numbers you add when you break one of the factors into a sum of its parts in order to calculate a product

> PRACTICE

3

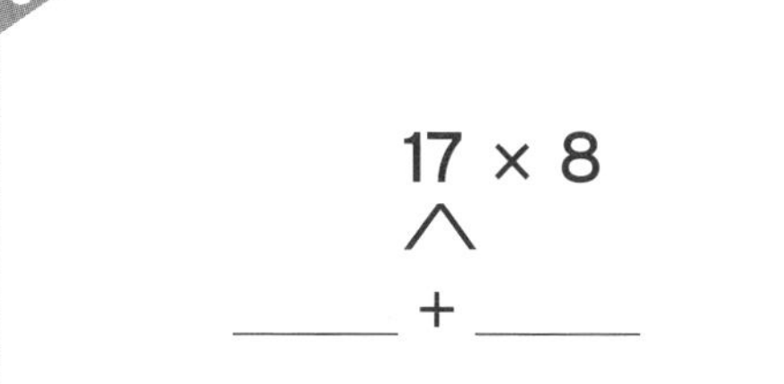

17×8

_____ + _____

_____ is _____ ten and _____ ones.

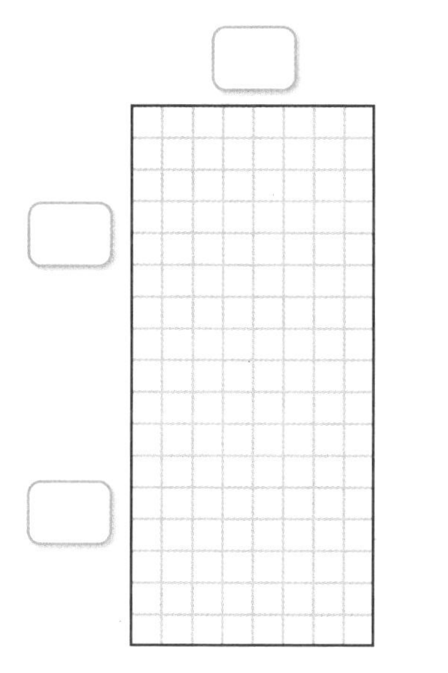

Equation 1 → ______________

Equation 2 → ______________

_____ + _____ = _____

$17 \times 8 =$ _____

4

9×16

_____ + _____

_____ is _____ ten and _____ ones.

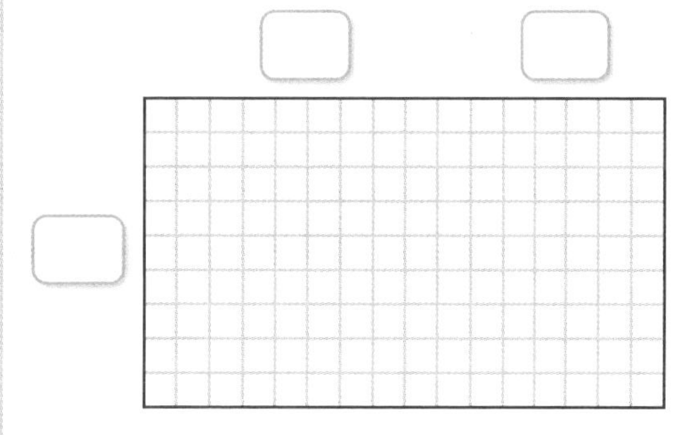

Equation 1 → ______________

Equation 2 → ______________

_____ + _____ = _____

$9 \times 16 =$ _____

EXIT
Ticket

BLOCK 2

> **Find the product.**

6×13

_____ + _____

_____ is _____ ten and _____ ones.

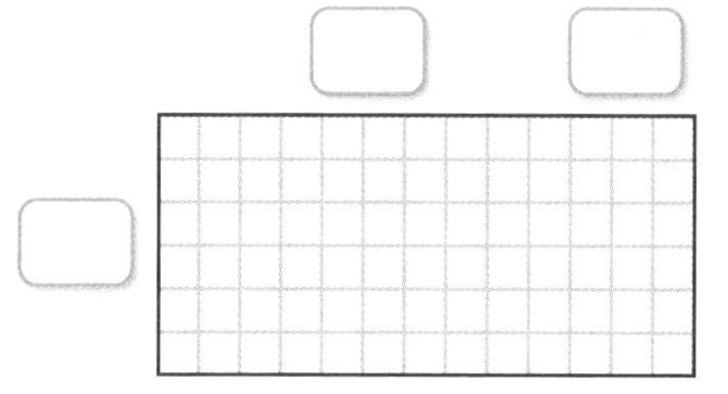

Equation 1 → ______________

Equation 2 → ______________

_____ + _____ = _____

$6 \times 13 =$ _____

> **Why do you think it is better to split 13 into 10 + 3 instead of 8 + 5 or 6 + 7?**

It is better to split 13 into 10 + 3 because ______________

____

____

SCORE 0 1 2

TOPIC 3

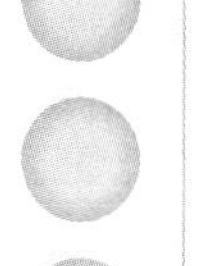

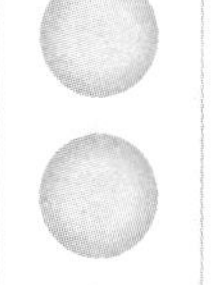

TOPIC 2

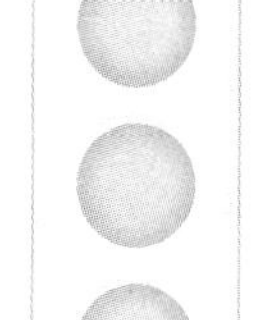

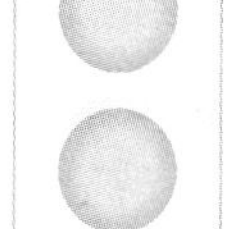

TOPIC 1

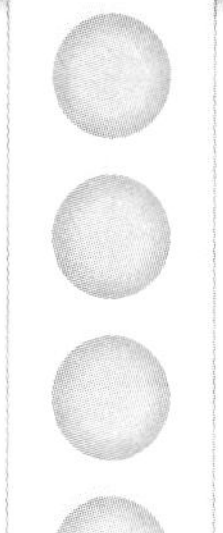

Develop Reasoning With Multiplication

RULES

Roll 2 Win (Level 1)

What You Need

- *mSpace* pages 58–61
- decahedron (black, 0–9)

What to Know

- Players take turns to complete a round.
- Players roll again if they roll a zero.
- Partners record each other's work.

How to Win

- After every round, each player records the product in the score box.
- After four rounds, players add their scores. The player with the greater total score wins.

> HOW TO PLAY

STEP 1 Roll the decahedron two times. Record each number in an empty box.

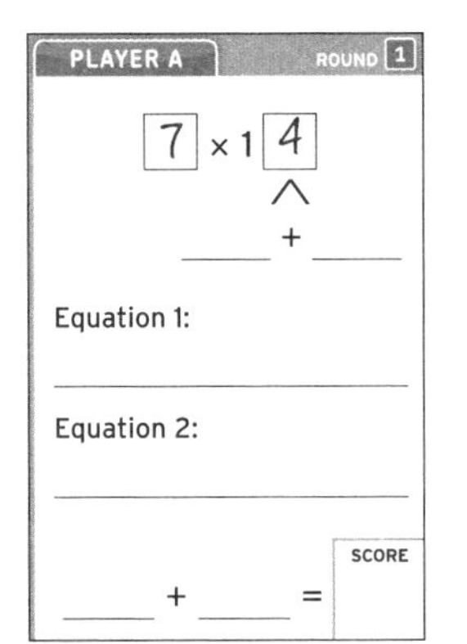

STEP 2 Split the factor greater than 10.

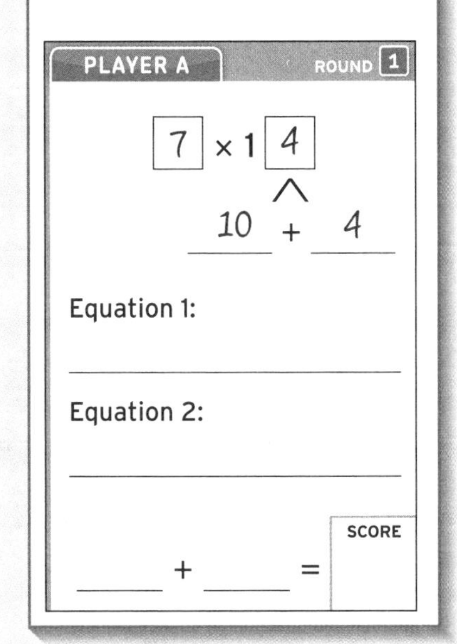

STEP 3 Find the partial products.

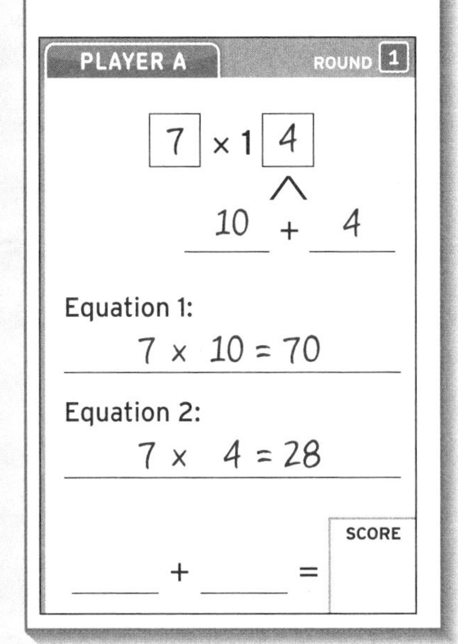

STEP 4 Add the partial products. Record your score.

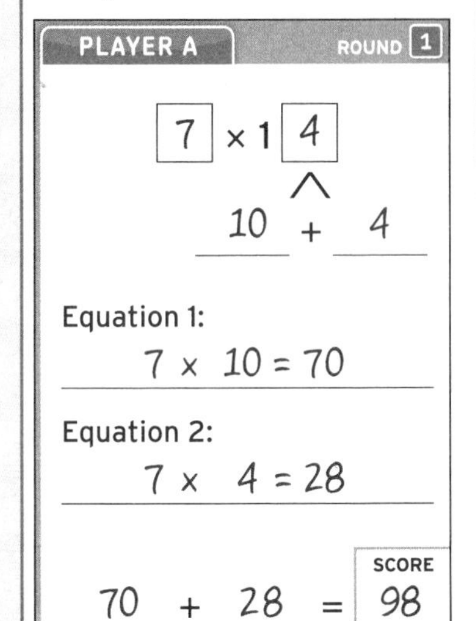

RECORDING SHEET

Roll 2 Win (Level 1)

> Record your equations and your partner's equations.
Optional: Use the grid paper on page 61 to draw and split rectangles.

PLAYER A

ROUND 1	ROUND 2	ROUND 3	ROUND 4	ADD YOUR SCORES
☐ × 1☐ ^ ___ + ___	☐ × 1☐ ^ ___ + ___	☐ × 1☐ ^ ___ + ___	☐ × 1☐ ^ ___ + ___	
Equation 1: ________	Equation 1: ________	Equation 1: ________	Equation 1: ________	
Equation 2: ________	Equation 2: ________	Equation 2: ________	Equation 2: ________	
___ + ___ = SCORE	___ + ___ = SCORE	___ + ___ = SCORE	___ + ___ = SCORE	

PLAYER B

ROUND 1	ROUND 2	ROUND 3	ROUND 4	ADD YOUR SCORES
☐ × 1☐ ^ ___ + ___	☐ × 1☐ ^ ___ + ___	☐ × 1☐ ^ ___ + ___	☐ × 1☐ ^ ___ + ___	
Equation 1: ________	Equation 1: ________	Equation 1: ________	Equation 1: ________	
Equation 2: ________	Equation 2: ________	Equation 2: ________	Equation 2: ________	
___ + ___ = SCORE	___ + ___ = SCORE	___ + ___ = SCORE	___ + ___ = SCORE	

RECORDING SHEET

Roll 2 Win (Level 1)

Record your equations and your partner's equations.
Optional: Use the grid paper on page 61 to draw and split rectangles.

PLAYER A

ROUND 1	ROUND 2	ROUND 3	ROUND 4	ADD YOUR SCORES
☐ × 1☐	☐ × 1☐	☐ × 1☐	☐ × 1☐	
____ + ____	____ + ____	____ + ____	____ + ____	
Equation 1: ________	Equation 1: ________	Equation 1: ________	Equation 1: ________	
Equation 2: ________	Equation 2: ________	Equation 2: ________	Equation 2: ________	
____ + ____ = SCORE	____ + ____ = SCORE	____ + ____ = SCORE	____ + ____ = SCORE	

PLAYER B

ROUND 1	ROUND 2	ROUND 3	ROUND 4	ADD YOUR SCORES
☐ × 1☐	☐ × 1☐	☐ × 1☐	☐ × 1☐	
____ + ____	____ + ____	____ + ____	____ + ____	
Equation 1: ________	Equation 1: ________	Equation 1: ________	Equation 1: ________	
Equation 2: ________	Equation 2: ________	Equation 2: ________	Equation 2: ________	
____ + ____ = SCORE	____ + ____ = SCORE	____ + ____ = SCORE	____ + ____ = SCORE	

Optional: Draw and split rectangles to help you multiply.

EXIT Ticket

BLOCK 2

> **Answer this question.**

What strategy could you use to win a game of *Roll 2 Win*?

The strategy I could use to win the game is ______________________

____

____

____

____

____

____

SCORE (0) (1) (2)

CAREER EXPLORATION

> **Architects use mathematics to make drawings of buildings.**

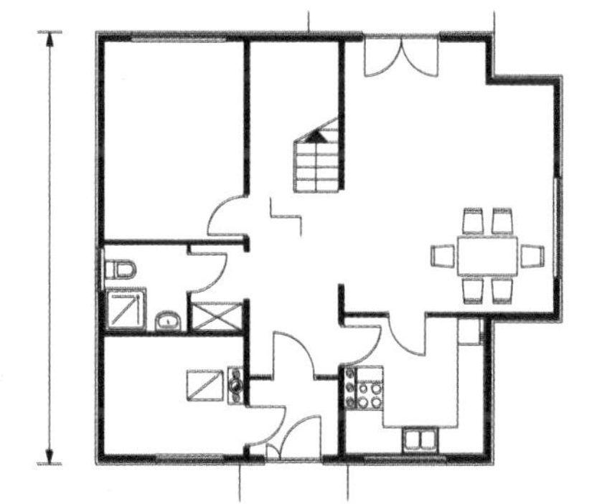

How could an architect use an area model to show the amount of carpet needed for a bedroom?

TOPIC 3

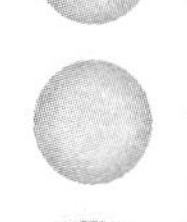

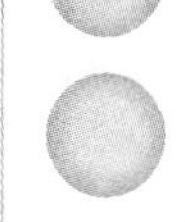

TOPIC 2

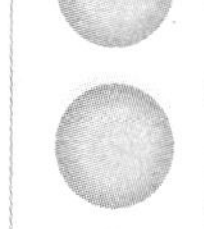

TOPIC 1

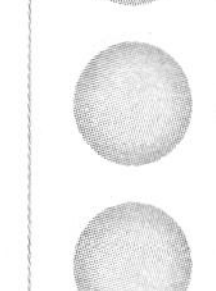
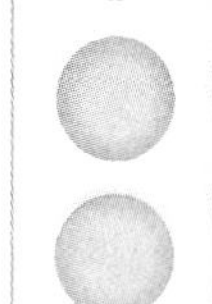
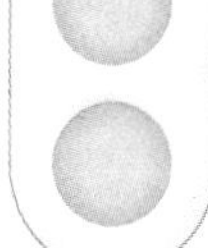

Apply the Distributive Property to Multiply

WORKED EXAMPLE

STEP 1 Split the factor greater than 10.

8×16

$16 = 10 + 6$

STEP 2 Rewrite the multiplication expression.

$8 \times (10 + 6)$

STEP 3 Find the partial products.

$(8 \times 10) + (8 \times 6)$

80 48

STEP 4 Find the partial products.

$80 + 48 = 128$

$8 \times 16 = 128$

TRY IT

1

STEP 1 Split the factor greater than 10.

17×5

_____ + _____

STEP 2 Rewrite the multiplication expression.

STEP 3 Find the partial products.

STEP 4 Add the partial products.

PRACTICE

2

STEP 1 Split the factor greater than 10.

3×15

_____ + _____

STEP 2 Rewrite the multiplication expression.

STEP 3 Find the partial products.

STEP 4 Add the partial products.

Distributive Property *(n)* Multiplying a sum by a number is the same as adding the partial products.

> PRACTICE

3 4×17

4 16×9

5 13×8

6 14×4

7 19×7

8 6×15

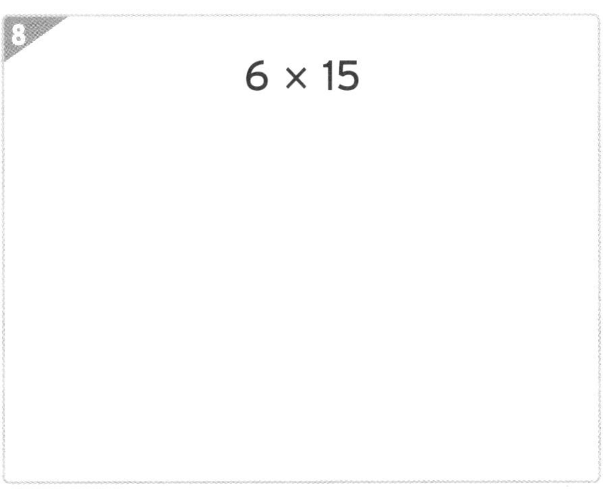

EXIT Ticket

BLOCK 2

TOPIC 3

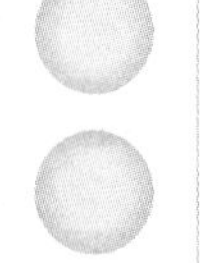

> **Find the product.**

18×4

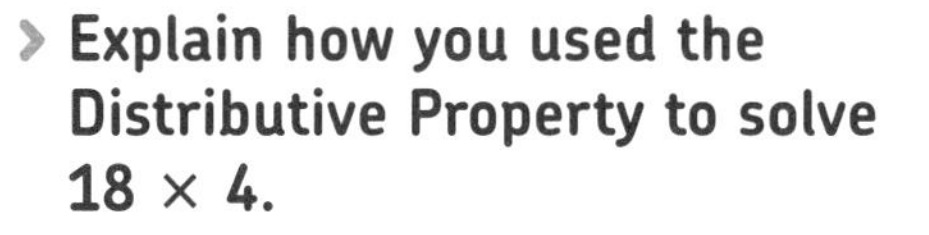

> **Explain how you used the Distributive Property to solve 18 × 4.**

TOPIC 2

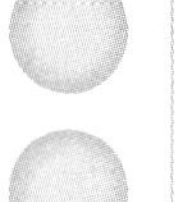
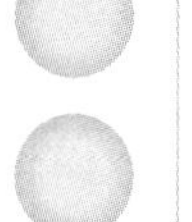
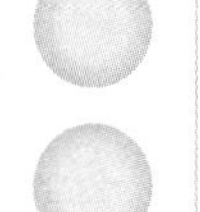

First, I split ______ into

______ + ______.

Then, I rewrote the problem like this:

____

Next, I found the partial products.

TOPIC 1

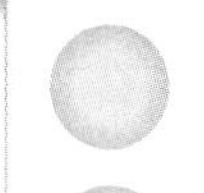

______ × ______ = ______ and

______ × ______ = ______

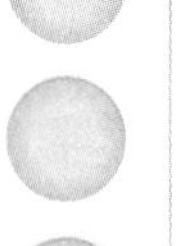

Finally, I ______________________

____

____

SCORE (0) (1) (2)

Multiply 1-Digit by 2-Digit Factors

> WORKED EXAMPLE

STEP 1 Split the factor greater than 10.

7×46

40 + 6

STEP 2 Rewrite the multiplication expression.

$7 \times (40 + 6)$

STEP 3 Find the partial products.

$(7 \times 40) + (7 \times 6)$

280 42

STEP 4 Add the partial products.

$280 + 42 = 322$

$7 \times 46 = 322$

> TRY IT

1

STEP 1 Split the factor greater than 10.

87×4

_____ + _____

STEP 2 Rewrite the multiplication expression.

STEP 3 Find the partial products.

STEP 4 Add the partial products.

> PRACTICE

2

STEP 1 Split the factor greater than 10.

7×35

_____ + _____

STEP 2 Rewrite the multiplication expression.

STEP 3 Find the partial products.

STEP 4 Add the partial products.

expression *(n)* A grouping of numbers and/or variables and operations symbols; does not have an equal sign or is on one side of an equal sign.

> PRACTICE

3 3×92

4 56×9

5 38×5

6 7×51

7 6×62

8 69×8

EXIT Ticket

BLOCK 2

TOPIC 3 · TOPIC 2 · TOPIC 1

> **Find the errors and fix them.**

43×6

$40 + 3$

$(40 + 3) \times 6$

$(4 \times 6) + (3 \times 6)$

24   18

$24 + 18 = 42$

$43 \times 6 = 42$

> **Explain how you know there are errors.**

I know there are errors because

___

___

___

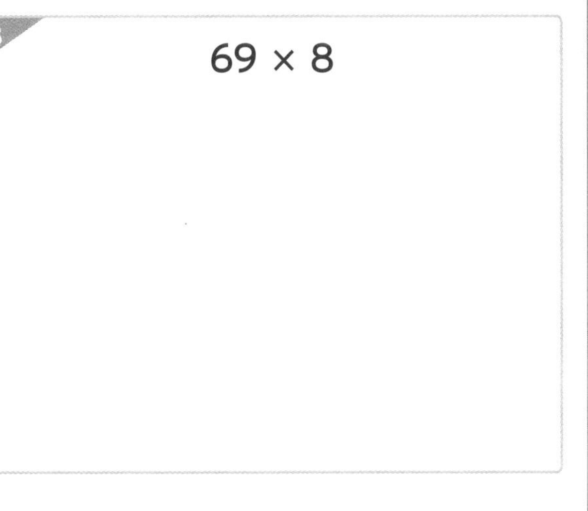

SCORE ⓪ ① ②

LESSON 5

PROBLEM SOLVING

Solve Equal Groups and Compare Problems

> WORKED EXAMPLE

Read It! **Read and identify the problem.**

APP DESIGNER

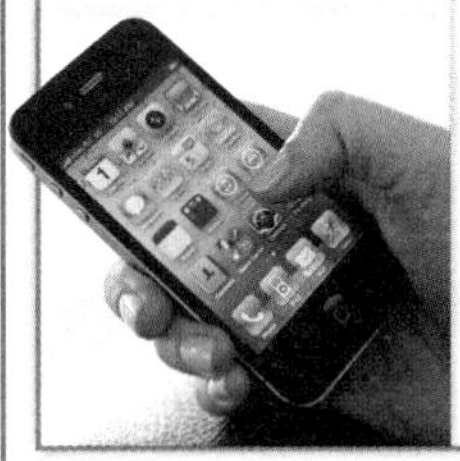

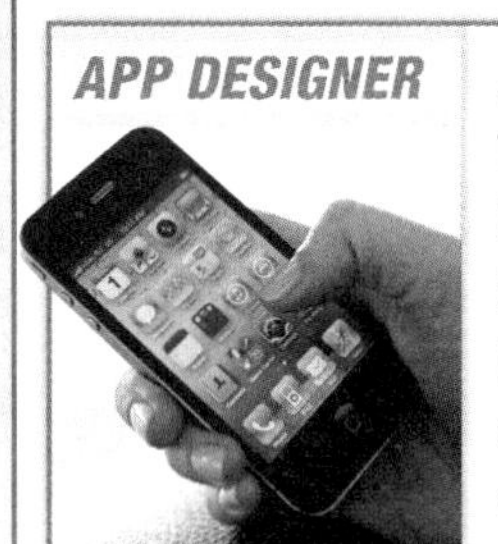

Jason created 13 cell phone apps. Dakota created 5 times as many. How many more cell phone apps did Dakota create?

PROBLEM TYPE *Compare Problem*

Show It! **Represent the problem.**

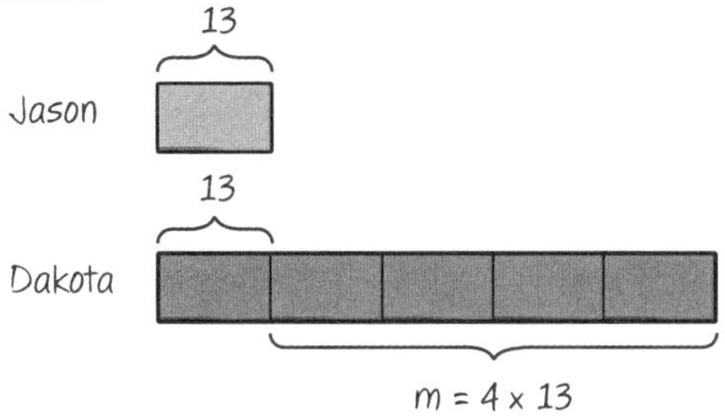

Solve It! **Solve the problem.**

$$4 \times 13 = (4 \times 10) + (4 \times 3)$$
$$= \quad 40 \quad + \quad 12$$
$$m = 52$$

Check It! **Check your work.**

> TRY IT

1

Read It! **Read and identify the problem.**

INDUSTRIAL DESIGNER

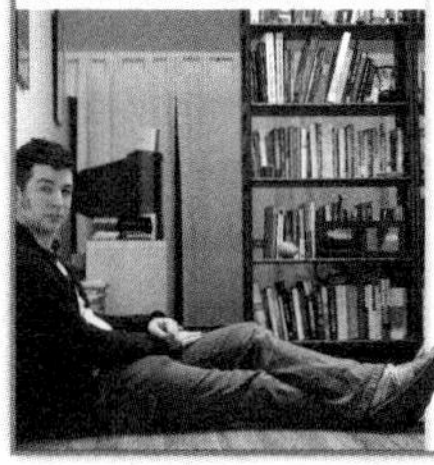

Lee designed a bookshelf with 6 shelves. Each shelf weighs 12 pounds. The frame weighs 38 pounds. What does the bookshelf weigh?

PROBLEM TYPE ____________________

Show It! **Represent the problem.**

Solve It! **Solve the problem.**

Check It! **Check your work.**

> PRACTICE

2

Read It! **Read and identify the problem.**

INTERIOR DESIGNER

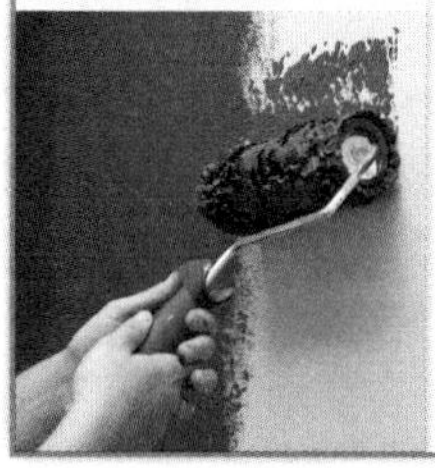

Jenna is painting her bedroom. The first wall is 72 square feet. The second wall is 3 times the size of the first wall. How many more square feet is the second wall?

PROBLEM TYPE ____________________

Show It! **Represent the problem.**

Solve It! **Solve the problem.**

Check It! **Check your work.**

> PRACTICE

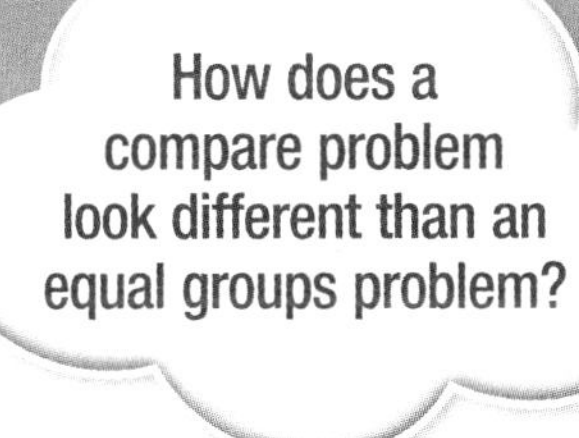

3

ARCHITECT

Jada designed a school basement. She made 8 computer labs that were 75 square feet each. The hallway was 81 square feet. How many square feet is the basement?

PROBLEM TYPE ______________________

4

ARCHITECT

The new wing of an art museum has 3 times as many windows as the old wing. Together, both wings have 32 windows. How many windows are in the new wing?

PROBLEM TYPE ______________________

EXIT Ticket

BLOCK 2

> **Solve this problem.**

You are designing a new movie complex. There are 14 movie theaters and 3 exits per theater. The food area has 9 exits. How many exits are there altogether?

PROBLEM TYPE ______________________

TOPIC 3

TOPIC 2

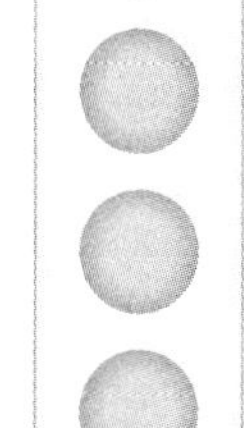

TOPIC 1

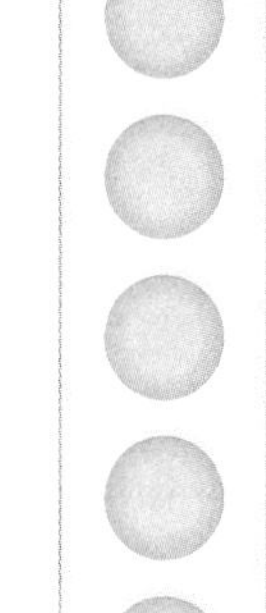

SCORE (0) (1) (2)

Strategies for Multiplication

LESSON 1

Find the Pattern

> **Find the rule. Then, write a number in the circle using the rule.**

Inside the circle: 3, 21, 27, 30, 39, 51

Outside the circle: 5, 40, 62, 46, 58

> **Why does the number you wrote belong in the circle?**

I wrote ________ in the circle because ________________

____

____

LESSON 2

Brain Teaser

> **Solve this riddle.**

Vicki is in elementary school. She is exactly half the age of her sister. What could be the ages of Vicki and her sister?

Vicki could be ______ years old.

Her sister would be ______ years old.

> **How did you begin working on this riddle?**

I began working on this riddle by

____

____

____

LESSON 3

Who's Right?

> **Bill was playing *Roll 2 Win* with Jayla. Bill rolled a 3 and a 9.**

Bill decided to place his rolls like this: 3 × 19. Jayla said, "I would have made 9 × 13." Who's right? ________

> **Do you agree with Bill or Jayla? Explain your reasoning.**

I agree with ________________

because ________________

____

____

LESSON 4

Which Does Not Belong?

› These numbers form a pattern. Circle the number that does not belong.

7, 14, 21, 28, 36, 42

› **What rule describes this pattern?**

The rule that describes this pattern is ______________________

____

____

LESSON 5

Brain Teaser

› Complete the puzzle.

9	×		=	27
−		+		−
	×		=	
=		=		=
3	×	5	=	

› **How would you know if you wrote a wrong answer in the puzzle?**

I would know if I wrote a wrong answer in the puzzle because

____

____

Sum It Up!

› **In this Topic, you learned how to multiply 1-digit by 3-digit numbers using the Distributive Property.**

I solved the problem $6 \times 285 = 1710$. How can I check whether my product is reasonable?

You can estimate by multiplying 6×300 to get 1800. Since the two products are close, the answer is reasonable.

Multiply With a 3-Digit Factor

> WORKED EXAMPLE

STEP 1 Split the 3-digit factor.

245 × 6

200 + 40 + 5

STEP 2 Split and label the rectangle.

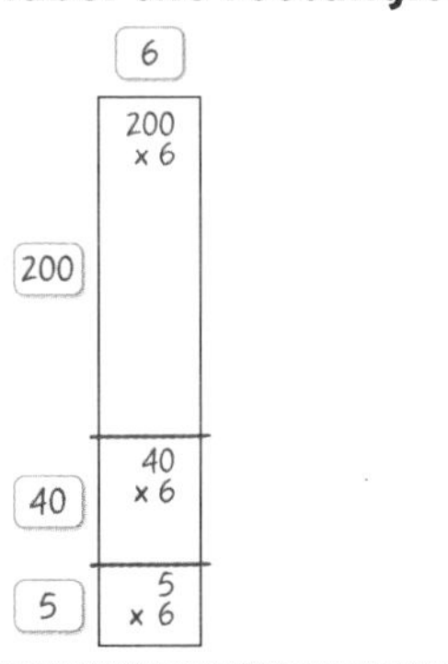

STEP 3 Find the partial products.

Equation 1 → 200 × 6 = 1200

Equation 2 → 40 × 6 = 240

Equation 3 → 5 × 6 = 30

STEP 4 Add the partial products.

$$\begin{array}{r} 1200 \\ 240 \\ +\ 30 \\ \hline 1470 \end{array}$$

245 × 6 = 1470

> TRY IT

1

STEP 1 Split the 3-digit factor.

3 × 178

_____ + _____ + _____

STEP 2 Split and label the rectangle.

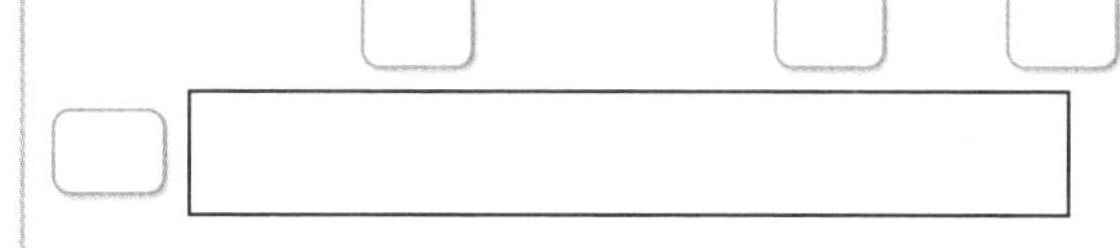

STEP 3 Find the partial products.

Equation 1 → _______________

Equation 2 → _______________

Equation 3 → _______________

STEP 4 Add the partial products.

3 × 178 = _____

> PRACTICE

2

STEP 1 Split the 3-digit factor.

4 × 356

_____ + _____ + _____

STEP 2 Split and label the rectangle.

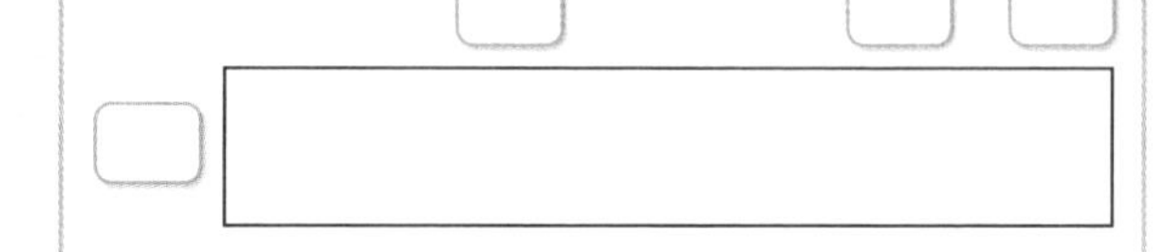

STEP 3 Find the partial products.

Equation 1 → _______________

Equation 2 → _______________

Equation 3 → _______________

STEP 4 Add the partial products.

4 × 356 = _____

› PRACTICE

3

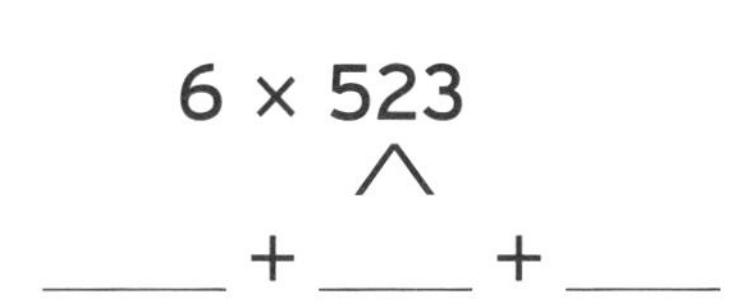

6×523

____ + ____ + ____

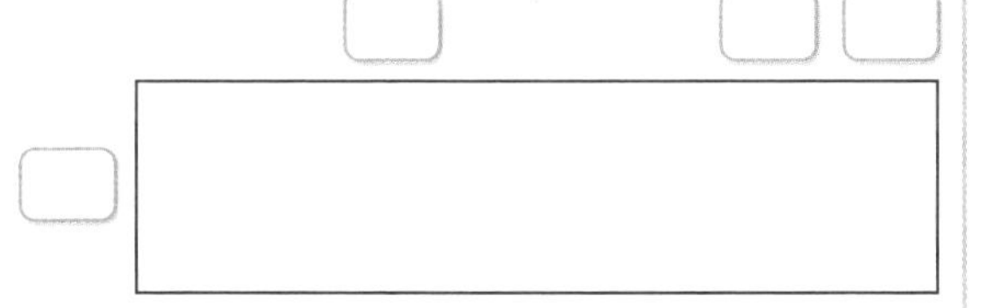

Equation 1 → ____________

Equation 2 → ____________

Equation 3 → ____________

$6 \times 523 =$ ____

4

186×9

____ + ____ + ____

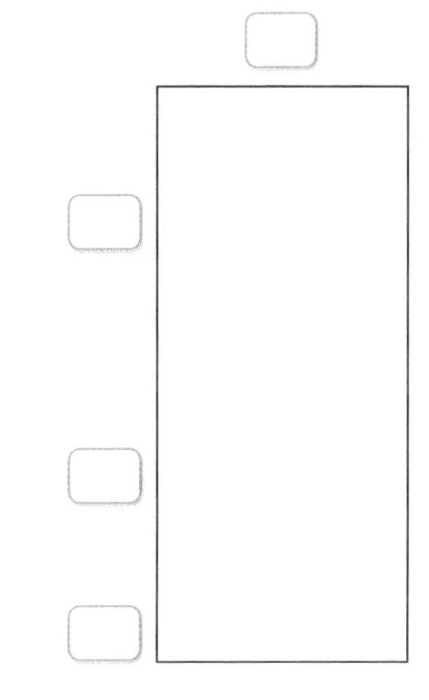

Equation 1 → ____________

Equation 2 → ____________

Equation 3 → ____________

$186 \times 9 =$ ____

EXIT Ticket

BLOCK 2

› Find the product.

4×352

____ + ____ + ____

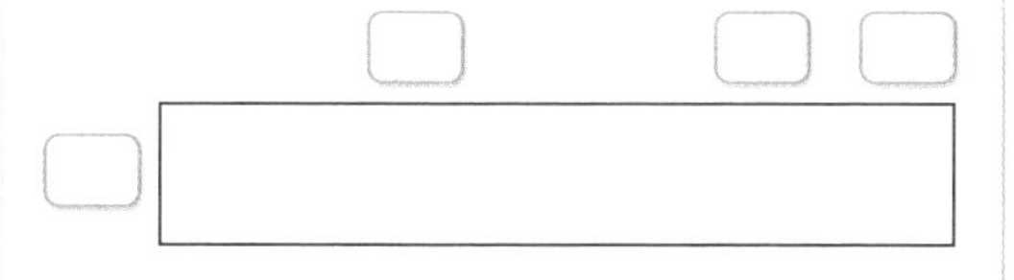

Equation 1 → ____________

Equation 2 → ____________

Equation 3 → ____________

$4 \times 352 =$ ____

› How does splitting a rectangle help you multiply 4 × 352?

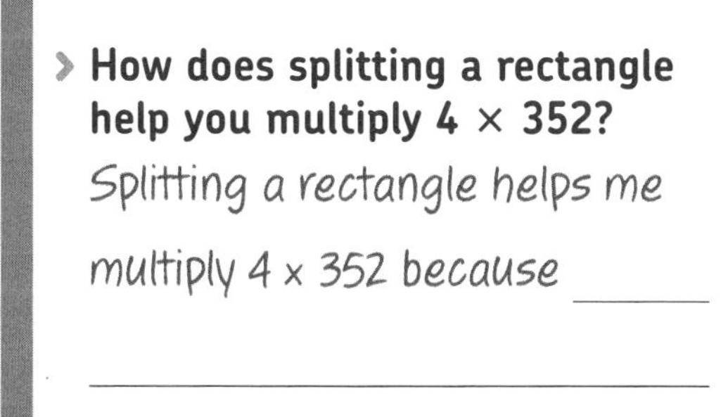

Splitting a rectangle helps me multiply 4 x 352 because ________

____

____

SCORE

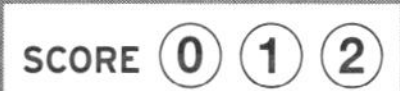

TOPIC 3

TOPIC 2

TOPIC 1

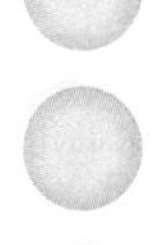

Estimate and Compare Products

> WORKED EXAMPLE

STEP 1 **Estimate the product.**

3 × 487

Estimate: 3 × 500 = 1500

STEP 2 **Rename the 3-digit factor.**

3 x (400 + 80 + 7)

STEP 3 **Find the partial products.**

(3 x 400) + (3 x 80) + (3 x 7)

3 x 400 = 1200

3 x 80 = 240

3 x 7 = 21

STEP 4 **Add the partial products.**

$$\begin{array}{r} 1200 \\ 240 \\ +\ 21 \\ \hline 1461 \end{array}$$

3 × 487 = 1461

Is your answer reasonable? yes

> TRY IT

1

STEP 1 **Estimate the product.**

6 × 723

Estimate: ______ × ______ = ______

STEP 2 **Rename the 3-digit factor.**

STEP 3 **Find the partial products.**

STEP 4 **Add the partial products.**

6 × 723 = ______

Is your answer reasonable? ______

> PRACTICE

2

STEP 1 **Estimate the product.**

5 × 614

Estimate: ______ × ______ = ______

STEP 2 **Rename the 3-digit factor.**

STEP 3 **Find the partial products.**

STEP 4 **Add the partial products.**

5 × 614 = ______

Is your answer reasonable? ______

estimate *(n)* A number that is close to the exact answer.

estimate *(v)* To approximate a calculation using numbers that are easier to work with.

> PRACTICE

3

7×296

Estimate: _____ × _____ = _____

$7 \times 296 =$ _____

Is your answer reasonable? _____

4

4×438

Estimate: _____ × _____ = _____

$4 \times 438 =$ _____

Is your answer reasonable? _____

EXIT Ticket

BLOCK 2

> **Answer this question.**

Is 5600 a reasonable estimate for the product of 7×841? Why or why not?

5600 is/is not a reasonable estimate for the product of 7 x 841 because ____________

____

____

____

____

If my estimate is close to the product I found, I know my solution is probably correct.

TOPIC 3

TOPIC 2

TOPIC 1

SCORE ⓪ ① ②

Develop Estimation Strategies

RULES

Roll 2 Win (Level 2)

What You Need

- *mSpace* pages 74–77
- decahedron (black, 0–9)

What to Know

- Players take turns to complete a round.
- Players roll again if they roll a zero.
- Partners record each other's work.

How to Win

- After every round, each player records the product in the score box.
- After four rounds, players add their scores. The player with the greater total score wins.

▼ WORKED EXAMPLE

STEP 1 Roll the decahedron four times. Record each number to make the greatest product.

STEP 2 Split the 3-digit factor.

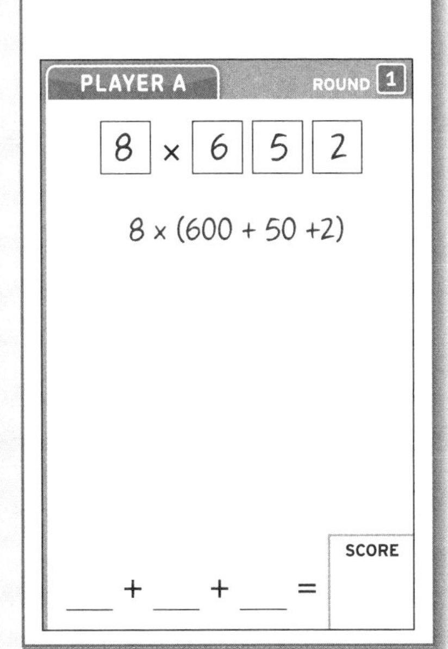

STEP 3 Find the partial products.

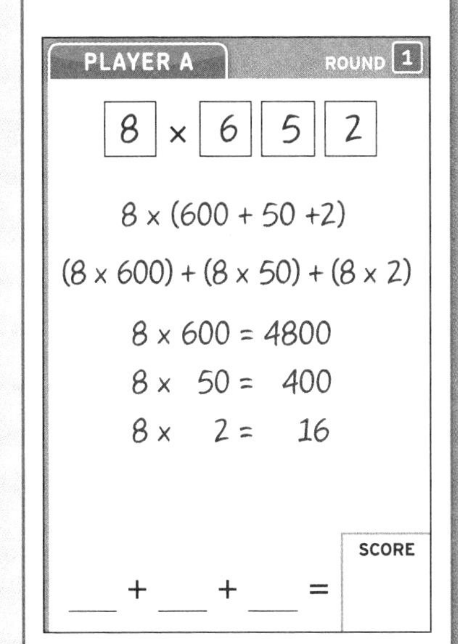

STEP 4 Add the partial products. Record your score.

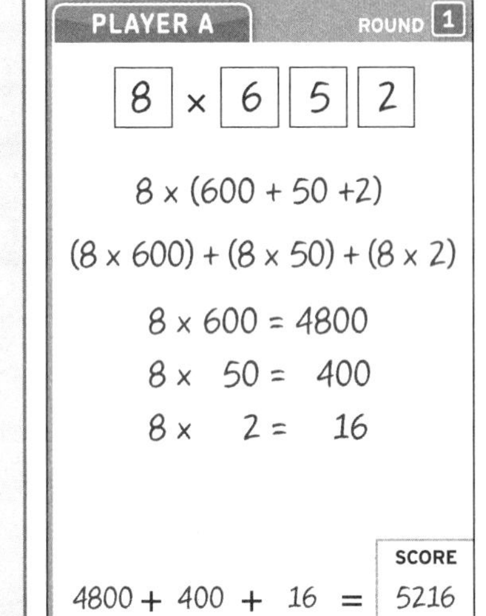

RECORDING SHEET

Roll 2 Win (Level 2)

Record your equations and your partner's equations. Optional: Use page 77 if you need extra space to work or to draw and split rectangles.

PLAYER A

ROUND 1	ROUND 2	ROUND 3	ROUND 4	ADD YOUR SCORES
☐ × ☐☐☐	☐ × ☐☐☐	☐ × ☐☐☐	☐ × ☐☐☐	
__ + __ + __ = SCORE	__ + __ + __ = SCORE	__ + __ + __ = SCORE	__ + __ + __ = SCORE	

PLAYER B

ROUND 1	ROUND 2	ROUND 3	ROUND 4	ADD YOUR SCORES
☐ × ☐☐☐	☐ × ☐☐☐	☐ × ☐☐☐	☐ × ☐☐☐	
__ + __ + __ = SCORE	__ + __ + __ = SCORE	__ + __ + __ = SCORE	__ + __ + __ = SCORE	

RECORDING SHEET

Roll 2 Win (Level 2)

Record your equations and your partner's equations. Optional: Use page 77 if you need extra space or want to draw and split rectangles.

PLAYER A

ROUND 1	ROUND 2	ROUND 3	ROUND 4	ADD YOUR SCORES
☐ × ☐☐☐	☐ × ☐☐☐	☐ × ☐☐☐	☐ × ☐☐☐	
___ + ___ + ___ = SCORE	___ + ___ + ___ = SCORE	___ + ___ + ___ = SCORE	___ + ___ + ___ = SCORE	

PLAYER B

ROUND 1	ROUND 2	ROUND 3	ROUND 4	ADD YOUR SCORES
☐ × ☐☐☐	☐ × ☐☐☐	☐ × ☐☐☐	☐ × ☐☐☐	
___ + ___ + ___ = SCORE	___ + ___ + ___ = SCORE	___ + ___ + ___ = SCORE	___ + ___ + ___ = SCORE	

> Optional: Use this page if you need extra space to work or if you want to draw and split rectangles to help you multiply.

EXIT Ticket

BLOCK 2

> Find the errors and fix them.

PLAYER A ROUND 1

3 × 5 7 8

3 x 700 = 2100

3 x 80 = 240

3 x 5 = 15

2100 + 240 + 15 = SCORE 2355

SCORE 0 1 2

CAREER EXPLORATION

> Web designers use mathematics to create layouts for web pages.

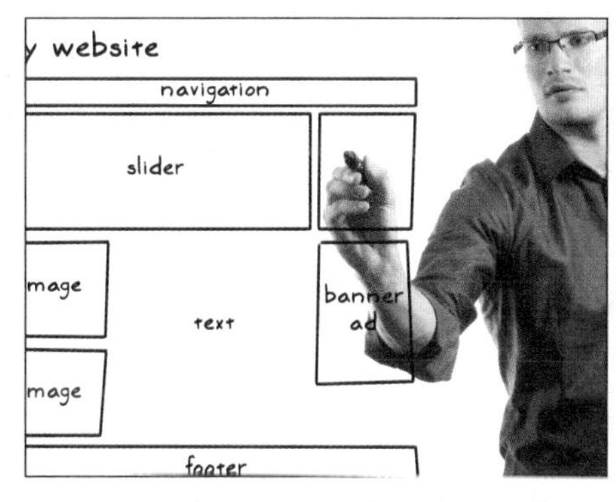

How could a web designer use an area model to design a web page?

TOPIC 3

TOPIC 2

TOPIC 1

Identify a Rule

> WORKED EXAMPLE

STEP 1 **Find the rule.**

INPUT	EQUATIONS	OUTPUT
1		8
2		16
3		24
4		32
5	5 x 8 = 40	40

Output = 8 × Input

STEP 2 **Express the rule with a variable.**

Output = 8 × n

Output = $8n$

STEP 3 **Complete the missing outputs.**

INPUT	EQUATIONS	OUTPUT
1		8
2		16
3		24
4		32
5	5 x 8 = 40	40
10	10 x 8 = 80	80
12	12 x 8 = 96	96

STEP 4 **Apply the rule using a different input.**

If the input is 20, then the output is 160.

> TRY IT

1

STEP 1 **Find the rule.**

INPUT	EQUATIONS	OUTPUT
2		12
4		24
6		36
8		48
10		

Output = ______ × Input

STEP 2 **Express the rule with a variable.**

Output = ______ × ______

Output = ______

STEP 3 **Complete the missing outputs.**

INPUT	EQUATIONS	OUTPUT
2		12
4		24
6		36
8		48
10		
12		
20		

STEP 4 **Apply the rule using a different input.**

If the input is 30, then the output is ______.

> PRACTICE

2

STEP 1 **Find the rule.**

INPUT	EQUATIONS	OUTPUT
1		10
2		20
3		30
4		40
5		

Output = ______ × Input

STEP 2 **Express the rule with a variable.**

Output = ______ × ______

Output = ______

STEP 3 **Complete the missing outputs.**

INPUT	EQUATIONS	OUTPUT
1		10
2		20
3		30
4		40
5		
6		
7		

STEP 4 **Apply the rule using a different input.**

If the input is 15, then the output is ______.

variable *(n)* A symbol in an expression that represents a value that may change or be unknown.

> PRACTICE

3

INPUT	EQUATIONS	OUTPUT
2		14
4		28
6		42
8		56
10		

Output = ______ × Input

Output = ______ × _____

Output = ______

INPUT	EQUATIONS	OUTPUT
2		14
4		28
6		42
8		56
10		
12		
14		

If the input is 25, then the output is ______.

4

INPUT	EQUATIONS	OUTPUT
2		22
4		44
6		66
8		88
10		

Output = ______ × Input

Output = ______ × _____

Output = ______

INPUT	EQUATIONS	OUTPUT
2		22
4		44
6		66
8		88
10		
12		
14		

If the input is 20, then the output is ______.

EXIT Ticket

BLOCK 2

> **Complete the function table.**

INPUT	EQUATIONS	OUTPUT
3		6
6		12
9		18
12		
15		
18		36
21		

> **Identify the rule, and complete the sentence frames.**

For every input *n*, the value of the output is ______.

If the input is 45, then the output is ______.

SCORE ⓪ ① ②

TOPIC 3

TOPIC 2

TOPIC 1

Solve Multi-Step Problems

> WORKED EXAMPLE

Read It! Read and identify the problem.

ARTIST

In Round 1 of a contest, 68 of 86 artists bought supplies online. The rest went to a store. In Round 2, twice as many artists went to the store. How many artists went to the store in Round 2?

PROBLEM TYPE: *Change Problem*

Show It! Represent the problem.

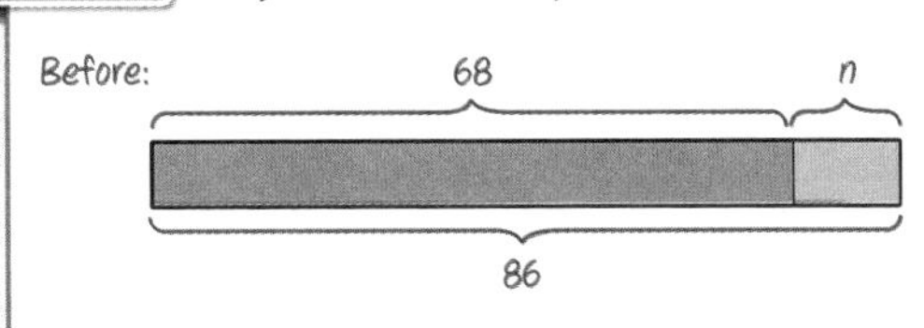

Solve It! Solve the problem.

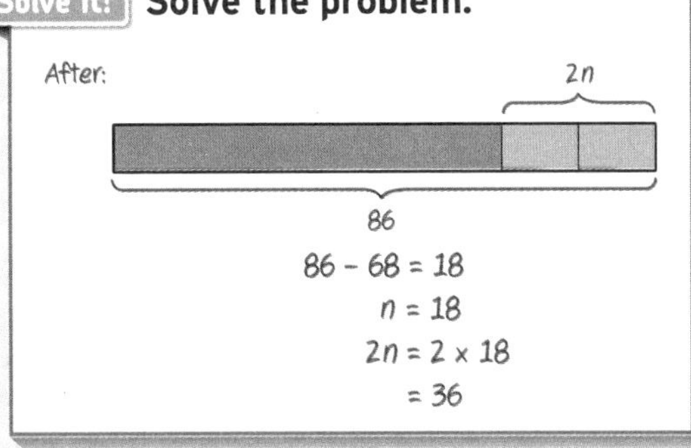

Check It! Check your work.

> TRY IT

1

Read It! Read and identify the problem.

ARTIST

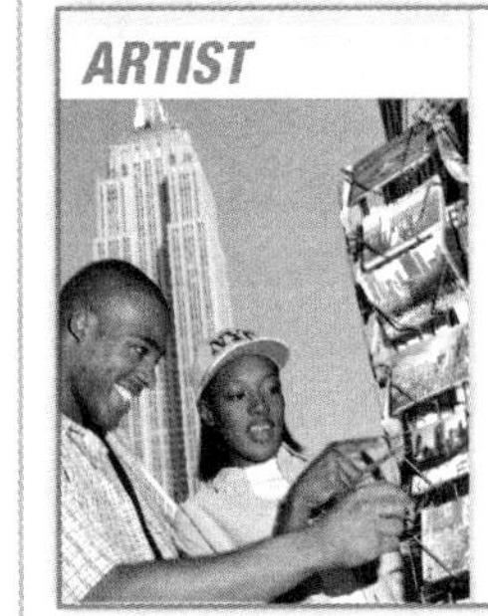

Dylan sold 175 paintings. He sold 8 times as many postcards. How many more postcards than paintings did Dylan sell?

PROBLEM TYPE: ______________________

Show It! Represent the problem.

Solve It! Solve the problem.

Check It! Check your work.

> PRACTICE

2

Read It! Read and identify the problem.

ARCHITECT

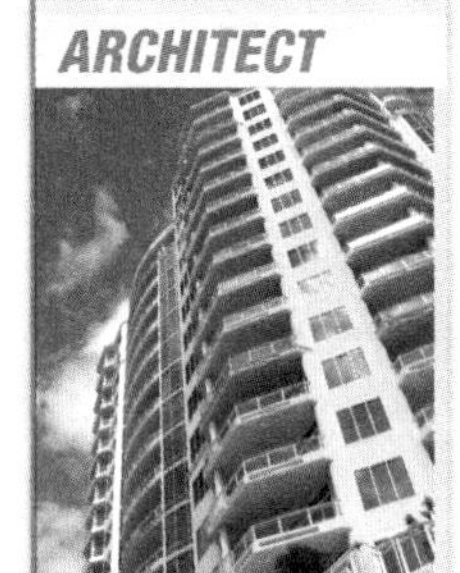

A new apartment building has 17 apartments on each of the first 9 floors. On the tenth floor, there are 6 apartments. How many apartments does it have altogether?

PROBLEM TYPE: ______________________

Show It! Represent the problem.

Solve It! Solve the problem.

Check It! Check your work.

> PRACTICE

3

SHOE DESIGNER

Jane designed 124 pairs of sneakers for her shoe store. She sold half during a sale and gave 20 pairs to a nearby school. How many pairs are left?

PROBLEM TYPE: ______________________

4

APPAREL DESIGNER

Tyra made 8 fewer jackets than Zack. They made 48 jackets altogether. How many jackets did Zack make?

PROBLEM TYPE: ______________________

EXIT Ticket

BLOCK 2

> **Solve this problem.**

Tom created a mixed-media mural of a flag to celebrate the 4th of July. He spent $57 on paint and 4 times as much on fabric. How much money did he spend altogether?

PROBLEM TYPE ______________________

TOPIC 3

TOPIC 2

TOPIC 1

I check my work by estimating and comparing the answer to the estimate.

SCORE (0) (1) (2)

Two-Digit Multiplication

LESSON 1

Number Strings

> Add this set of expressions mentally.

29 + 31
29 + 16
19 + 26
19 + 19

> Pick one of the expressions and explain how you solved it.

I solved ____ + ____ by ________

____

____

____

LESSON 2

Make an Estimate

> Estimate the product of 26 × 8.

____ × ____ = ____

> Will the actual product be greater or less than your estimate? How do you know?

The actual product will be ________

than my estimate because ______

____

LESSON 3

Build It

> Use each of these digits to create a 1-digit factor and a 3-digit factor that creates the greatest possible product.

3 4 5 7

____ × ____ ____ ____ = ____

> Explain how you know you created the greatest possible product.

I know I created the greatest possible product because ________

____

____

LESSON 4

Missing Numbers

› **Find the missing numbers by multiplying and finding the partial products.**

____ × 60 = 2400

____ × 7 = 280

2400 + 280 = ____

____ × 67 = ____

› **What was your strategy for solving this problem?**

My strategy for solving this problem was ________________

____

____

LESSON 5

Brain Teaser

› **Solve this riddle.**

Kim is 3 times the age of her younger sister, Jasmine. If Jasmine will be 6 years old in two years, how old will Kim be?

› **What was the first step you took to solve this riddle?**

The first step I took to solve this riddle was ________________

____

____

Sum It Up!

› **In this Topic, you learned how to multiply two 2-digit numbers using the Distributive Property.**

How can I be sure I found the partial products when multiplying 38 × 67?

You can draw and split a rectangle to help you visualize the partial products.

	60	7
30	30 x 60	30 x 7
8	8 x 60	8 x 7

Multiply 2-Digit Factors

WORKED EXAMPLE

STEP 1 Split both factors.

23 × 37

20 + 3   30 + 7

STEP 2 Split and label the rectangle.

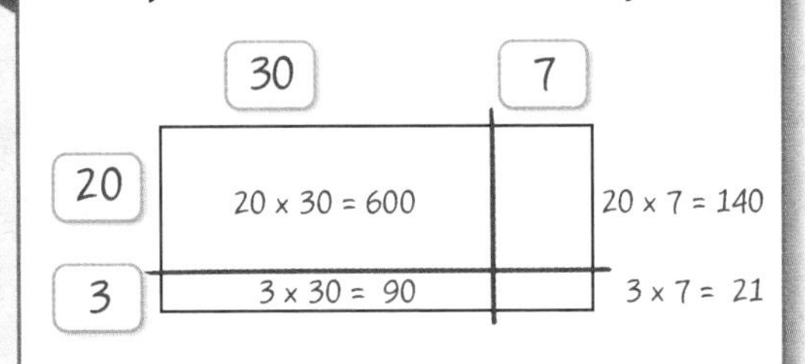

STEP 3 Find the partial products.

Equation 1 → 20 x 30 = 600

Equation 2 → 20 x 7 = 140

Equation 3 → 3 x 30 = 90

Equation 4 → 3 x 7 = 21

STEP 4 Add the partial products.

600
140
90
+ 21
700
150
+ 1

23 × 37 = 851

TRY IT

1

STEP 1 Split both factors.

48 × 72

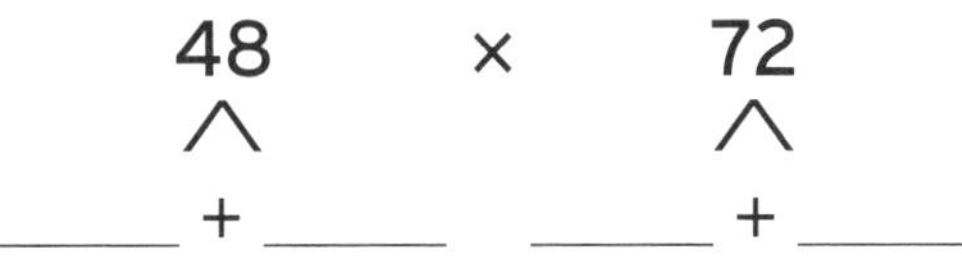

____ + ____   ____ + ____

STEP 2 Split and label the rectangle.

STEP 3 Find the partial products.

Equation 1 → ________

Equation 2 → ________

Equation 3 → ________

Equation 4 → ________

STEP 4 Add the partial products.

48 × 72 = ____

PRACTICE

2

STEP 1 Split both factors.

57 × 32

____ + ____   ____ + ____

STEP 2 Split and label the rectangle.

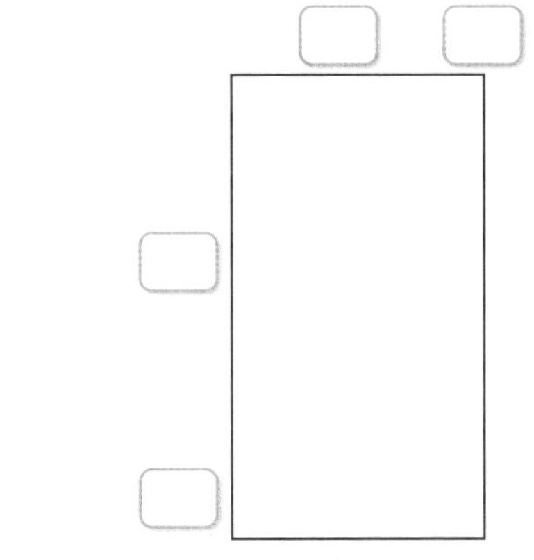

STEP 3 Find the partial products.

Equation 1 → ________

Equation 2 → ________

Equation 3 → ________

Equation 4 → ________

STEP 4 Add the partial products.

57 × 32 = ____

PRACTICE

3

$$29 \times 65$$

___ + ___   ___ + ___

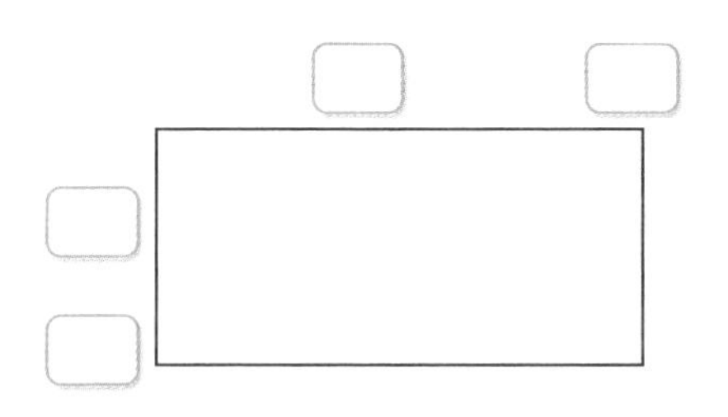

Equation 1 → ______________

Equation 2 → ______________

Equation 3 → ______________

Equation 4 → ______________

29 × 65 = ______

4

$$82 \times 43$$

___ + ___   ___ + ___

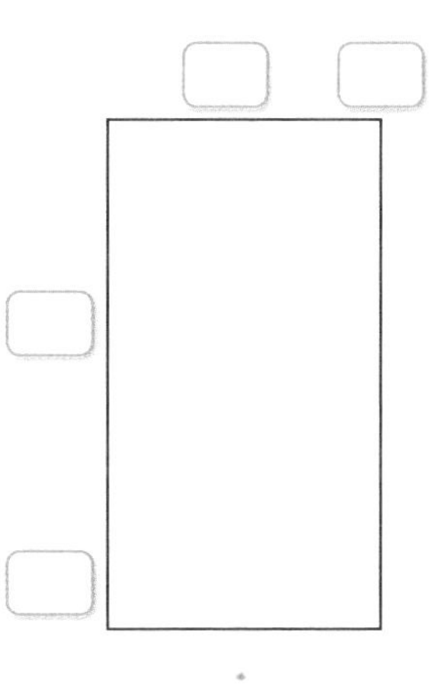

Equation 1 → ______________

Equation 2 → ______________

Equation 3 → ______________

Equation 4 → ______________

82 × 43 = ______

EXIT Ticket

TOPIC 3

> **Find the product.**

$$32 \times 76$$

___ + ___   ___ + ___

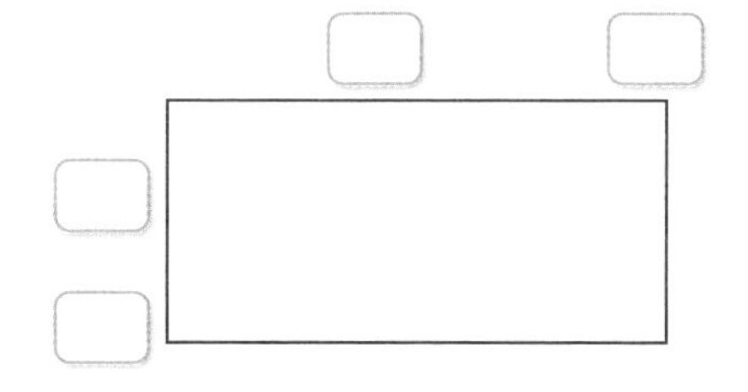

Equation 1 → ______________

Equation 2 → ______________

Equation 3 → ______________

Equation 4 → ______________

32 × 76 = ______

TOPIC 2

> **How does splitting the rectangle help you multiply with greater factors?**

Splitting the rectangle helps me multiply with greater factors by

____

____

____

TOPIC 1

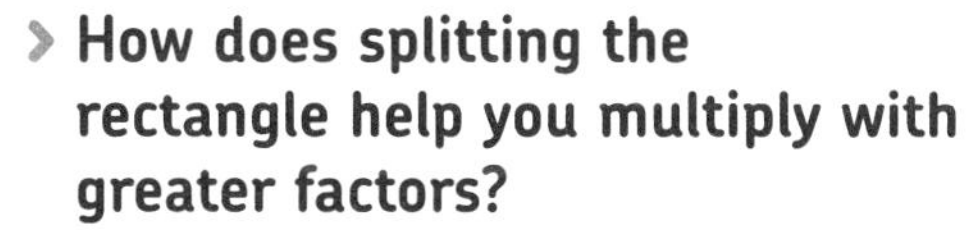

SCORE ⓪ ① ②

Multiply 2-Digit Factors Using the Distributive Property

> WORKED EXAMPLE

STEP 1 **Estimate the product.**

52 × 36

Estimate: 50 × 40 = 2000

STEP 2 **Rename both factors.**

52 × 36 = (50 + 2) × (30 + 6)

52 × 36 =

(50 × 30) + (50 × 6) +

(2 × 30) + (2 × 6)

STEP 3 **Find the partial products.**

50 × 30 = 1500
50 × 6 = 300
2 × 30 = 60
2 × 6 = 12

STEP 4 **Add the partial products.**

50 × 30 = 1500
50 × 6 = 300
2 × 30 = 60
2 × 6 = 12

1872

Is your answer reasonable? yes

> TRY IT

1

STEP 1 **Estimate the product.**

23 × 79

Estimate: ____ × ____ = ____

STEP 2 **Rename both factors.**

23 × 79 = (___ + ___) × (___ + ___)

23 × 79 = (___ × ___) + (___ × ___) +

(___ × ___) + (___ × ___)

STEP 3 **Find the partial products.**

STEP 4 **Add the partial products.**

23 × 79 = ____

Is your answer reasonable? ____

> PRACTICE

2

STEP 1 **Estimate the product.**

47 × 88

Estimate: ____ × ____ = ____

STEP 2 **Rename both factors.**

47 × 88 = (___ + ___) × (___ + ___)

47 × 88 = (___ × ___) + (___ × ___) +

(___ × ___) + (___ × ___)

STEP 3 **Find the partial products.**

STEP 4 **Add the partial products.**

47 × 88 = ____

Is your answer reasonable? ____

> PRACTICE

3

61×69

Estimate: ______ × ______ = ______

$61 \times 69 = (\_\_ + \_\_) \times (\_\_ + \_\_)$

$61 \times 69 = (\_\_ \times \_\_) + (\_\_ \times \_\_) +$

$(\_\_ \times \_\_) + (\_\_ \times \_\_)$

$61 \times 69 =$ ______

Is your answer reasonable? ______

4

38×73

Estimate: ______ × ______ = ______

$38 \times 73 = (\_\_ + \_\_) \times (\_\_ + \_\_)$

$38 \times 73 = (\_\_ \times \_\_) + (\_\_ \times \_\_) +$

$(\_\_ \times \_\_) + (\_\_ \times \_\_)$

$38 \times 73 =$ ______

Is your answer reasonable? ______

EXIT Ticket

BLOCK 2

> **Find the product.**

74×28

$74 \times 28 = (\_\_ + \_\_) \times (\_\_ + \_\_)$

$74 \times 28 = (\_\_ \times \_\_) + (\_\_ \times \_\_) +$

$(\_\_ \times \_\_) + (\_\_ \times \_\_)$

$74 \times 28 =$ ______

> **How is splitting two 2-digit factors similar to splitting rectangles to multiply?**

Splitting two 2-digit factors is similar to splitting rectangles to multiply because ______________________

____

____

____

____

SCORE ⓪ ① ②

TOPIC 3

TOPIC 2

TOPIC 1

Strengthen Estimation Strategies

RULES

Roll 2 Win (Level 3)

What You Need
- *mSpace* pages 88–91
- decahedron (black, 0–9)

What To Know
- Players select a target number.
- Players create two 2-digit factors from the numbers rolled to make an estimate of the product.
- Partners record and check each other's estimates.

How To Win
- After each round, players calculate the difference between the target number and their estimates. They record the difference in the score box.
- After 4 rounds, players add their scores. The winner is the player with the LEAST number of points.

WORKED EXAMPLE

STEP 1 Choose a target number and write it on the recording sheet.

TARGET NUMBER: 4500
PLAYER A ROUND 1
☐☐ × ☐☐
Estimate
___ × ___ = ___
___ − ___ = SCORE

STEP 2 Roll the decahedron four times. Record each number in an empty box.

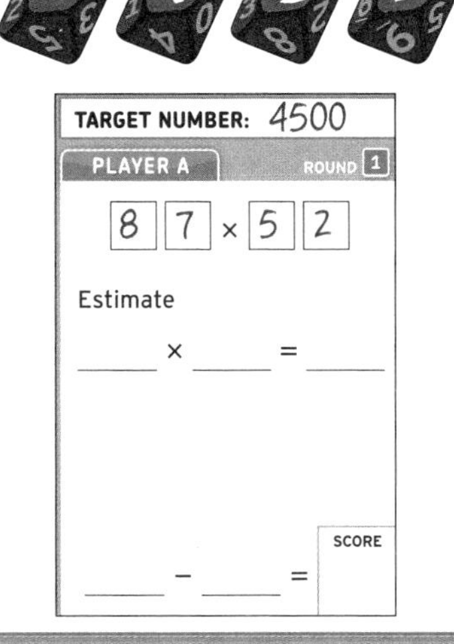

STEP 3 Use the factors to make an estimate that is as close to your target number as possible.

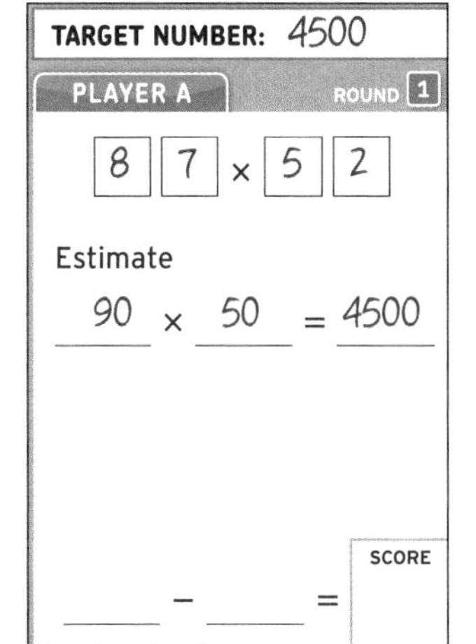

STEP 4 Subtract to compare your estimate to the target number. Record the difference as your score.

TARGET NUMBER: 4500
PLAYER A ROUND 1
8 7 × 5 2
Estimate
90 × 50 = 4500
4500 − 4500 = SCORE 0

RECORDING SHEET

Roll 2 Win (Level 3)

Choose a target number from this list: 600, 1200, 1800, 2400, 3000, 3600, 4500, 4800. Record your equations and your partner's equations.

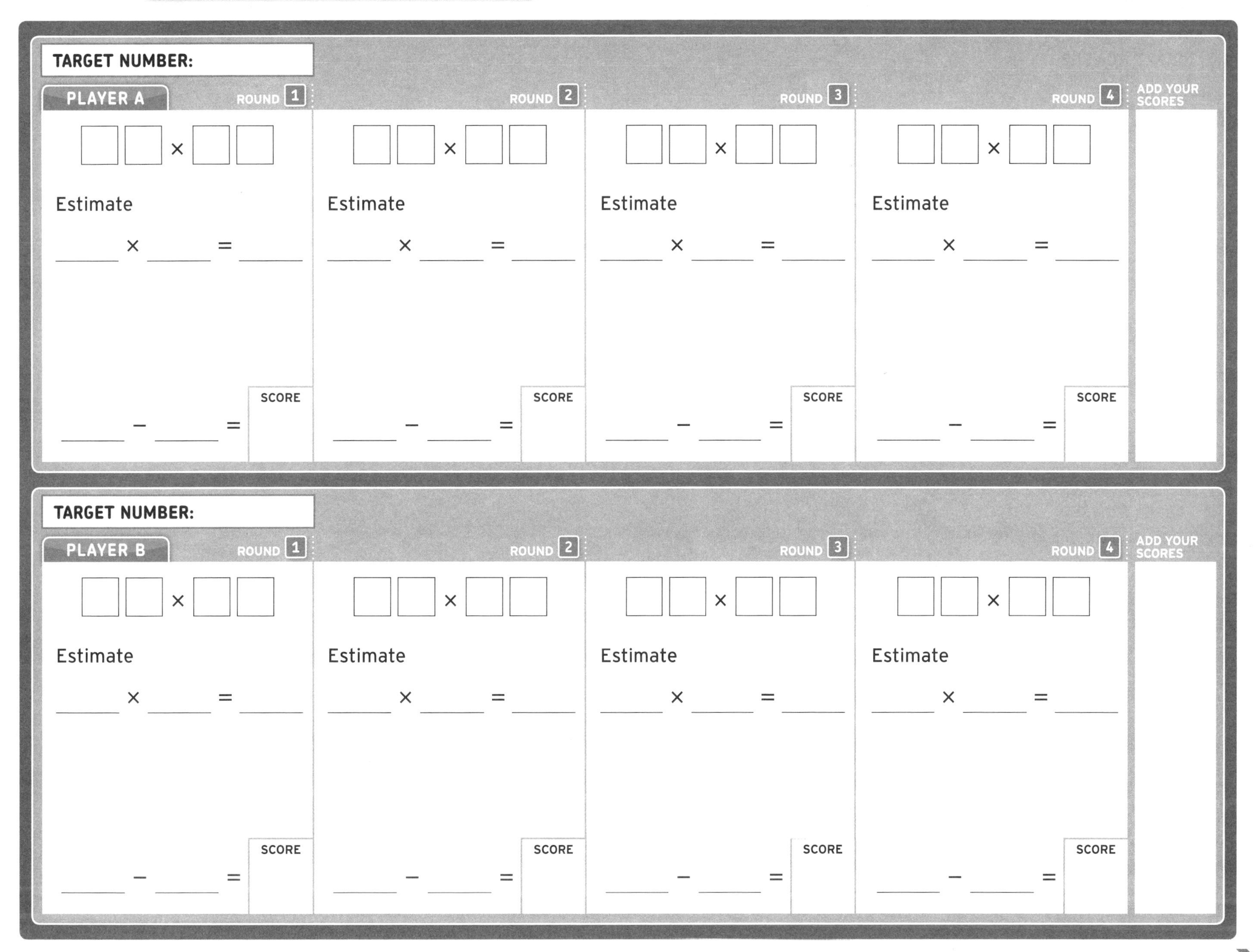

RECORDING SHEET

Roll 2 Win (Level 3)

Choose a target number from this list: 600, 1200, 1800, 2400, 3000, 3600, 4500, 4800. Record your and your partner's equations.

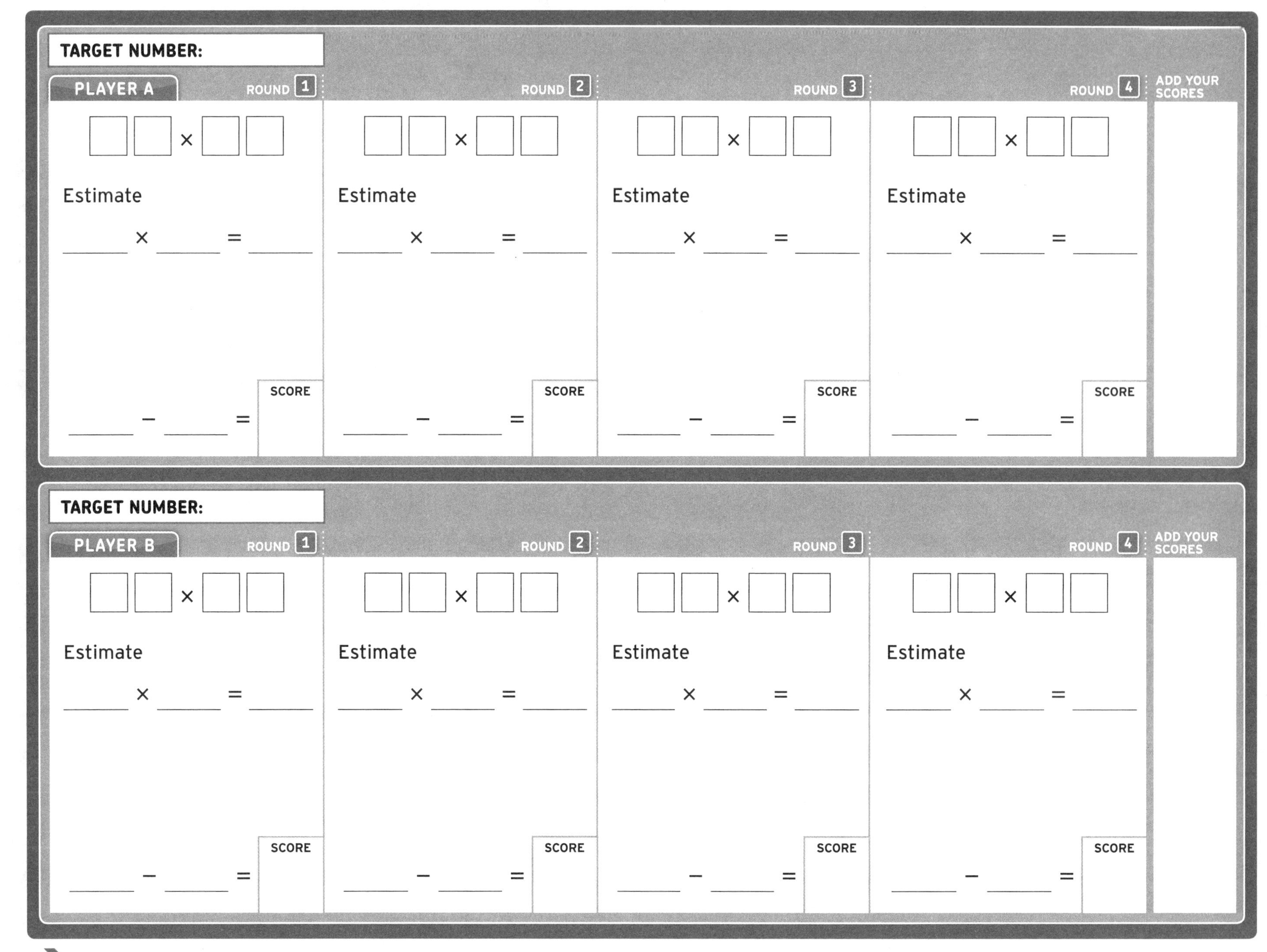

› Optional: Use this page if you need extra space to work.

EXIT Ticket

BLOCK 2

TOPIC 3

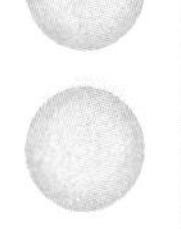

› **Answer this question.**

If you rolled a 2, 3, 7, and 8, how would you arrange the numbers to reach a Target Number of 2400?

I would arrange the numbers as

☐☐ × ☐☐

because ______________________

____

____

____

SCORE (0) (1) (2)

TOPIC 2

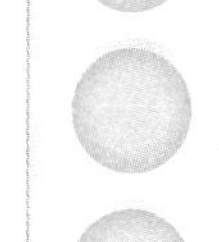

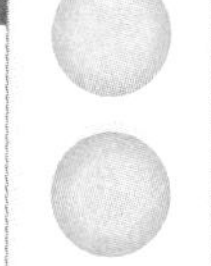

CAREER EXPLORATION

› **Fashion designers use math to decide how much material they need to create an item of clothing.**

TOPIC 1

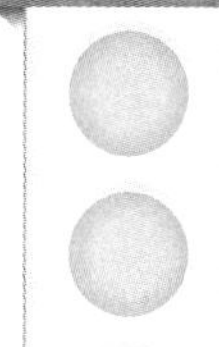

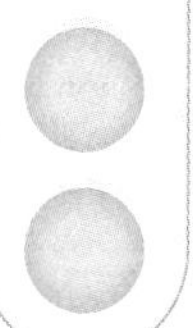

How could a fashion designer estimate to find out how much fabric he needs for one shirt?

Write Multiplication Problems

WORKED EXAMPLE

STEP 1 **Read the expression.**

12 × 36

STEP 2 **Write a problem.**

12 designers each created a tile in a large mural. Each tile was 36 square feet. How many square feet is the mural?

STEP 3 **Draw a model.**

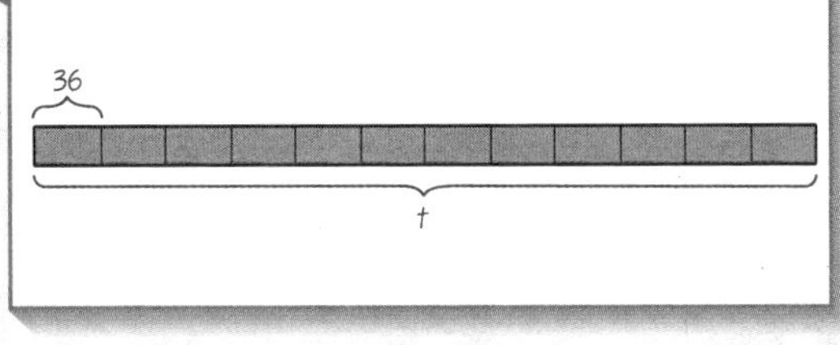

STEP 4 **Solve the problem.**

$t = 12 \times 36$
$= (10 + 2) \times (30 + 6)$

$10 \times 30 = 300$
$10 \times 6 = 60$
$2 \times 30 = 60$
$2 \times 6 = 12$

432 ft^2

TRY IT

1

STEP 1 **Read the expression.**

13 × 75

STEP 2 **Write a problem.**

An art gallery had ______ visitors. Another gallery had ______ times the same number of visitors. How many fewer visitors were in the first art gallery?

STEP 3 **Draw a model.**

STEP 4 **Solve the problem.**

PRACTICE

2

STEP 1 **Read the expression.**

16 × 53

STEP 2 **Write a problem.**

A designer sold ______ pairs of jeans for $ ______ each. How much money did she make altogether?

STEP 3 **Draw a model.**

STEP 4 **Solve the problem.**

BLOCK 2

> PRACTICE

3

24×13

I spent $ ______ on canvases and ______ times as much on acrylic paints. How much more did I spend on the paint?

4

62×38

An art exhibition had ______ participants displaying their work. Each artist paid $ ______ in registration fees. How much money was paid for registration fees?

EXIT
Ticket

BLOCK 2

TOPIC 3

TOPIC 2

TOPIC 1

> **Find the mistake in the problem.**

Ben wrote a problem for this equation.

80×13

I spent $80 on art supplies. I spent 14 times as much on a new camera. How much did I spend on my new camera?

What mistake did Ben make?

____

____

____

____

____

> **Rewrite the word problem so that it matches the expression.**

____

____

____

____

____

SCORE (0) (1) (2)

Solve Complex Multiplication Problems

> WORKED EXAMPLE

Read It! Read and identify the problem.

APPAREL DESIGNER

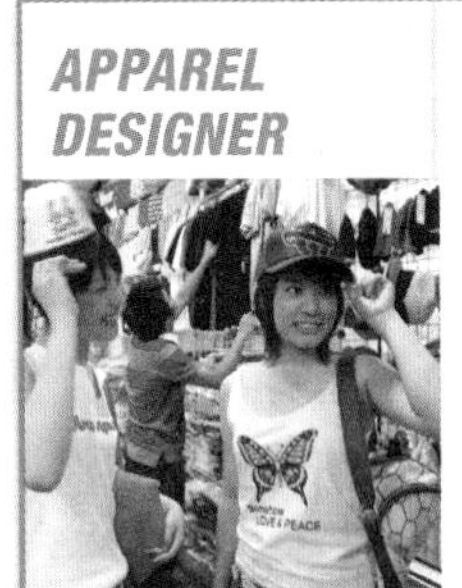

Hayley designed and sold 35 hats for $11 each. She spent $200 on making the hats. How much profit did she make?

PROBLEM TYPE Equal Groups Problem

Show It! Represent the problem.

$11

35

Solve It! Solve the problem.

$35 \times \$11 = \$385$

$\$385 - \$200 = \$185$

$p = \$185$

Check It! Check your work.

> TRY IT

1

Read It! Read and identify the problem.

INDUSTRIAL DESIGNER

Jamie and Sara have 112 model planes altogether. Sara has 6 times as many model planes as Jamie. How many planes does Jamie have?

PROBLEM TYPE ______________________

Show It! Represent the problem.

Solve It! Solve the problem.

Check It! Check your work.

> PRACTICE

2

Read It! Read and identify the problem.

CARPENTER

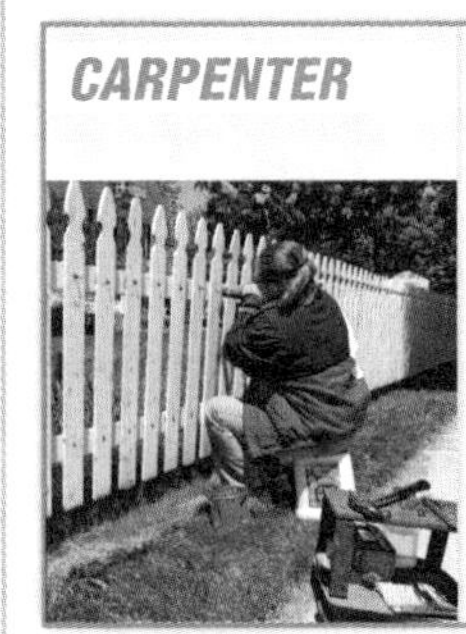

Lin built 17 sections of fence. Each section was 11 yards long. If 1 yard = 3 feet, what was the length of the entire fence in feet?

PROBLEM TYPE ______________________

Show It! Represent the problem.

Solve It! Solve the problem.

Check It! Check your work.

BLOCK 2

> PRACTICE

3

GRAPHIC DESIGNER

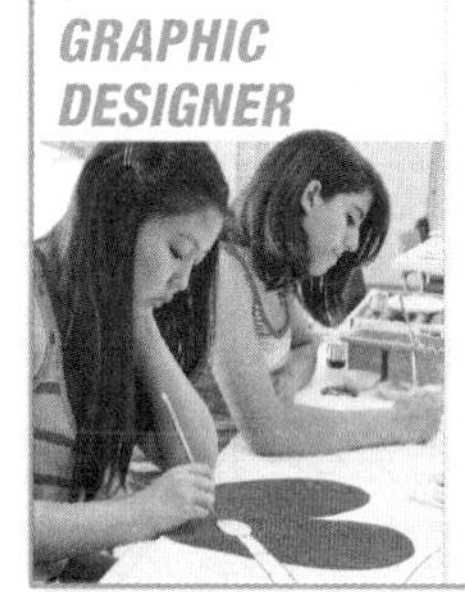

Nicole made two posters. The second poster was 3 times larger than the first. If the first poster was 78 square inches, how large were the posters altogether?

PROBLEM TYPE ______________________

4

GRAPHIC DESIGNER

Jerome and Cy created 250 comic book panels altogether. Jerome created 4 times as many panels as Cy. How many panels did Jerome create?

PROBLEM TYPE ______________________

EXIT Ticket

BLOCK 2

> **Solve this problem.**

A band designed 8 different album covers for their new album. Each cover cost $410 to design. They chose the 8th cover for their new album. How much money did they spend on the unused covers?

PROBLEM TYPE ______________________

Make an estimate to check if your answer is reasonable.
_____ × 400 is about _____.

SCORE ⓪ ① ②

TOPIC 3

TOPIC 2

TOPIC 1

BLOCK 2 PERFORMANCE TASK

> YOUR JOB
Artist

> YOUR TASK
Plan the painting of a mural by dividing it into small rectangular sections.

ANCHOR VIDEO CONNECTION

As the Anchor Video shows, artists may draw a model of a mural to help them plan it.

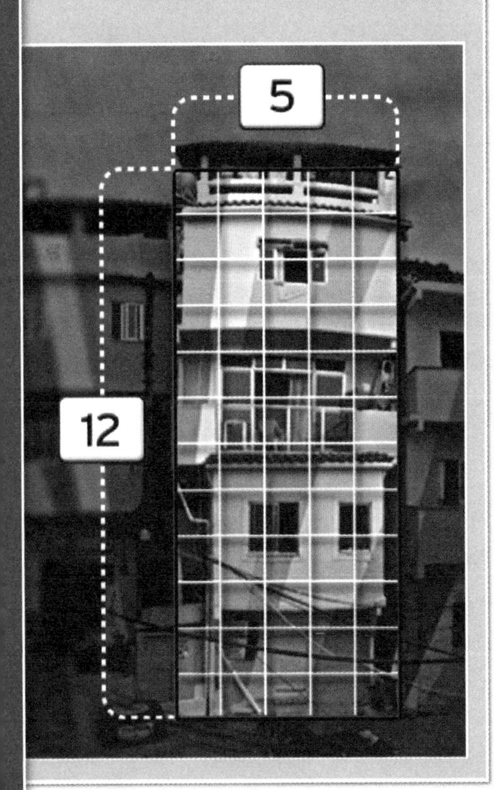

Design a Mural

> You have been hired to organize five teams of painters and artists to paint a large outdoor mural. The mural is 36 feet tall and 64 feet wide.

A EXPLORE

Draw and label four plans for dividing the mural into five smaller rectangles, one for each team. Try to make the five rectangles as equal in size as possible. Use whole numbers only. See the sample plan for an example.

SAMPLE PLAN

64 ft; 12 ft, 40 ft, 12 ft; 36 ft; 12 ft, 12 ft, 12 ft; sections 1, 2, 3, 4, 5

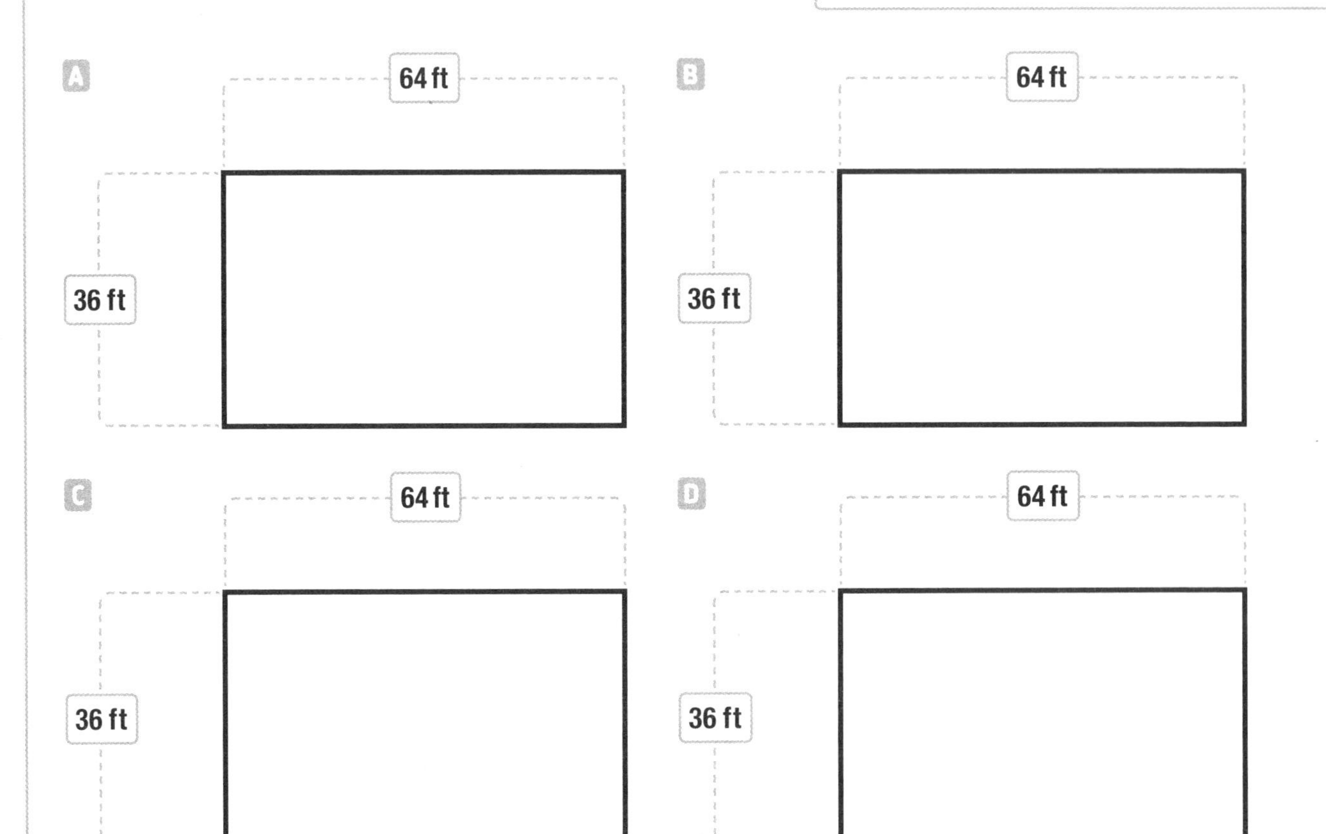

B APPLY

Choose two plans from Part A that you think work best. For each plan, complete the table to find the areas of the smaller rectangles.

PLAN ______

RECTANGLE	SIZE (ft × ft)	PARTIAL PRODUCTS	AREA (ft^2)
1	×		
2	×		
3	×		
4	×		
5	×		
TOTAL			

PLAN ______

RECTANGLE	SIZE (ft × ft)	PARTIAL PRODUCTS	AREA (ft^2)
1	×		
2	×		
3	×		
4	×		
5	×		
TOTAL			

C ANALYZE

INTERPRET Review the tables. In which plan are the smaller rectangles closest in size? Explain how you know.

____

____

____

REFLECT Why should the total area of the five smaller rectangles always be the same?

____

____

____

Evaluate

› **Rate how well you and your partner understood and completed each part of the performance task.**

Rating Scale			
None	Limited	Partial	Thorough
0	1	2	3

A Drew and labeled four different plans for the mural.

Me	0	1	2	3
Partner	0	1	2	3

B Calculated the areas of the smaller rectangles for two plans.

Me	0	1	2	3
Partner	0	1	2	3

C Answered each question accurately.

Me	0	1	2	3
Partner	0	1	2	3

EXTEND

If the size of the mural was changed to 18 ft. × 32 ft., would the area be half the area of the 36 ft. × 64 ft. mural? Show your work and explain your reasoning.

____

____

____

MINDSET SCAN

Scan Your Learning Attitudes

Congratulations! You've completed Block 2 of *MATH 180*. For each question, fill in the circle that best describes your mindset. Then complete the sentence frames.

A GETTING FOCUSED

Focusing your attention on a task, such as solving a math problem, is the first step to completing it successfully.

How well did you pay attention to the BLOCK 2 Instructional Videos?

① I let my mind wander and was easily distracted as I watched the Instructional Videos.

② I tried to watch each Instructional Video carefully, but sometimes my mind wandered. I usually did not replay the videos.

③ I watched the Instructional Videos carefully, sometimes repeating sections of a video to make sure I understood them.

I (did/did not) pay close attention to the Instructional Videos because ______________

____

____

____

B EXPANDING AND DEVELOPING BRAIN CONNECTIONS

New brain pathways and connections allow you to think in new ways and solve new problems.

Did you commit time and effort to solving practice problems during BLOCK 2?

① I solved a few practice problems, but often I tried to let classmates or the teacher solve the problems for me.

② I solved many practice problems, but only during class time.

③ I solved many practice problems in the *mSpace* and on the Brain Arcade. I practiced at home, during lunch, or after school.

I spent (little/some/a lot of) time on practice problems because ______________

____

____

C PERSISTENCE

When you keep trying new ways to solve difficult problems, you eventually will succeed.

What did you do when you struggled to solve difficult BLOCK 2 problems?

① I gave up on the problems very quickly.

② Sometimes I kept trying, or I asked a classmate or teacher for the answer.

③ I kept trying as much as possible and didn't give up. I reviewed earlier work, and I asked a classmate or teacher to help me understand.

I (never/sometimes/often) gave up on math problems because ______________

____

____

D KEEPING A POSITIVE MOOD AND MOTIVATION

Learning math can be challenging. Keeping a positive mood can help you succeed.

How did you respond when you did not understand a BLOCK 2 math concept?

① I told myself that I was bad at math and would never get any better at it.

② I laughed at my lack of understanding, and I told myself I would study harder next time.

③ I spent extra time studying and practicing, and I felt proud of my effort even if I needed more time than I expected to learn the math.

I responded to challenging math concepts by ______________

____

____

____

Score Your Mindset

Add up all the numbers that you checked (1, 2, or 3.) Then read the feedback in the chart.

TOTAL SCORE

If your total score was:	*You were in the:*
6 or less	**Fixed Mindset Zone** You were in the Fixed Mindset Zone this time. Your mindset may have held you back from doing your best.
7-10	**Mixed Mindset Zone** You were in the Mixed Mindset Zone this time. You may have used some Growth Mindset thinking, but in other ways you may have held yourself back.
11 or more	**Growth Mindset Zone** You were in the Growth Mindset Zone this time. You used strategies that will help you grow your brain and get smarter.

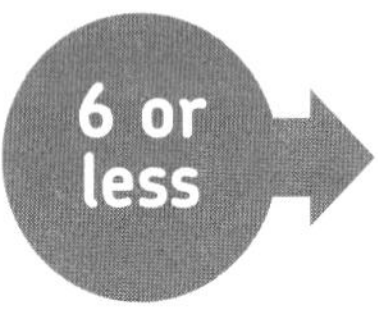

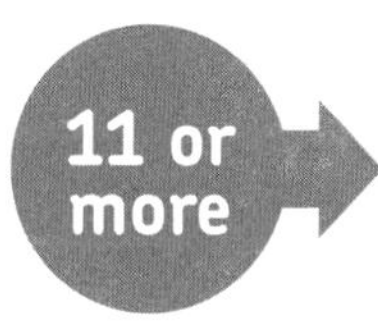

How can you develop a Growth Mindset?

- Read the statements in the Mindset Scan again.
- Make a plan to help you choose the third statement in each category when you take a scan like this one again. Include specific goals in your plan.
- Review your plan as you study. Try to meet the goals you set for yourself.

Brain Boosting

What will you do to help your brain stay in the Growth Zone?

I will work to:

- ☐ Stay focused
- ☐ Develop brain connections
- ☐ Be persistent
- ☐ Keep a positive mood

What will I do?	**Who** will help me?

When will I do it?	**How** will this help me to grow?

BLOCK 3

Division

On a Mission

VOCABULARY

- divide
- dividend
- divisible
- divisor
- equal groups
- partial quotient
- remainder
- Venn diagram

Global Soap

How can you help your community?

In this Anchor Video, one man is on a mission to bring every child a bar of soap.

Math in Service

In this Block, you will explore how math is used in community projects, social service, and public safety.

Police Officers

enforce laws to protect people and property. By **2020**, there will be over **800,000** police officers and detectives working in the United States.

CHARITY Fundraisers

raise money for charity by asking for donations and hosting special events. Americans donate more than **$250 billion** per year, or about **$1,000** per household.

There are **7.2 million**

Teachers AND College Professors

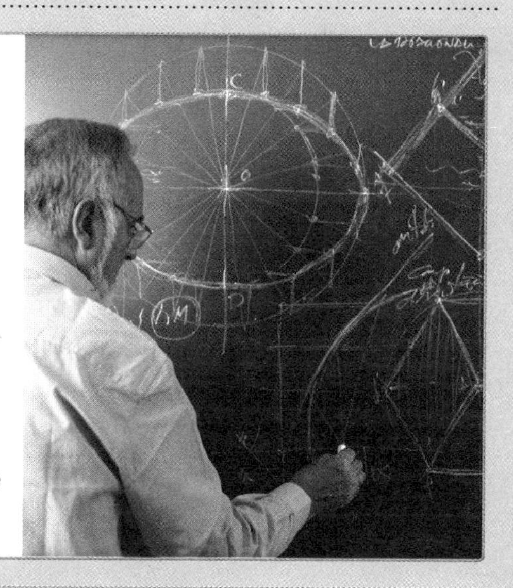

in the United States. They must earn **at least** a Bachelor's degree, but most teachers earn Master's degrees. Professors earn Doctorate degrees in their areas of expertise.

THE UNITED STATES Armed Forces

consist of **5 branches**: Army, Navy, Marine Corps, Air Force, and Coast Guard. The Army is the largest with more than **1 million** soldiers and an annual budget of more than **$100 billion**.

Health Educators

develop programs that encourage people and communities to make healthy choices. Experts say that with better diet and more exercise, US health-care costs could be reduced by more than **$70 billion** per year.

Equal Groups in Division

LESSON 1

Block Preview

> **Think about the Anchor Video and answer this question.**

What resource from your community would you share with the world?

> **Explain your choice of resource to share.**

I would share ______________ with the world because ______________

____

____

LESSON 2

Missing Numbers

> **Use the numbers 1 to 9 to complete these equations.**

$5 \times \_\_\_ = 35$ $\_\_\_ \times 9 = 18$ $\_\_\_ \times 5 = 45$

$\_\_\_ \times 3 = 18$ $7 \times \_\_\_ = 7$ $\_\_\_ \times 8 = 32$

$6 \times \_\_\_ = 30$ $5 \times \_\_\_ = 15$ $7 \times \_\_\_ = 56$

> **How did you find the missing numbers?**

I found the missing numbers by

____

____

____

LESSON 3

Which Does Not Belong?

> **Circle the number that does not belong.**

7, 17, 21, 28, 35, 42

> **How is one of the numbers different from the others?**

The number ________ is different because ______________

____

____

LESSON 4

Build It

> Use these numbers to write as many correct division equations without remainders as you can.

1	2	3	4	5	9	12	15

- ______________________
- ______________________
- ______________________
- ______________________

> **What strategy did you use to write as many equations as possible?**

The strategy I used to write the equations was ______________________

____

____

LESSON 5

Who's Right?

> Kal and Andy found different quotients for the same division problem.

Kal	Andy
$24 \div 3 = 7$ R4	$24 \div 3 = 8$

Who's right? __________

> **How do you know who is correct?**

I know _______ *is correct because*

____

____

____

____

Sum It Up!

> **In this Topic, you learned to divide whole numbers using models and multiplication.**

How can I use a model to show 21 divided by 3?

Make an array of 21 squares, with 3 squares in each row.

Divide by Taking Out Equal Groups

> WORKED EXAMPLE

STEP 1 Represent the problem with an array.

$24 \div 6$

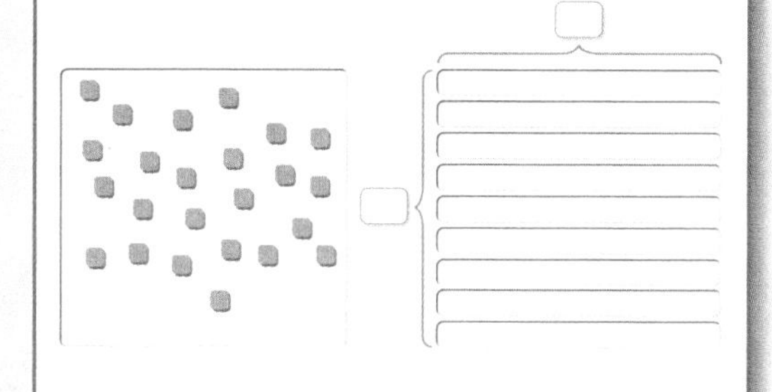

Total number of squares: 24

Number of squares in a row: 6

STEP 2 Use the array model to divide.

$24 \div 6$

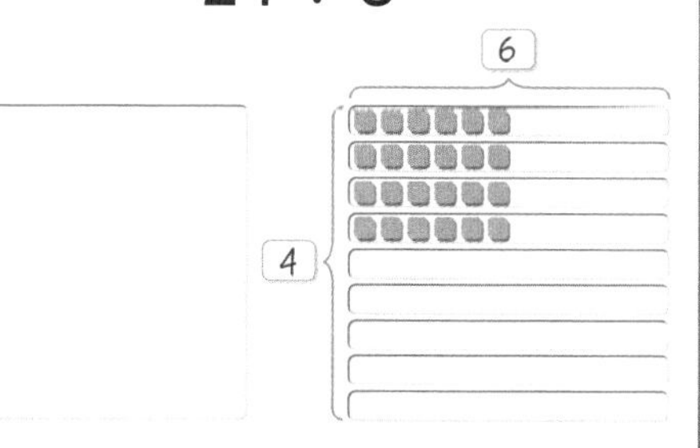

STEP 3 Write a division equation.

24 ÷ 6 = 4

> TRY IT

1

STEP 1 Represent the problem with an array.

$15 \div 3$

Total number of squares: ________

Number of squares in a row: ________

STEP 2 Use the array model to divide.

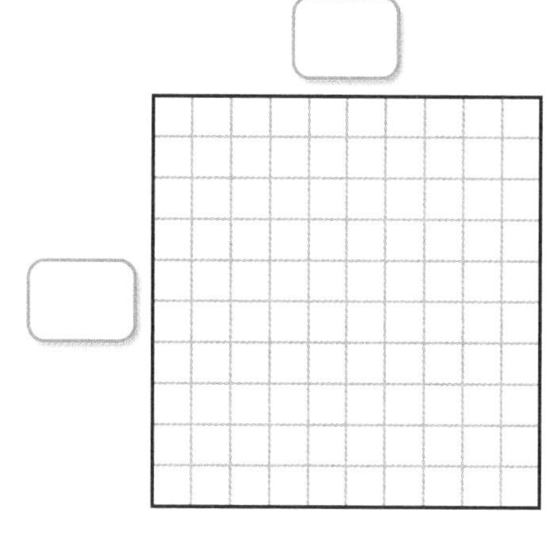

STEP 3 Write a division equation.

________ ÷ ________ = ________

> PRACTICE

2

STEP 1 Represent the problem with an array.

$16 \div 4$

Total number of squares: ________

Number of squares in a row: ________

STEP 2 Use the array model to divide.

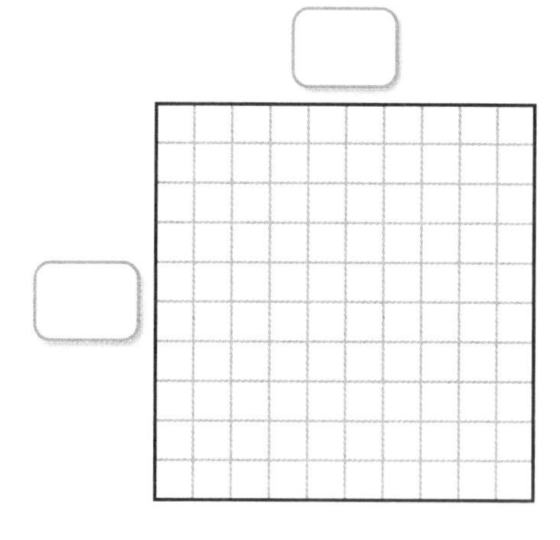

STEP 3 Write a division equation.

________ ÷ ________ = ________

divide *(v)* to split or separate a number into equal parts or equal groups

> PRACTICE

3

$18 \div 6$

Total number of squares: ________

Number of squares in a row: ________

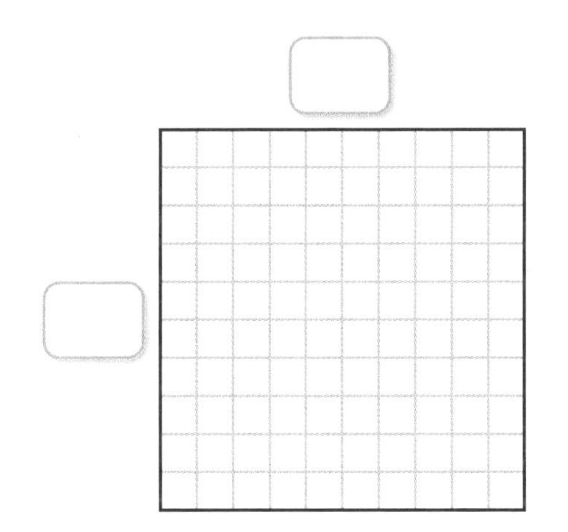

________ ÷ ________ = ________

4

$20 \div 4$

Total number of squares: ________

Number of squares in a row: ________

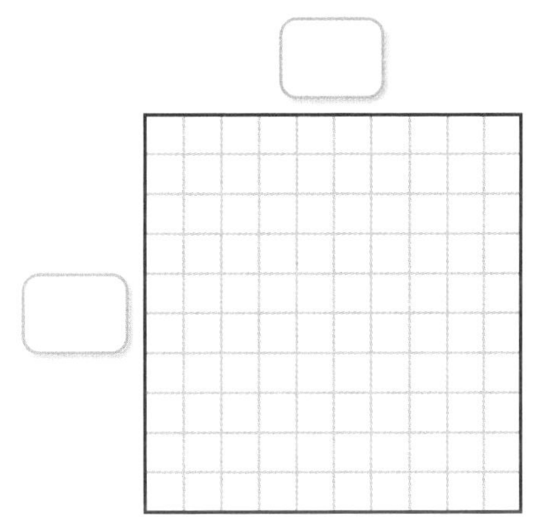

________ ÷ ________ = ________

EXIT Ticket

BLOCK 3

> **Solve this division problem.**

$21 \div 7$

Total number of squares: ________

Number of squares in a row: ______

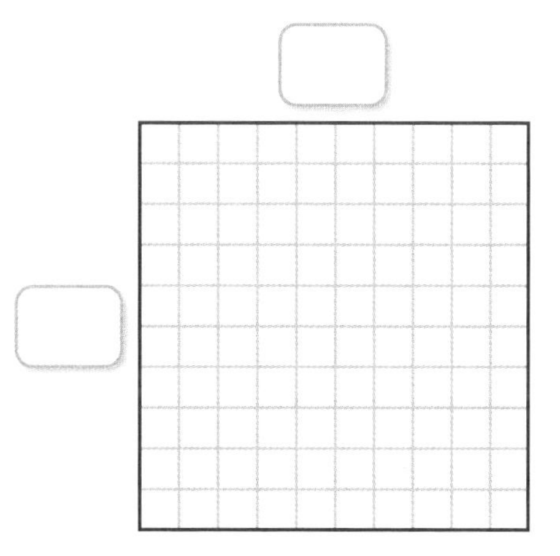

$21 \div 7 =$ ________

> **How does using an array model help solve this problem?**

Using an array model helps solve the problem because

____

____

____

SCORE (0) (1) (2)

TOPIC 3

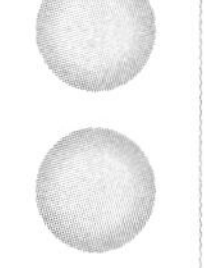

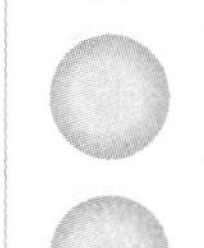

TOPIC 2

TOPIC 1

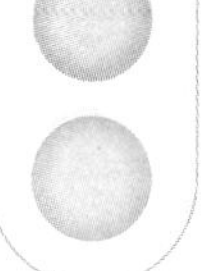

Use Multiplication to Divide

WORKED EXAMPLE

STEP 1 Write a multiplication equation.

$24 \div 3 =$ ______

______ $\times 3 = 24$

STEP 2 Use multiplication to find the quotient.

$24 \div 3 =$ 8

8 $\times 3 = 24$

STEP 3 Verify the quotient.

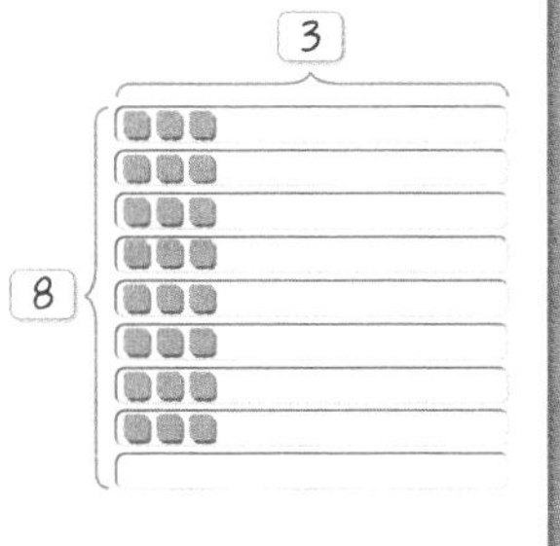

TRY IT

1

STEP 1 Write a multiplication equation.

$28 \div 4 =$ ______

STEP 2 Use multiplication to find the quotient.

STEP 3 Verify the quotient.

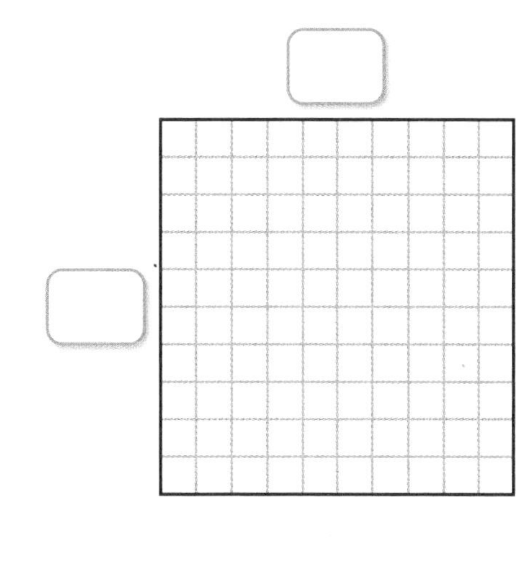

PRACTICE

2

STEP 1 Write a multiplication equation.

$30 \div 5 =$ ______

STEP 2 Use multiplication to find the quotient.

STEP 3 Verify the quotient.

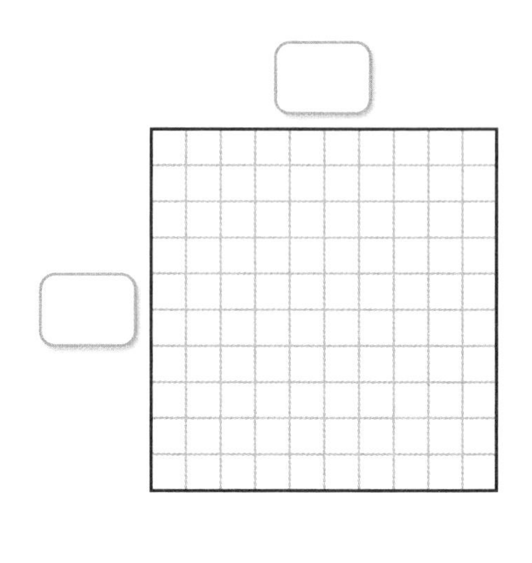

dividend *(n)* the number that is divided into equal parts or groups

divisor *(n)* the number you divide by

> PRACTICE

3. $42 \div 7 =$ ______

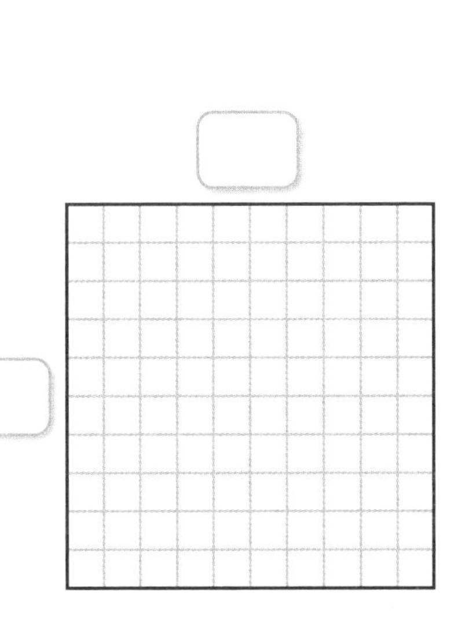

4. $56 \div 8 =$ ______

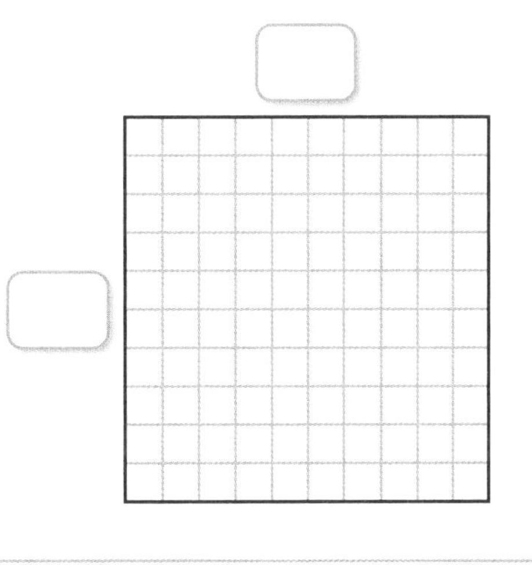

5. $48 \div 6 =$ ______

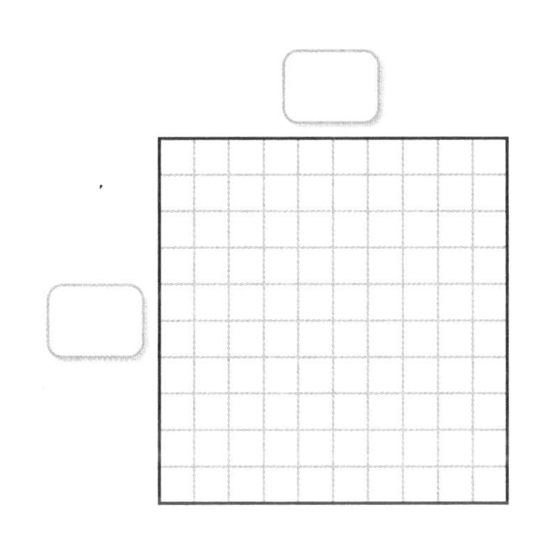

6. $27 \div 3 =$ ______

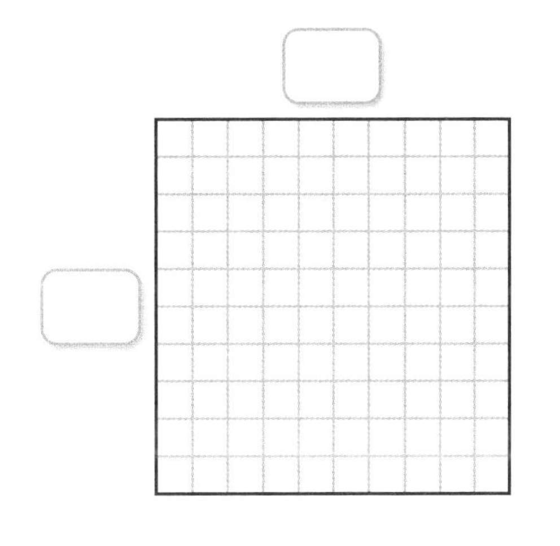

EXIT Ticket

BLOCK 3

> Use multiplication to solve this problem. Draw an array to verify the solution.

$54 \div 6 =$ ______

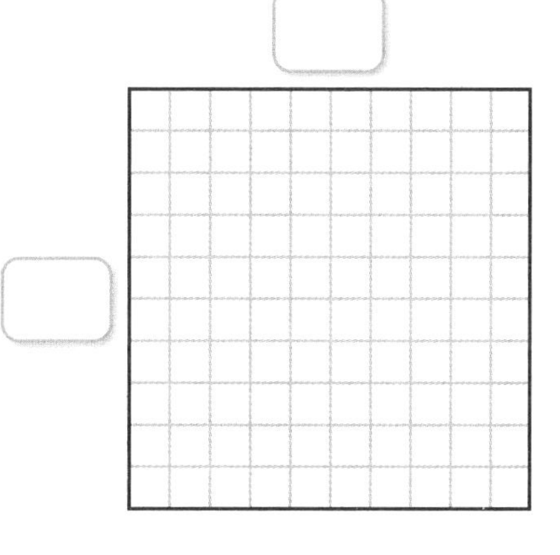

> How does knowing multiplication facts help you divide?

Knowing multiplication facts helps me divide because ______

______

______

______

______

SCORE ⓪ ① ②

TOPIC 3

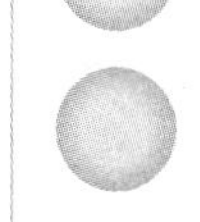

TOPIC 2

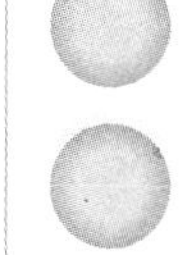

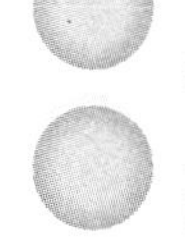

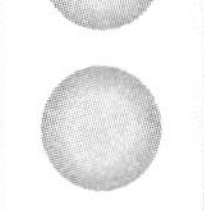

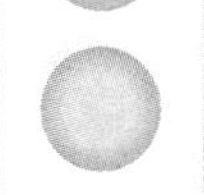

TOPIC 1

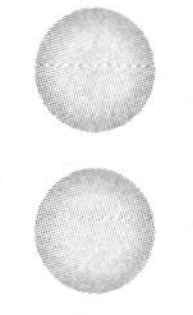

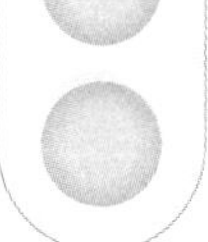

Interpret Remainders

> WORKED EXAMPLE

STEP 1 Represent the problem with an array.

$23 \div 3$

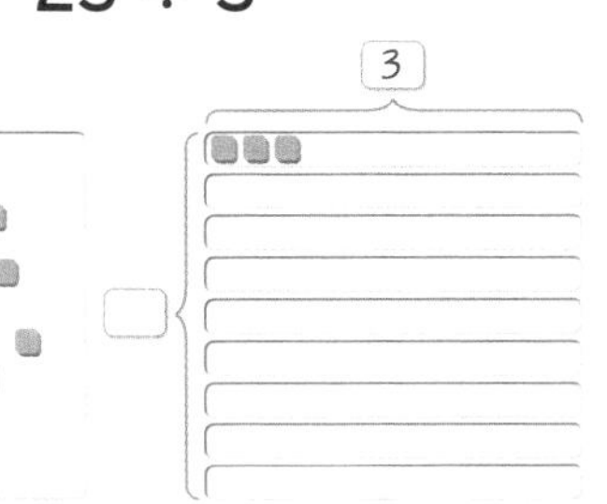

STEP 2 Use the array model to divide.

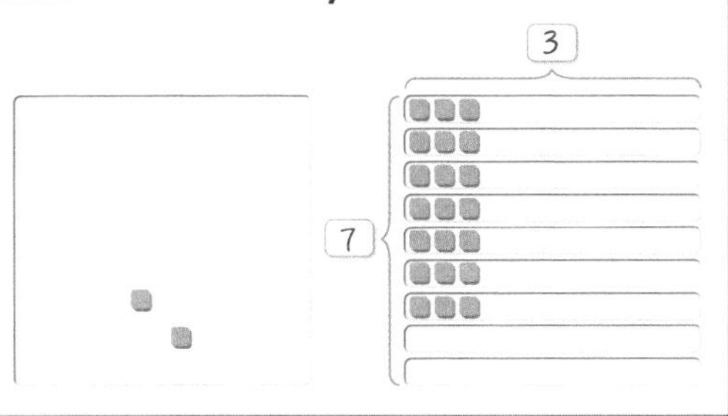

STEP 3 Write a division equation with a remainder.

$23 \div 3 =$ 7 R2

STEP 4 Solve the problem with multiplication.

$\_\_\_ \times 3 = 23$
$7 \times 3 = 21$
$8 \times 3 = 24$
$(7 \times 3) + 2 = 23$

$23 \div 3 =$ 7 R2

> TRY IT

1

STEP 1 Represent the problem with an array.

$19 \div 2$

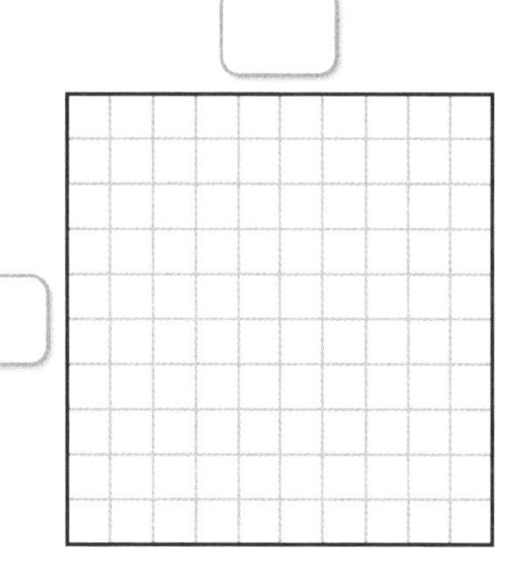

STEP 2 Use the array model to divide.

STEP 3 Write a division equation with a remainder.

$19 \div 2 =$ ________

STEP 4 Solve the problem with multiplication.

$19 \div 2 =$ ________

> PRACTICE

2

STEP 1 Represent the problem with an array.

$14 \div 4$

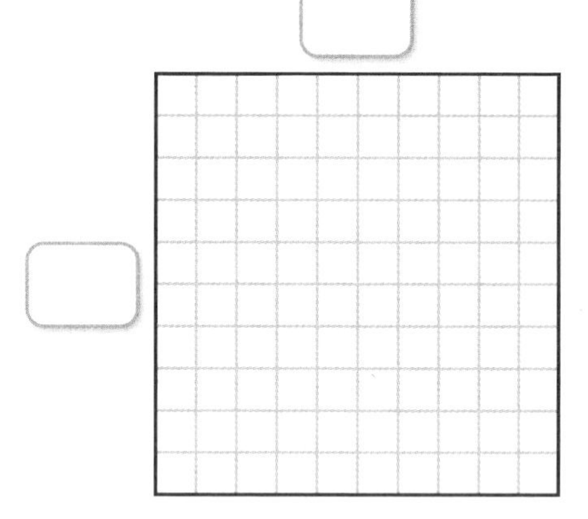

STEP 2 Use the array model to divide.

STEP 3 Write a division equation with a remainder.

$14 \div 4 =$ ________

STEP 4 Solve the problem with multiplication.

$14 \div 4 =$ ________

BLOCK 3

remainder *(n)* the whole number left over after division

divisible *(adj)* able to divide a dividend with no remainder

> PRACTICE

3

STEP 1 Represent the problem with an array.

$40 \div 6$

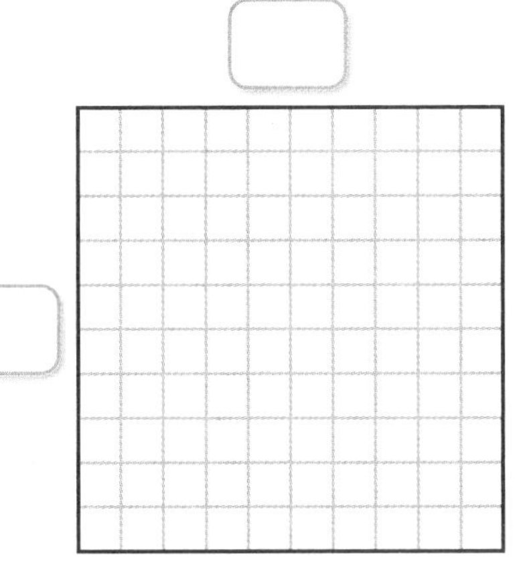

STEP 2 Use the array model to divide.

STEP 3 Write a division equation with a remainder.

$40 \div 6 =$ ______

STEP 4 Solve the problem with multiplication.

$40 \div 6 =$ ______

4

STEP 1 Represent the problem with an array.

$33 \div 5$

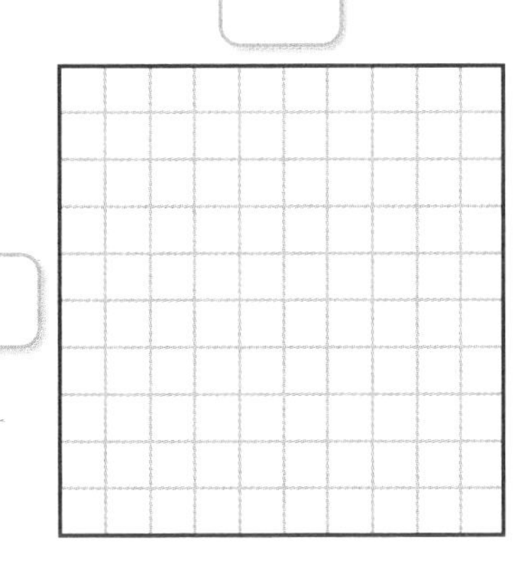

STEP 2 Use the array model to divide.

STEP 3 Write a division equation with a remainder.

$33 \div 5 =$ ______

STEP 4 Solve the problem with multiplication.

$33 \div 5 =$ ______

EXIT Ticket

BLOCK 3

> **Find the error and fix the math.**

$42 \div 5$

$8 \times 5 = 40$

$9 \times 5 = 45$

$(8 \times 5) + 2 = 42$

$42 \div 5 = 8\text{ R}5$

> **Describe the error and explain how you fixed it.**

The error is that ______

______

______

I fixed the error by ______

______

______

What number times 5 equals 42, or is close to 42?

TOPIC 3

TOPIC 2

TOPIC 1

SCORE ⓪ ① ②

Develop Reasoning With Division

RULES

Division Bingo (Level 1)

What You Need

- *mSpace* pages 108–111
- decahedron (white, 1–10)

What To Know

- Players decide who is X and who is O.
- Players take turns.
- Each player records the numbers and equations for both players in a round.

How To Win

- The winner is the first player to mark five boxes in a row—across, up and down, or from corner to corner.

> HOW TO PLAY

STEP 1 Roll the decahedron. Record this number as the divisor in the "number rolled" column.

PLAYER A

NUMBER ROLLED	NUMBER ON BINGO CARD	EQUATION
3		

STEP 2 Choose a dividend on the Bingo card that is divisible by the divisor rolled. Write the equation.

PLAYER A

NUMBER ROLLED	NUMBER ON BINGO CARD	EQUATION
3	45	$45 \div 3 = 15$

STEP 3 Ask your partner to check your equation. If it is correct, put your mark on the dividend.

36	10	21	25	32
9	16	~~45~~ (X)	72	40
20	49	Free Space	48	28
27	24	42	50	18
30	63	12	35	15

STEP 4 Trade turns. Record your partner's equation.

PLAYER A

NUMBER ROLLED	NUMBER ON BINGO CARD	EQUATION
3	45	$45 \div 3 = 15$

PLAYER B

NUMBER ROLLED	NUMBER ON BINGO CARD	EQUATION
6	30	$30 \div 6 = 5$

RECORDING SHEET

Division Bingo (Level 1)

> Record your equations and your partner's equations.
Optional: Use the space on page 111 for calculations.

36	10	21	25	32
9	16	45	72	40
20	49	Free Space	48	28
27	24	42	50	18
30	63	12	35	15

PLAYER A

NUMBER ROLLED	NUMBER ON BINGO CARD	EQUATION

PLAYER B

NUMBER ROLLED	NUMBER ON BINGO CARD	EQUATION

RECORDING SHEET

Division Bingo (Level 1)

> Record your equations and your partner's equations. Optional: Use the space on page 111 for calculations.

36	10	21	25	32
9	16	45	72	40
20	49	Free Space	48	28
27	24	42	50	18
30	63	12	35	15

PLAYER A

NUMBER ROLLED	NUMBER ON BINGO CARD	EQUATION

PLAYER B

NUMBER ROLLED	NUMBER ON BINGO CARD	EQUATION

Optional: Use this space for calculations.

EXIT
Ticket

BLOCK 3

TOPIC 3

TOPIC 2

TOPIC 1

Answer this question.

To win a round of *Division Bingo,* you need to mark the square with 36 inside. What divisors would you hope to roll in order to mark that square?

I would hope to roll ______________

____

because ______________________

____

____

____

SCORE (0) (1) (2)

CAREER EXPLORATION

Social workers meet with people to help them improve their lives.

How might a social worker use division to schedule sessions?

Solve Division Problems

> WORKED EXAMPLE

Read It! **Read and identify the problem.**

SOCIAL WORKER

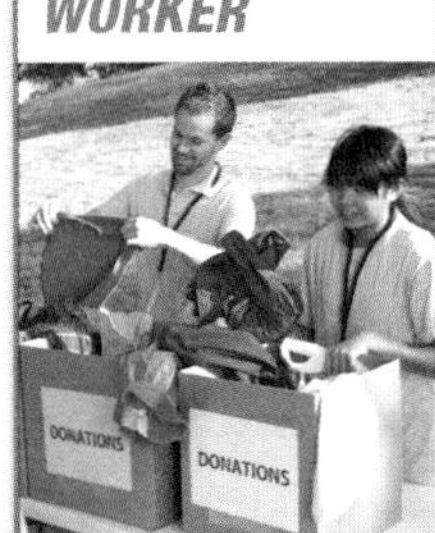

Tanya collected 42 winter coats to donate to a shelter. She packs them in boxes that hold 5 coats each. How many boxes does she need?

PROBLEM TYPE Equal Groups Problem

Show It! **Represent the problem.**

42 coats

5 coats/ 1 box

Solve It! **Solve the problem.**

$8 \times 5 = 40$

$9 \times 5 = 45$

$42 \div 5 = 8\ R2$

Tanya needs 9 boxes.

Check It! **Check your work.**

> TRY IT

1

Read It! **Read and identify the problem.**

FIREFIGHTER

A fire department receives 39 helmets. Each of its firefighting teams gets 7 helmets. How many helmets are left over?

PROBLEM TYPE ______________________

Show It! **Represent the problem.**

Solve It! **Solve the problem.**

Check It! **Check your work.**

> PRACTICE

2

Read It! **Read and identify the problem.**

ENVIRONMENTALIST

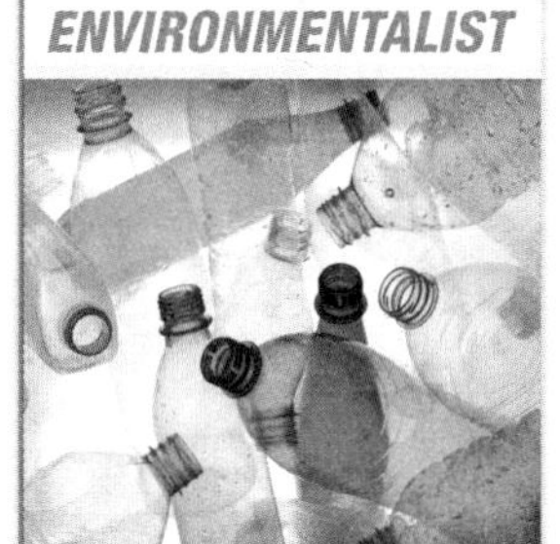

Ava recycled 78 plastic bottles. She received a coupon for every 12 bottles she recycled. How many coupons did she get?

PROBLEM TYPE ______________________

Show It! **Represent the problem.**

Solve It! **Solve the problem.**

Check It! **Check your work.**

> PRACTICE

3

POLICE OFFICER

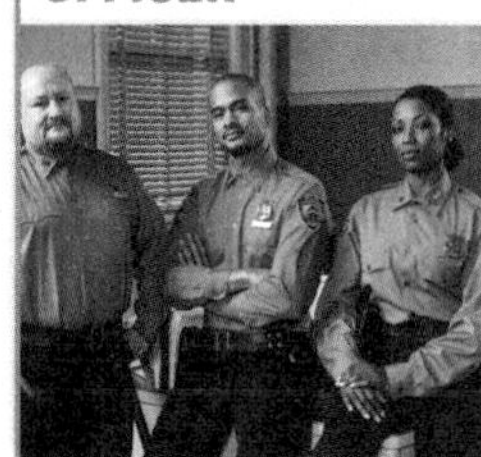

The police chief buys 52 flashlights. He gives each squad 8 flashlights, and then has 4 flashlights left over. How many squads are there?

PROBLEM TYPE ______________________

4

DOG WALKER

Rachel gets paid $11 for every hour that she walks and feeds a dog. She is also paid a tip on her total wage. If she earned a total of $85, how much was her tip?

PROBLEM TYPE ______________________

EXIT Ticket

BLOCK 3

> **Solve this problem.**

You are donating old books to a youth camp. You have 47 books that you need to pack in boxes of 8. How many boxes do you need?

Which problem asks me to find the quotient? Which problem asks me to find the remainder?

TOPIC 3

TOPIC 2

TOPIC 1

SCORE (0) (1) (2)

Strategies for Division

LESSON 1

Who's Right?

> Mark and Tyler found different answers to the same problem.

Mark	Tyler
33 ÷ 8 = 4 R1	33 ÷ 8 = 3 R9

Who's right? ______

> Explain why you know the person is right.

______ is right because ______

LESSON 2

Missing Numbers

> Fill in the missing numbers.

$(\_\_\_ \times 10) + 4 = 34$

$(\_\_\_ \times 10) + 7 = 67$

$(\_\_\_ \times 10) + \_\_\_ = 51$

$(\_\_\_ \times 10) + \_\_\_ = 93$

> How did place value help you find the missing numbers?

Place value helped me find the missing numbers because ______

LESSON 3

Build It

> Create as many division equations as you can with a remainder of 1. Use only these numbers.

1 2 3 4 5 6

- ______
- ______
- ______
- ______
- ______

> How can you create a division problem with a remainder of 1?

I can create a division problem with a remainder of 1 by ______

BLOCK 3

LESSON 4

Which Does Not Belong?

› **Circle the expression that does not belong.**

24 ÷ 2

75 ÷ 2

18 ÷ 3

75 ÷ 5

› **Explain your answer.**

The expression that does not belong is ____________ because

____

____

____

LESSON 5

Find the Pattern

› **Circle the number that does not follow the rule.**

6, 15, 18, 19, 21, 24, 30

› **How did you decide which number does not belong? Explain your reasoning.**

______ does not belong because

____

____

____

Sum It Up!

› **In this Topic, you learned to solve division problems by taking out partial quotients. Taking out multiples of 10 and 100 makes division easier.**

I want to divide 1,285 by 3. What's the first step?

Take out 400 groups of 3 because 400 × 3 equals 1200.

Divide by Taking Out 10s

WORKED EXAMPLE

STEP 1 Take out 10 groups of the divisor.

$43 \div 3$

```
     10
3 ) 43
  - 30      10 x 3 = 30
    13
```

STEP 2 Take out other partial quotients.

```
      4
     10
3 ) 43
  - 30      10 x 3 = 30
    13
  - 12      4 x 3 = 12
     1
```

STEP 3 Write the quotient and remainder.

```
      4     14 R1
     10
3 ) 43
  - 30      10 x 3 = 30
    13
  - 12      4 x 3 = 12
     1
```

$43 \div 3 =$ 14 R1

TRY IT

1

STEP 1 Take out 10 groups of the divisor.

$75 \div 6$

6) 75

STEP 2 Take out other partial quotients.

STEP 3 Write the quotient and remainder.

$75 \div 6 =$ ______

PRACTICE

2

STEP 1 Take out 10 groups of the divisor.

$62 \div 5$

5) 62

STEP 2 Take out other partial quotients.

STEP 3 Write the quotient and remainder.

$62 \div 5 =$ ______

partial quotients *(n)* numbers you can add to calculate a quotient

› PRACTICE

3

51 ÷ 3

51 ÷ 3 = ______

4

52 ÷ 2

52 ÷ 2 = ______

5

80 ÷ 6

80 ÷ 6 = ______

6

56 ÷ 5

56 ÷ 5 = ______

EXIT Ticket

BLOCK 3

› **Find the quotient.**

94 ÷ 7

94 ÷ 7 = ______

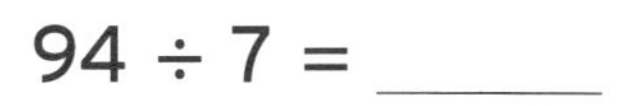

› **How can you use multiplication to check your answer?**

I can use multiplication to check my answer by ______

______

______

______

______

______

______

SCORE ⓪ ① ②

TOPIC 3

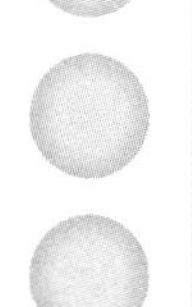

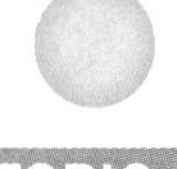

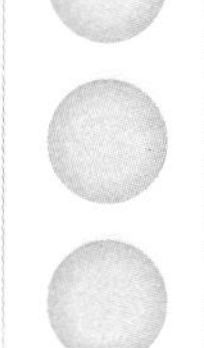

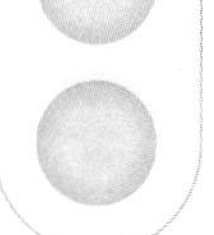

Divide by Taking Out Multiples of 10

> WORKED EXAMPLE

STEP 1 Take out multiples of 10 groups of the divisor.

78 ÷ 3

$$\begin{array}{r} 20 \\ 3\overline{)78} \\ -60 \\ \hline 18 \end{array} \quad 20 \times 3 = 60$$

STEP 2 Take out other partial quotients.

$$\begin{array}{r} 6 \\ 20 \\ 3\overline{)78} \\ -60 \\ \hline 18 \\ -18 \\ \hline 0 \end{array} \quad \begin{array}{l} 20 \times 3 = 60 \\ 6 \times 3 = 18 \end{array}$$

STEP 3 Write the quotient and remainder.

78 ÷ 3 = 26

> TRY IT

1

STEP 1 Take out multiples of 10 groups of the divisor.

157 ÷ 3

$3\overline{)157}$

STEP 2 Take out other partial quotients.

STEP 3 Write the quotient and remainder.

157 ÷ 3 = ______

> PRACTICE

2

STEP 1 Take out multiples of 10 groups of the divisor.

164 ÷ 4

$4\overline{)164}$

STEP 2 Take out other partial quotients.

STEP 3 Write the quotient and remainder.

164 ÷ 4 = ______

BLOCK 3

multiple of 10 *(n)* a number that has a factor of 10

› PRACTICE

3

$128 \div 4$

$4\overline{)128}$

$128 \div 4 =$ ______

4

$362 \div 7$

$7\overline{)362}$

$362 \div 7 =$ ______

5

$285 \div 9$

$9\overline{)285}$

$285 \div 9 =$ ______

6

$375 \div 6$

$6\overline{)375}$

$375 \div 6 =$ ______

EXIT Ticket

BLOCK 3

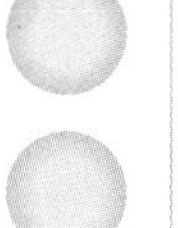

TOPIC 3

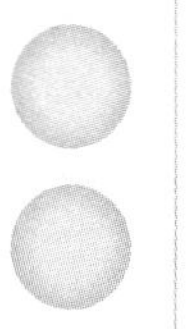

TOPIC 2

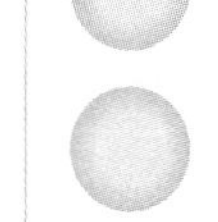

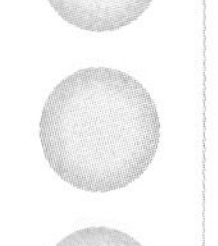

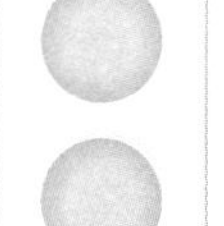

TOPIC 1

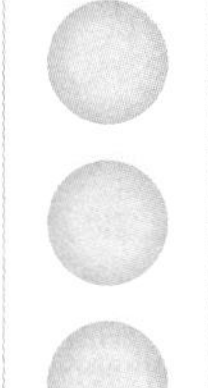

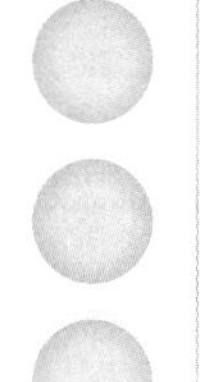

› **Find the quotient.**

$94 \div 3$

$3\overline{)94}$

$94 \div 3 =$ ______

I can use multiplication to check the answer to a division problem.

SCORE (0) (1) (2)

Divide by Taking Out Multiples of 100

WORKED EXAMPLE

STEP 1 Take out multiples of 100 groups of the divisor.

1575 ÷ 6

```
      200
 6 )1575
  - 1200     200 x 6 = 1200
     375
```

STEP 2 Take out multiples of 10 groups of the divisor.

```
       50
      200
 6 )1575
  - 1200     200 x 6 = 1200
     375
   - 300      50 x 6 =  300
      75
```

STEP 3 Take out other partial quotients and write the quotient.

```
        2
       10
       50     262 R3
      200
 6 )1575
  - 1200     200 x 6 = 1200
     375
   - 300      50 x 6 =  300
      75
    - 60      10 x 6 =   60
      15
      12       2 x 6 =   12
       3
```

1575 ÷ 6 = 262 R3

TRY IT

1

STEP 1 Take out multiples of 100 groups of the divisor.

995 ÷ 2

2)995

STEP 2 Take out multiples of 10 groups of the divisor.

STEP 3 Take out other partial quotients and write the quotient.

995 ÷ 2 = ______

PRACTICE

2

STEP 1 Take out multiples of 100 groups of the divisor.

1250 ÷ 5

5)1250

STEP 2 Take out multiples of 10 groups of the divisor.

STEP 3 Take out other partial quotients and write the quotient.

1250 ÷ 5 = ______

> PRACTICE

3

775 ÷ 3

$3\overline{)775}$

775 ÷ 3 = ______

4

1000 ÷ 3

$3\overline{)1000}$

1000 ÷ 3 = ______

5

1825 ÷ 6

$6\overline{)1825}$

1825 ÷ 6 = ______

6

6005 ÷ 8

$8\overline{)6005}$

6005 ÷ 8 = ______

EXIT
Ticket

BLOCK 3

TOPIC 3

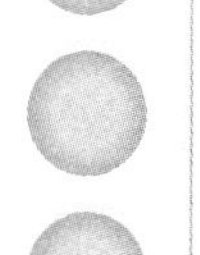

> **Find the error and fix the math.**

4150 ÷ 7

```
      2
     90        598
    500
 7)4150
  -3500        500 × 7 = 3500
    650
    630         90 × 7 =  630
     20
    -14          2 × 7 =   14
      6
```

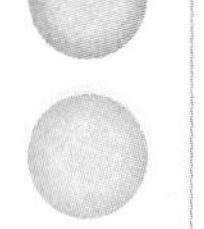

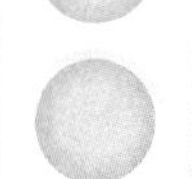

> **What error was made in this solution?**

The error is that ______________________

____

____

____

____

____

____

The correct answer is ______.

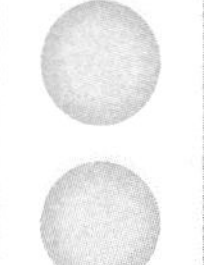

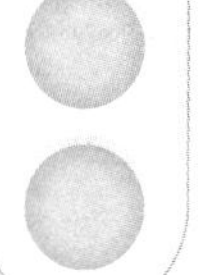

SCORE (0) (1) (2)

Develop Reasoning About Remainders

RULES

Division Bingo (Level 2)

What You Need
- *mSpace* pages 122–125
- decahedron (white, 1–10)

What to Know
- Players decide who is X and who is O.
- Players take turns.
- Each player records the numbers and equations for both players in a round.

How to Win
- The winner is the first player to mark five boxes in a row—across, up and down, or from corner to corner.

HOW TO PLAY

STEP 1 Roll the decahedron. Record this number as the divisor in the "Number Rolled" column.

PLAYER A

NUMBER ROLLED	NUMBER ON BINGO CARD	EQUATION
3		

STEP 2 Choose a dividend on the Bingo card that is divisible by the divisor you rolled. Write the equation.

PLAYER A

NUMBER ROLLED	NUMBER ON BINGO CARD	EQUATION
3	51	$51 \div 3 = 17$

STEP 3 Ask your partner to check your equation. If it is correct, put your mark on the dividend.

49	56	44	60	75
54	68	63	48	64
52	42	Free Space	55	85
70	72	51 (X)	78	45
90	65	50	96	84

STEP 4 Trade turns. Record your partner's equations.

PLAYER A

NUMBER ROLLED	NUMBER ON BINGO CARD	EQUATION
3	51	$51 \div 3 = 17$

PLAYER B

NUMBER ROLLED	NUMBER ON BINGO CARD	EQUATION
6	60	$60 \div 6 = 10$

RECORDING SHEET

Division Bingo (Level 2)

› Record your equations and your partner's equations.
Optional: Use the space on page 125 for calculations.

49	56	44	60	75
54	68	63	48	64
52	42	Free Space	55	85
70	72	51	78	45
90	65	50	96	84

PLAYER A

NUMBER ROLLED	NUMBER ON BINGO CARD	EQUATION

PLAYER B

NUMBER ROLLED	NUMBER ON BINGO CARD	EQUATION

RECORDING SHEET

Division Bingo (Level 2)

> Record your equations and your partner's equations.
Optional: Use the space on page 125 for calculations.

49	56	44	60	75
54	68	63	48	64
52	42	Free Space	55	85
70	72	51	78	45
90	65	50	96	84

PLAYER A

NUMBER ROLLED	NUMBER ON BINGO CARD	EQUATION

PLAYER B

NUMBER ROLLED	NUMBER ON BINGO CARD	EQUATION

> Optional: Use this space for calculations.

EXIT
Ticket

BLOCK 3

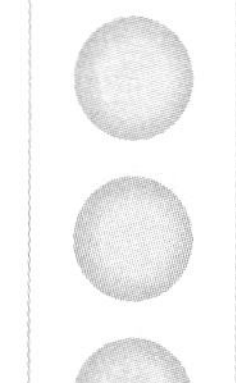

> **Answer this question.**

You rolled a number that allows you to place your mark on any dividend on the Bingo card. What number did you roll? Explain your thinking.

The number that lets you place your mark on any dividend is _______ because _______________

____

____

____

SCORE (0) (1) (2)

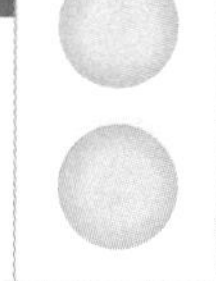

CAREER EXPLORATION

> **Health educators teach kids and adults how to eat healthy.**

How could a health educator use division to decide how many brochures to bring each class?

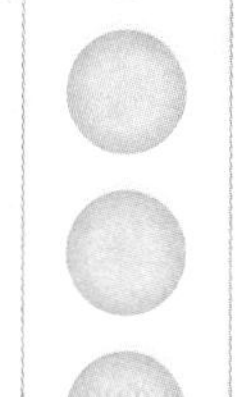

Use Divisibility to Solve Problems

> WORKED EXAMPLE

STEP 1 **Analyze the problem.**

Classify these numbers.

2, 3, 6, 8, 9, 12, 13, 15, 18

CIRCLE A Numbers divisible by 2

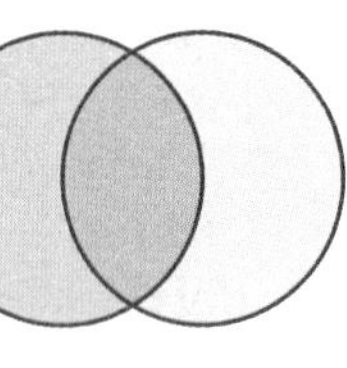

CIRCLE B Numbers divisible by 3

STEP 2 **List the multiples.**

Multiples of 2: 2, 4, 6, 8, 10, 12, 14, 16, 18

Multiples of 3: 3, 6, 9, 12, 15, 18

STEP 3 **Identify the numbers in the circles and intersection.**

Circle A: 2, (6), 8, (12), (18)

Circle B: 3, (6), 9, (12), 15, (18)

STEP 4 **Complete the Venn diagram.**

CIRCLE A Numbers divisible by 2

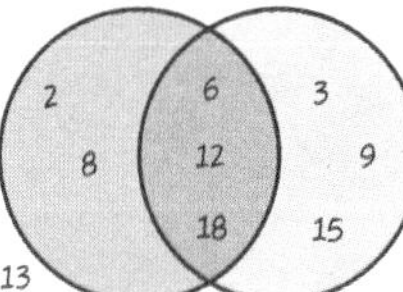

CIRCLE B Numbers divisible by 3

> TRY IT

1

STEP 1 **Analyze the problem.**

Classify these numbers.

7, 10, 12, 14, 24, 28, 36, 42

CIRCLE A Numbers divisible by 6

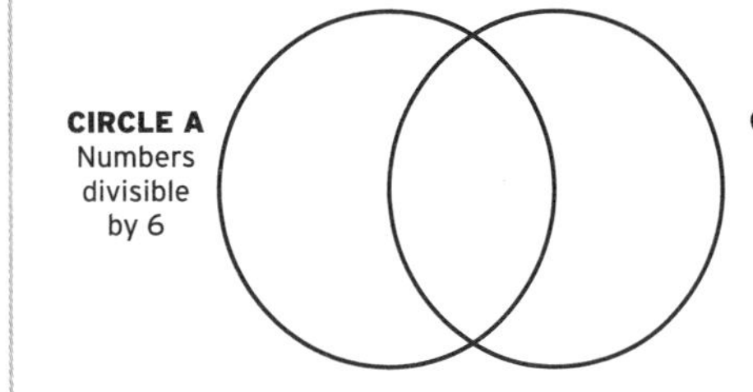

CIRCLE B Numbers divisible by 7

STEP 2 **List the multiples.**

Multiples of 6: ______________________

Multiples of 7: ______________________

STEP 3 **Identify the numbers in the circles and intersection.**

Circle A: ______________________

Circle B: ______________________

STEP 4 **Complete the Venn diagram.**

> PRACTICE

2

STEP 1 **Analyze the problem.**

Classify these numbers.

4, 10, 12, 17, 25, 32, 38, 40

CIRCLE A Numbers divisible by 4

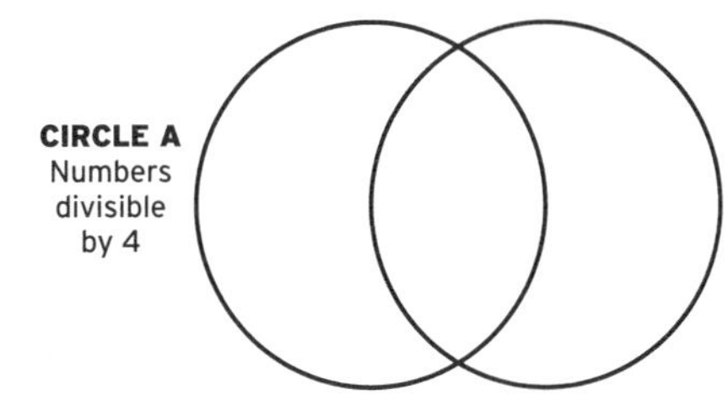

CIRCLE B Numbers divisible by 5

STEP 2 **List the multiples.**

Multiples of 4: ______________________

Multiples of 5: ______________________

STEP 3 **Identify the numbers in the circles and intersection.**

Circle A: ______________________

Circle B: ______________________

STEP 4 **Complete the Venn diagram.**

BLOCK 3

> PRACTICE

3

STEP 1 **Analyze the problem.**

Classify these numbers.

6, 14, 15, 18, 28, 30, 33, 35, 42

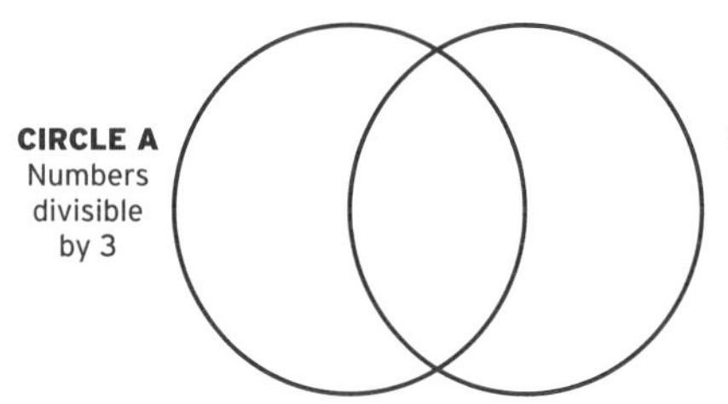

STEP 2 **List the multiples.**

Multiples of 3:

____

Multiples of 7:

____

STEP 3 **Identify the numbers in the circles and intersection.**

Circle A:

____

Circle B:

____

STEP 4 **Complete the Venn diagram.**

4

STEP 1 **Analyze the problem.**

Classify these numbers.

9, 16, 20, 24, 30, 36, 45, 54

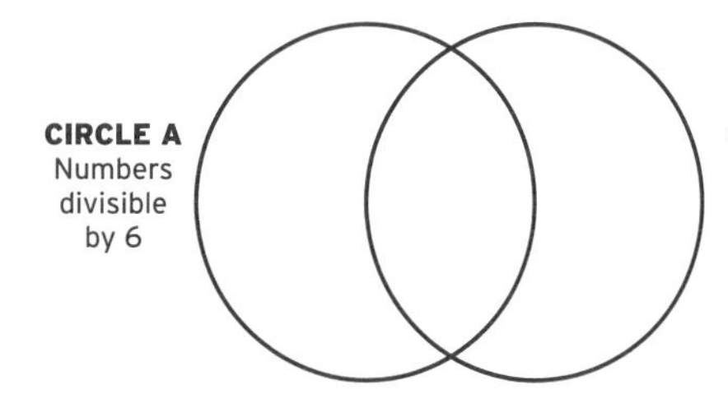

STEP 2 **List the multiples.**

Multiples of 6:

____

Multiples of 9:

____

STEP 3 **Identify the numbers in the circles and intersection.**

Circle A:

____

Circle B:

____

STEP 4 **Complete the Venn diagram.**

EXIT Ticket

BLOCK 3

TOPIC 3 · TOPIC 2 · TOPIC 1

> **Classify these numbers using the Venn diagram.**

5, 6, 12, 16, 20, 24, 28, 30

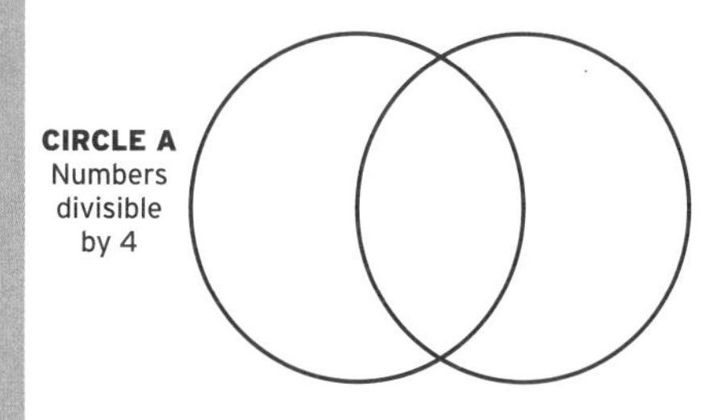

Multiples of 4:

____

Multiples of 6:

____

> **Identify the numbers in the circles and intersection.**

Circle A:

____

Circle B:

____

SCORE (0) (1) (2)

Partial Quotient Strategy

LESSON 1

Number Strings

> Divide this set of expressions mentally.

$40 \div 4$

$80 \div 4$

$16 \div 4$

$96 \div 4$

> Pick two expressions and explain how they are related.

The expressions ____________ and ____________ are related because ______________________________

____

LESSON 2

Brain Teaser

> Solve the problems without finding the number in each box.

1. If $\square \times 2 = 30$, what is $\square \times 4$? ____
2. If $\square \times 5 = 65$, what is $\square \times 10$? ____
3. If $40 \times \square = 800$, what is $400 \times \square$? ____

> Pick one problem and explain how you found the product.

I found the product for Problem ___ by ______________________________

____

____

LESSON 3

Missing Numbers

> Fill in the missing digits and complete the division.

$$\begin{array}{r} 20\,\overline{)\,91\square} \\ -\;800 \\ \hline 1\square 5 \end{array}$$

> How did you begin solving this problem?

I began solving this problem by ______________________________

____

____

LESSON 4

Make an Estimate

> Estimate the quotients. Circle the expression with the greater quotient.

$165 \div 21$ $268 \div 29$

> How did you decide which quotient is greater?

I decided which quotient is greater by ______

______

______

LESSON 5

Find the Pattern

> Classify these numbers in the Venn diagram.

6, 18, 26, 54, 60

CIRCLE A Numbers divisible by 6

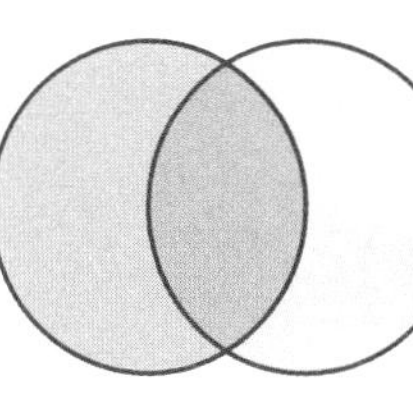

CIRCLE B Numbers divisible by 9

> Name three more numbers that can be placed in the intersection.

Three possible numbers are ______

______

______

Sum It Up!

> In this Topic, we learned how to divide by 10 and multiples of 10. Then we divided by 2-digit divisors.

What's the first step you'd take to find 156 divided by 33?

I'd make an estimate. 150 divided by 30 is 5, so 5 is a useful estimate.

$156 \div 33$

Estimate: $150 \div 30 = 5$

Divide by 10 and Multiples of 10

> WORKED EXAMPLE

STEP 1 Divide by a multiple of 10.

692 ÷ 20

```
       30
20 ) 692
    - 600     30 x 20 = 600
       92
```

STEP 2 Take out other partial quotients.

```
        4
       30
20 ) 692
    - 600     30 x 20 = 600
       92
     - 80      4 x 20 =  80
       12
```

STEP 3 Find the quotient and the remainder.

```
        4         34 R 12
       30
20 ) 692
    - 600     30 x 20 = 600
       92
     - 80      4 x 20 =  80
       12
```

692 ÷ 20 = 34 R12

> TRY IT

1

STEP 1 Divide by a multiple of 10.

985 ÷ 30

30) 985

STEP 2 Take out other partial quotients.

STEP 3 Find the quotient and the remainder.

985 ÷ 30 = ______

> PRACTICE

2

STEP 1 Divide by a multiple of 10.

745 ÷ 30

30) 745

STEP 2 Take out other partial quotients.

STEP 3 Find the quotient and the remainder.

745 ÷ 30 = ______

BLOCK 3

> PRACTICE

3

862 ÷ 20

862 ÷ 20 = ________

4

756 ÷ 10

756 ÷ 10 = ________

5

930 ÷ 30

930 ÷ 30 = ________

6

370 ÷ 20

370 ÷ 20 = ________

EXIT
Ticket

BLOCK 3

TOPIC 3

> **Find the errors and fix the math.**

965 ÷ 30

```
       2      5 R5
       3
30 ) 965
    −900      3 × 30 = 900
      65
     −60      2 × 30 =  60
       5
```

965 ÷ 30 = 5 R5

TOPIC 2

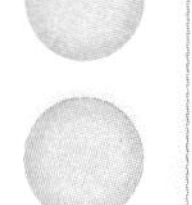

> **Write the correct quotient and remainder. Then explain how the error was made.**

The quotient and remainder are ________.

The error was made because

____

____

____

____

TOPIC 1

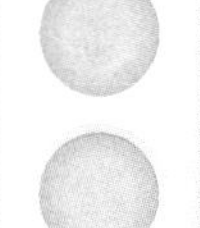

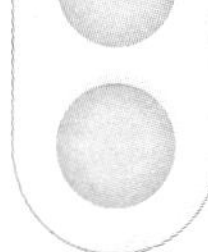

SCORE ⓪ ① ②

Divide by 2-Digit Divisors

> WORKED EXAMPLE

STEP 1 **Estimate the quotient.**

$68 \div 13$

Estimate: 70 ÷ 10 = 7

STEP 2 **Take out equal groups.**

$$
\begin{array}{r|l}
1 & 5\ R3 \\
4 & \\
13\overline{)68} & \\
-52 & 4 \times 13 = 52 \\
16 & \\
-13 & 1 \times 13 = 13 \\
3 &
\end{array}
$$

STEP 3 **Calculate the quotient and the remainder.**

$68 \div 13 =$ 5 R3

STEP 4 **Compare the quotient with the estimate.**

Is your answer reasonable? yes

> TRY IT

1

STEP 1 **Estimate the quotient.**

$98 \div 18$

Estimate: ______ ÷ ______ = ______

STEP 2 **Take out equal groups.**

$18\overline{)98}$

STEP 3 **Calculate the quotient and the remainder.**

$95 \div 18 =$ ________

STEP 4 **Compare the quotient with the estimate.**

Is your answer reasonable? ________

> PRACTICE

2

STEP 1 **Estimate the quotient.**

$75 \div 12$

Estimate: ______ ÷ ______ = ______

STEP 2 **Take out equal groups.**

$12\overline{)75}$

STEP 3 **Calculate the quotient and the remainder.**

$75 \div 12 =$ ________

STEP 4 **Compare the quotient with the estimate.**

Is your answer reasonable? ________

estimate *(n)* a number that is an approximate calculation based on numbers that are easier to work with

> PRACTICE

3

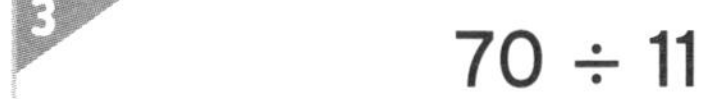

70 ÷ 11

Estimate: ______ ÷ ______ = ______

$11 \overline{)70}$

70 ÷ 11 = ________

Is your answer reasonable? ________

4

58 ÷ 15

Estimate: ______ ÷ ______ = ______

$15 \overline{)58}$

58 ÷ 15 = ________

Is your answer reasonable? ________

5

37 ÷ 17

Estimate: ______ ÷ ______ = ______

$17 \overline{)37}$

37 ÷ 17 = ________

Is your answer reasonable? ________

6

83 ÷ 19

Estimate: ______ ÷ ______ = ______

$19 \overline{)83}$

83 ÷ 19 = ________

Is your answer reasonable? ________

EXIT Ticket

BLOCK 3

TOPIC 3

TOPIC 2

TOPIC 1

> **Find the quotient.**

56 ÷ 12

Estimate: _____ ÷ _____ = _____

$12 \overline{)56}$

56 ÷ 12 = ______

Is your answer reasonable: _____

> **Explain how making an estimate is useful.**

Making an estimate is useful because ________________

____

____

____

____

____

SCORE ⓪ ① ②

Estimate and Divide Greater Numbers

> WORKED EXAMPLE

STEP 1 **Estimate the quotient.**

$792 \div 18$

Estimate: 800 ÷ 20 = 40

STEP 2 **Take out equal groups.**

$$\begin{array}{r} 4 \\ 40 \\ 18\overline{)792} \\ -720 \\ \hline 72 \\ -72 \\ \hline 0 \end{array}$$

44

$40 \times 18 = 720$

$4 \times 18 = 72$

STEP 3 **Find the quotient and the remainder.**

$792 \div 18 =$ 44

STEP 4 **Compare the quotient with the estimate.**

Is your answer reasonable? yes

> TRY IT

1

STEP 1 **Estimate the quotient.**

$1325 \div 41$

Estimate: _____ ÷ _____ = _____

STEP 2 **Take out equal groups.**

$41\overline{)1325}$

STEP 3 **Find the quotient and the remainder.**

$1325 \div 41 =$ _________

STEP 4 **Compare the quotient with the estimate.**

Is your answer reasonable? _____

> PRACTICE

2

STEP 1 **Estimate the quotient.**

$775 \div 12$

Estimate: _____ ÷ _____ = _____

STEP 2 **Take out equal groups.**

$12\overline{)775}$

STEP 3 **Find the quotient and the remainder.**

$775 \div 12 =$ _________

STEP 4 **Compare the quotient with the estimate.**

Is your answer reasonable? _____

PRACTICE

3

$365 \div 12$

Estimate: ______ ÷ ______ = ______

$12\overline{)365}$

$365 \div 12 =$ ________

Is your answer reasonable? ______

4

$1620 \div 24$

Estimate: ______ ÷ ______ = ______

$24\overline{)1620}$

$1620 \div 24 =$ ________

Is your answer reasonable? ______

EXIT
Ticket

BLOCK 3

TOPIC 3

TOPIC 2

TOPIC 1

Find the quotient.

$776 \div 22$

Estimate: ____ ÷ ____ = ____

$22\overline{)776}$

$776 \div 22 =$ ______

How do you know your answer is reasonable?

I know my answer is reasonable because ________________

____

____

____

____

SCORE ⓪ ① ②

Develop Divisibility Strategies

RULES

Division Bingo (Level 3)

What You Need

- *mSpace* pages 136–139
- decahedron (white, 1–10)

What to Know

- Players decide who is X and who is O.
- Players take turns.
- Each player records the numbers and equations for both players in a round.

How to Win

- The winner is the first player to mark five boxes in a row—across, up and down, or from corner to corner.

> HOW TO PLAY

STEP 1 Roll the decahedron. Record this number as the divisor in the "Number Rolled" column.

PLAYER A

NUMBER ROLLED	NUMBER ON BINGO CARD	EQUATION
3		

STEP 2 Choose a dividend on the Bingo card that is divisible by the divisor you rolled. Write the equation.

PLAYER A

NUMBER ROLLED	NUMBER ON BINGO CARD	EQUATION
3	180	$180 \div 3 = 60$

STEP 3 Ask your partner to check your equation. If it is correct, put your mark on the dividend.

144	156	98	93	88
121	132	102	140	78
108	200	Free Space	120	104
126	150	180 (marked X)	99	136
160	105	128	100	122

STEP 4 Trade turns. Record your partner's equation.

PLAYER A

NUMBER ROLLED	NUMBER ON BINGO CARD	EQUATION
3	180	$180 \div 3 = 60$

PLAYER B

NUMBER ROLLED	NUMBER ON BINGO CARD	EQUATION
6	144	$144 \div 6 = 24$

RECORDING SHEET

Division Bingo (Level 3)

> Record your equations and your partner's equations.
> Optional: Use the space on page 139 for calculations.

144	156	98	93	88
121	132	102	140	78
108	200	Free Space	120	104
126	150	180	99	136
160	105	128	100	122

PLAYER A

NUMBER ROLLED	NUMBER ON BINGO CARD	EQUATION

PLAYER B

NUMBER ROLLED	NUMBER ON BINGO CARD	EQUATION

RECORDING SHEET

Division Bingo (Level 3)

> Record your equations and your partner's equations.
> Optional: Use the space on page 139 for calculations.

144	156	98	93	88
121	132	102	140	78
108	200	Free Space	120	104
126	150	180	99	136
160	105	128	100	122

PLAYER A

NUMBER ROLLED	NUMBER ON BINGO CARD	EQUATION

PLAYER B

NUMBER ROLLED	NUMBER ON BINGO CARD	EQUATION

> Use this space for calculations.

EXIT Ticket

TOPIC 3

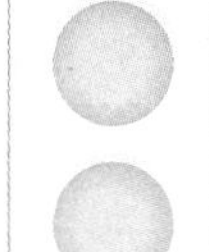

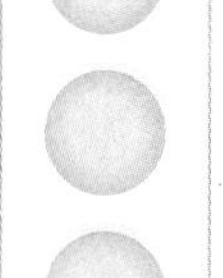

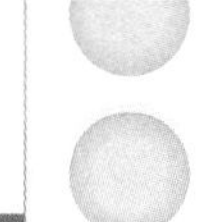

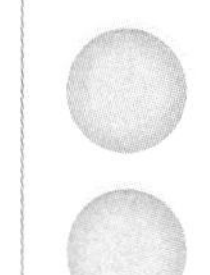

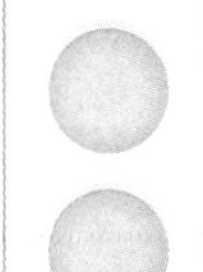

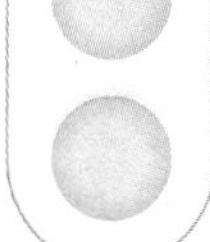

> **Answer these questions.**

Julio needs to mark 122 to win the game. What numbers would Julio need to roll to win?

Julio needs to roll ____________,

because ____________

____

Is Julio likely to roll a 1 or 2? Why or why not?

Julio is/is not likely to roll a 1 or 2 because ____________

____

SCORE (0) (1) (2)

CAREER EXPLORATION

> **Charity fundraisers gather donations for their organizations.**

How might a fundraiser use division to determine how to distribute the money raised?

Solve Multi-Step Division Problems

> WORKED EXAMPLE

Read It! Read and identify the problem.

VOLUNTEER

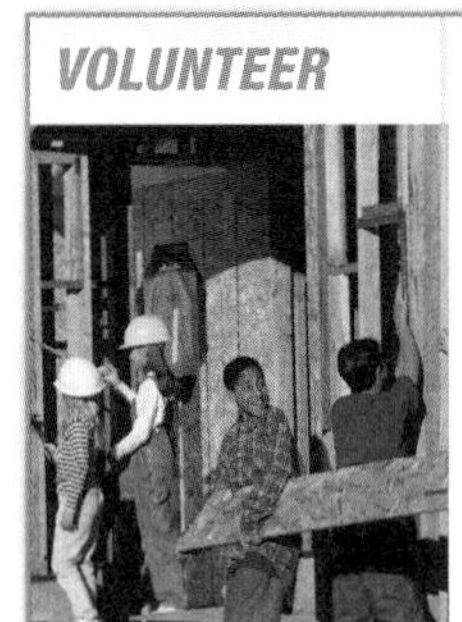

There are 4 times as many girls as boys in a volunteer program. The program has 180 girls. How many more girls than boys are there?

PROBLEM TYPE Compare Problem

Show It! Represent the problem.

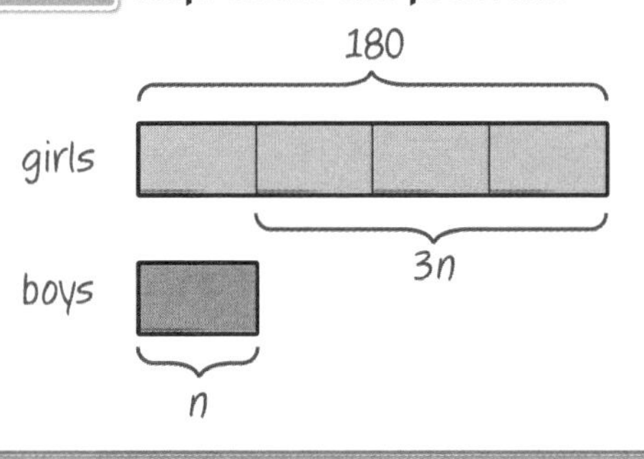

Solve It! Solve the problem.

$$n = 180 \div 4$$
$$= 45$$
$$3n = 3 \times 45$$
$$= 135$$

Check It! Check your work.

> TRY IT

1

Read It! Read and identify the problem.

ANIMAL RIGHTS ACTIVIST

Miguel and Anne rescued 133 abandoned dogs last year. Miguel rescued 6 times as many dogs as Anne. How many dogs did Anne rescue?

PROBLEM TYPE ______________________

Show It! Represent the problem.

Solve It! Solve the problem.

Check It! Check your work.

> PRACTICE

2

Read It! Read and identify the problem.

MUSICIAN

Jin donated earnings from 2 songs to a charity. He donated $864 altogether. If Jin's second song earned 5 times as much as his first song, how much did his first song earn?

PROBLEM TYPE ______________________

Show It! Represent the problem.

Solve It! Solve the problem.

Check It! Check your work.

> PRACTICE

3

ENVIRONMENTALIST

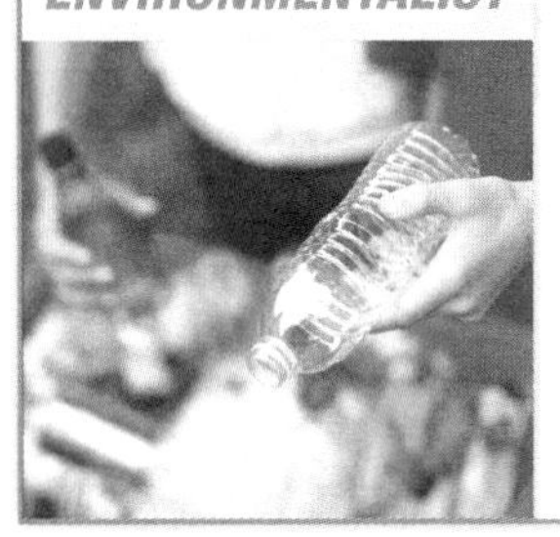

Taylor recycled 3600 bottles and cans. She recycled 8 times more cans than bottles. How many more cans than bottles did she recycle?

PROBLEM TYPE ______________________

4

AMBULANCE DRIVER

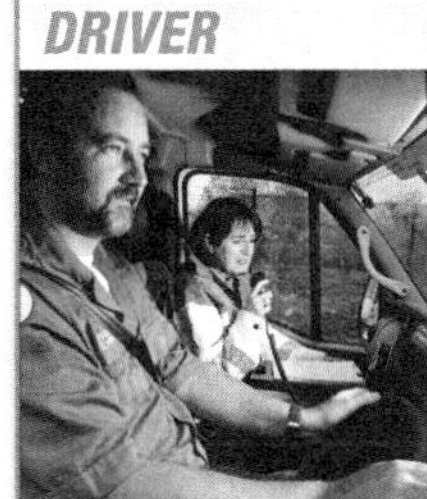

Amir received 442 emergency calls last year. He received 12 times as many calls from the city as the suburbs. How many calls did he receive from the suburbs?

PROBLEM TYPE ______________________

EXIT Ticket

BLOCK 3

> **Solve this problem.**

You sold $5040 in tickets for a fundraising concert. You sold 8 times as many Level 1 tickets as Level 2 tickets. How much more did you make in Level 1 tickets?

PROBLEM TYPE ______________________

Which of these compare problems ask me to find the value of one unit?

SCORE (0) (1) (2)

TOPIC 3

TOPIC 2

TOPIC 1

BLOCK 3 **PERFORMANCE TASK**

> YOUR JOB
Charity Fundraiser

> YOUR TASK
Distribute books collected for charity to libraries around the world.

ANCHOR VIDEO CONNECTION

As the Anchor Video shows, charities gather money and goods, and then distribute them to people in need.

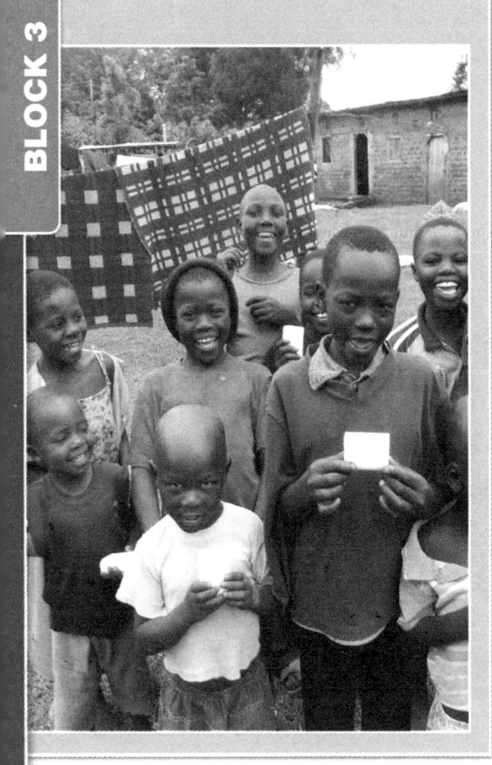

BLOCK 3

Organize a Book Drive

> **Students at seven schools collected books for charity. Make a plan to send the books to libraries around the world.**

A EXPLORE

1 Make a dot plot of the books collected from each school. First name each value in the table to the closest hundred. Then draw a dot above that number on the line.

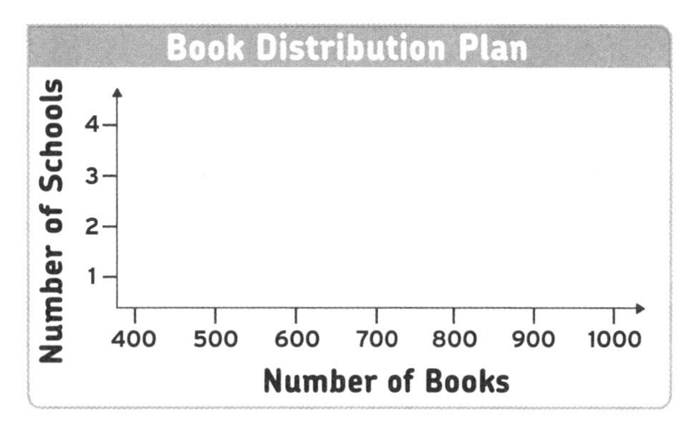

2 Choose a city for each school to send its books. You will choose some cities 2 or 3 times. Try to send each library about the same number of books.

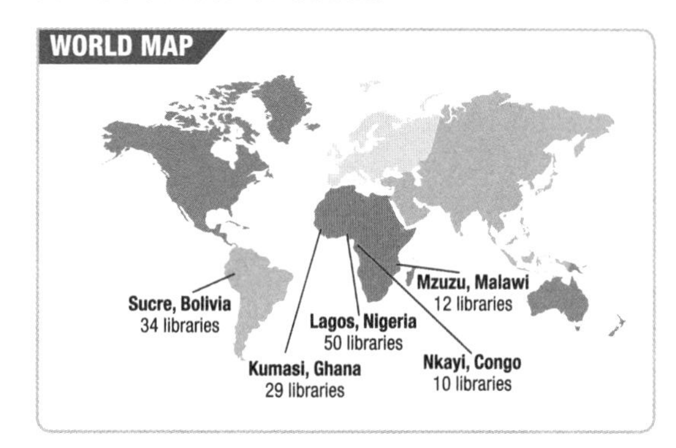

What does the dot plot show about the data? ____________________

Book Distribution Plan			
School	**Books Collected**	**Destination**	**Number of Libraries**
Andrews	360		
Cranston	711		
Las Palmas	1044		
Lincoln	1002		
Main Street	798		
M. L. King, Jr.	513		
Sierra	432		

B APPLY

Find the total number of books that each city receives. Then divide to find the number of books for each library.

DESTINATION	NUMBER OF BOOKS	NUMBER OF BOOKS ÷ NUMBER OF LIBRARIES	BOOKS PER LIBRARY	BOOKS LEFT OVER
Sucre, Bolivia		______ ÷ 34		
Nkayi, Congo		______ ÷ 10		
Kumasi, Ghana		______ ÷ 29		
Mzuzu, Malawi		______ ÷ 12		
Lagos, Nigeria		______ ÷ 50		

Draw another dot plot to show the books that each library receives. Rename each number to the closest ten. Then draw a dot above that number on the line.

Book Distribution Plan

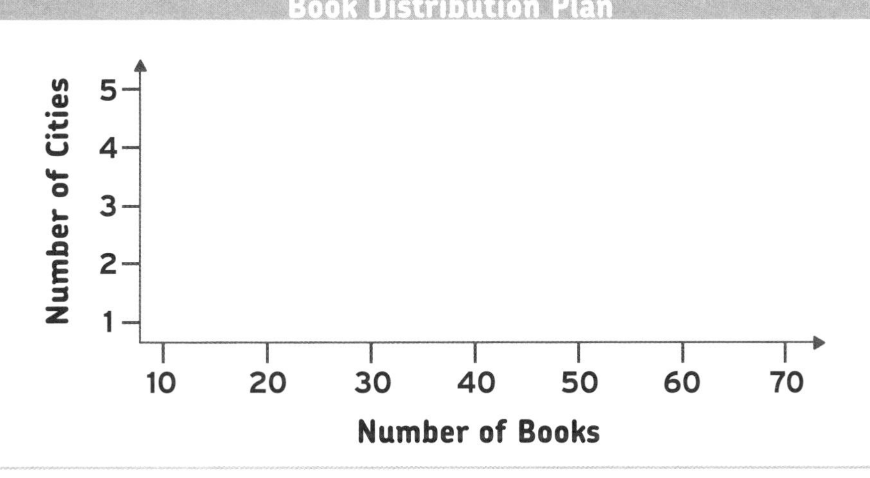

C ANALYZE

EXPLAIN How well does the plan share the books among the libraries? Use the dot plot to support your answer.

____

____

____

REFLECT Why must some cities receive books from more than one school?

____

____

____

Evaluate

› **Rate how well you and your partner understood and completed each part of the performance task.**

Rating Scale

None	Limited	Partial	Thorough
0	1	2	3

A Used the dot plot to match schools and destination cities.

Me	0	1	2	3
Partner	0	1	2	3

B Calculated the number of books per library.

Me	0	1	2	3
Partner	0	1	2	3

C Answered each question accurately.

Me	0	1	2	3
Partner	0	1	2	3

EXTEND

If Lagos, Nigeria, stopped accepting books, would the equal share for each remaining library increase or decrease? Explain your answer.

____

____

____

____

____

BLOCK 3 MINDSET SCAN

Reflect on Your Learning Strategies

Congratulations! You've completed Block 3 of *MATH 180*. Respond to these questions by checking EACH sentence that describes your mindset.

A CHALLENGE SEEKING

When you take on new challenges, you learn more and your brain becomes stronger and smarter.

What challenges did you set for yourself and meet during BLOCK 3?

- ☐ I solved all the practice problems in my *mSpace*.
- ☐ To test my knowledge and skills, sometimes I made up and solved new problems, or I asked a partner to make up new math problems for me.
- ☐ After I solved the easier problems in the Success Zone, I tried solving more challenging problems.
- ☐ I looked for and found the ideal response to the Performance Task.

☐ Other *(please describe)*:

____

____

____

____

____

B EFFORT, PRACTICE, AND PERSISTENCE

Practice is like exercise for your brain. Keep practicing, and you will develop your "brain muscle" over time.

How did you learn the math concepts of BLOCK 3?

- ☐ I asked a classmate, my teacher, or a family member for help when I didn't understand a math concept.
- ☐ I revised or recalculated my answers to challenging math problems, sometimes more than once, to find the correct answers.
- ☐ I played each Brain Arcade game many times, stopping only when I knew I understood the math concepts and could answer the questions easily.
- ☐ I reviewed all the math concepts of Block 3 to prepare for the *mSkills* Assessment.

☐ Other *(please describe)*:

____

____

____

____

____

____

C LEARNING FROM MISTAKES AND FEEDBACK

Mistakes can help you learn if you recognize and correct them.

How did you respond to mistakes you made on BLOCK 3 math problems?

- ☐ I figured out what I did wrong, and then solved the problem correctly.
- ☐ I accepted suggestions from my teacher to improve my math skills.
- ☐ When I solved similar problems, I reviewed my work to make sure I did not make the same mistakes again.
- ☐ I kept a positive attitude by thinking of mistakes as an opportunity to learn and improve.
- ☐ I practiced calming strategies like taking deep breaths, remembering a fun time, or thinking of things I enjoy doing.

☐ Other *(please describe)*:

____

____

____

____

____

Score Your Mindset

Count up all your checks and write the total here:

TOTAL CHECKS

If you checked: | *You were in the following zone, which means:*

Fixed Mindset Zone

You didn't use many brain-wise learning strategies this time. Your mindset may have held you back from doing your best.

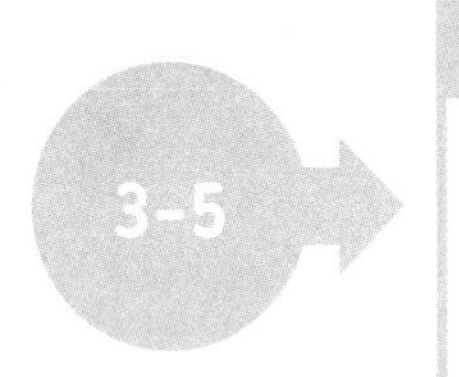

Mixed Mindset Zone

You used some good strategies but skipped some others. Your mindset may have held you back from doing your best.

Growth Mindset Zone

Overall, your use of learning strategies was in the Growth Zone this time. You used lots of good strategies that will help you grow your brain and get smarter.

What can you do about it?

- Review the strategies listed in the Mindset Scan.
- Choose one strategy from each category that you think would help you learn. Copy these strategies into your journal or notebook.
- Try each strategy as you study the math concepts of the next Block.

Brain Boosting

What will you do to help your brain stay in the Growth Zone?

I will focus on:

- ☐ Challenge seeking
- ☐ Effort, practice, and persistence
- ☐ Learning from mistakes and feedback

"I've failed over and over and over again in my life. And that is why I succeed."

Michael Jordan
Basketball star

What will I do?	**Who** will help me?
When will I do it?	**How** will this help me to grow?

BLOCK 4

Fraction Concepts

Be My Guest

VOCABULARY

- denominator
- equivalent
- fraction
- inequality
- mixed number
- numerator
- simplest form
- unit fraction

Making the Cut

Do you have what it takes to be a professional chef?

In this Anchor Video, students use fractions in a culinary arts class to compete for college scholarships.

Math in Food and Hospitality

In this Block, you will explore how math is used in the hospitality and tourism industry.

Tour GUIDES

lead visitors in museums, on cruise ships, and even through the 277-mile long by 1-mile deep Grand Canyon.

Hotel MANAGERS

are in demand. This career is expected to grow nearly 44% in the next 10 years.

Do you love organizing events?

Event PLANNERS

make up one of the 10 fastest growing careers in the United States.

Do you like being your own boss? Nearly $\frac{1}{3}$ of

Floral DESIGNERS

are self-employed.

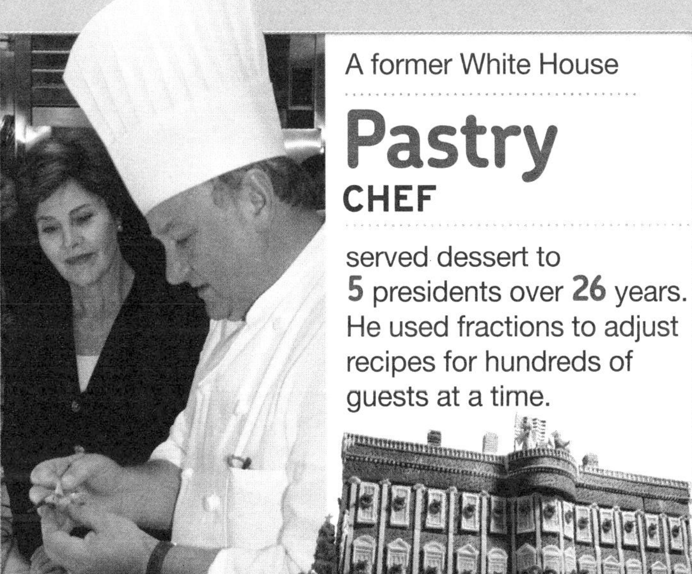

A former White House

Pastry CHEF

served dessert to 5 presidents over 26 years. He used fractions to adjust recipes for hundreds of guests at a time.

Understanding Fractions

LESSON 1

Block Preview

> **Think about the Anchor Video and answer this question.**

How could you change a recipe from 8 servings to 4?

> **Explain your strategy.**

I could change the recipe by ______________________

____

____

____

LESSON 2

Number Strings

> **Multiply this set of expressions mentally.**

5×5

5×10

5×20

5×19

> **How does knowing 5×20 help you solve 5×19?**

Knowing 5 x 20 helps me solve 5 x 19 because ______________________

____

____

LESSON 3

Build It

> **Write as many fractions as possible that have these properties:**

- numerators and denominators can be made with 1, 2, 4, 8, 16.
- fractions are less than or equal to 1.

> **What is your strategy for building as many fractions as possible?**

My strategy for building as many fractions as possible is ______________________

____

____

LESSON 4

Which Does Not Belong?

› Phil has 6 fraction pieces. He uses 5 to make a row the same length as a one-whole piece.

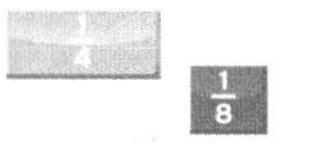

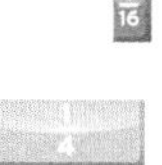

› Which fraction does not belong?

____

› How did you know which fraction piece did not belong?

I knew that the fraction ____ did not belong because _______________

____

____

LESSON 5

Brain Teaser

› Use fraction pieces to make one whole. You must use:

- 4 fraction pieces
- 3 different sizes

› Use as many of these pieces as you need:

› What was the first step you used to solve this problem?

The first step I used to solve this problem was _______________

____

____

Sum It Up!

› In this Topic, you learned to model and compare fractions using fraction pieces.

Is $\frac{3}{4}$ greater than or less than $\frac{1}{2}$? How can you tell?

I'll build the fractions using fraction pieces. I can see that $\frac{3}{4} > \frac{1}{2}$.

Model Fractions as Parts of a Whole

> WORKED EXAMPLE

STEP 1 Divide one whole into 2 equal parts.

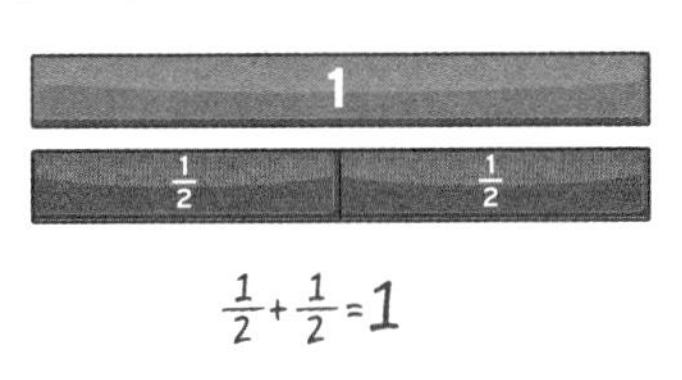

$\frac{1}{2}+\frac{1}{2}=1$

STEP 2 Divide one whole into 4 equal parts.

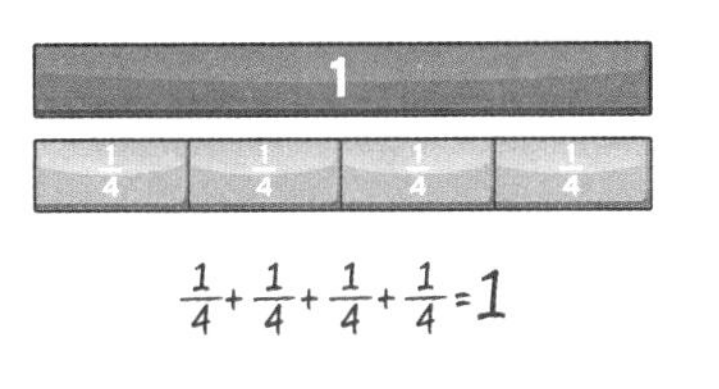

$\frac{1}{4}+\frac{1}{4}+\frac{1}{4}+\frac{1}{4}=1$

STEP 3 Divide one whole into 8 equal parts.

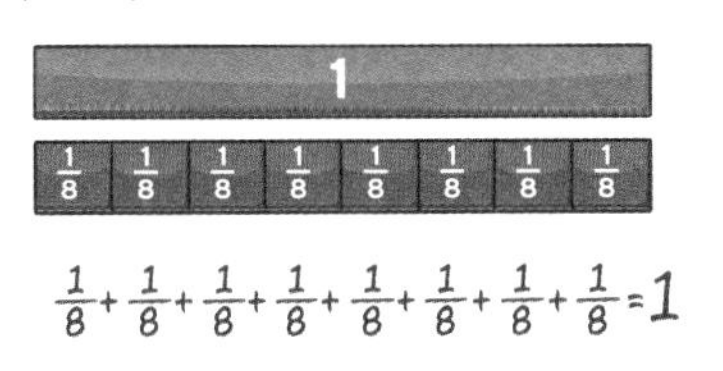

$\frac{1}{8}+\frac{1}{8}+\frac{1}{8}+\frac{1}{8}+\frac{1}{8}+\frac{1}{8}+\frac{1}{8}+\frac{1}{8}=1$

STEP 4 Divide one whole into 16 equal parts.

$\frac{1}{16}+\frac{1}{16}+\frac{1}{16}+\frac{1}{16}+\frac{1}{16}+\frac{1}{16}+\frac{1}{16}+\frac{1}{16}+$
$\frac{1}{16}+\frac{1}{16}+\frac{1}{16}+\frac{1}{16}+\frac{1}{16}+\frac{1}{16}+\frac{1}{16}+\frac{1}{16}=1$

> TRY IT

1

STEP 1 Show the fraction using fraction pieces.

How many $\frac{1}{8}$ pieces are in $\frac{3}{4}$?

STEP 2 Make the same length using different size pieces.

STEP 3 Write equations for each fraction row.

Equation 1 →

____

Equation 2 →

____

STEP 4 Write a pair of equal fractions.

$\frac{3}{4}=\frac{\square}{8}$

> PRACTICE

2

STEP 1 Show the fraction using fraction pieces.

How many $\frac{1}{2}$ pieces are in $\frac{8}{8}$?

STEP 2 Make the same length using different size pieces.

STEP 3 Write equations for each fraction row.

Equation 1 →

____

Equation 2 →

____

STEP 4 Write a pair of equal fractions.

$\frac{8}{8}=\frac{\square}{2}$

numerator *(n)* Tells how many equal parts of the whole a fraction is describing.

denominator *(n)* Tells the total number of equal parts in the whole in a fraction.

> PRACTICE

3 How many $\frac{1}{8}$ pieces are in $\frac{1}{4}$?

Equation 1 → ______

Equation 2 → ______

$\frac{1}{4} = \frac{\square}{8}$

4 How many $\frac{1}{16}$ pieces are in $\frac{2}{8}$?

Equation 1 → ______

Equation 2 → ______

$\frac{2}{8} = \frac{\square}{16}$

5 How many $\frac{1}{8}$ pieces are in $\frac{10}{16}$?

Equation 1 → ______

Equation 2 → ______

$\frac{10}{16} = \frac{\square}{8}$

6 How many $\frac{1}{8}$ pieces are in $\frac{4}{4}$?

Equation 1 → ______

Equation 2 → ______

$\frac{4}{4} = \frac{\square}{8}$

EXIT Ticket

BLOCK 4

TOPIC 3 TOPIC 2 TOPIC 1

> **Solve this problem.**

How many $\frac{1}{16}$ pieces are in $\frac{3}{8}$?

Equation 1 → ______

Equation 2 → ______

$\frac{3}{8} = \frac{\square}{16}$

> **How do you know the fractions are equal?**

I know the fractions are equal because ______

______

______

I count the number of fraction pieces I use—that's the numerator.

SCORE ⓪ ① ②

Use Fraction Models

> WORKED EXAMPLE

STEP 1 Write an equation with fractions.

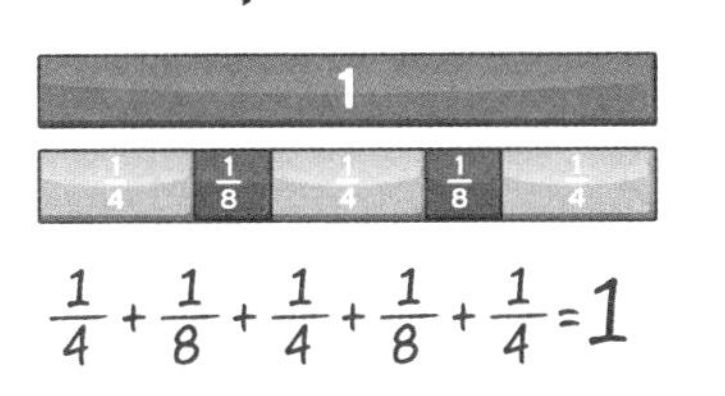

$\frac{1}{4} + \frac{1}{8} + \frac{1}{4} + \frac{1}{8} + \frac{1}{4} = 1$

STEP 2 Reorder the fraction pieces.

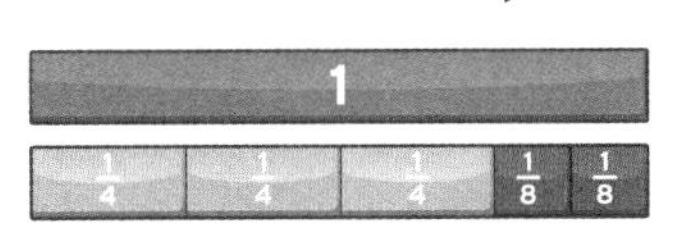

STEP 3 Rewrite the equation.

$\frac{1}{4} + \frac{1}{4} + \frac{1}{4} + \frac{1}{8} + \frac{1}{8} = 1$

STEP 4 Combine fractions.

$\frac{3}{4} + \frac{2}{8} = 1$

> TRY IT

1

STEP 1 Write an equation with fractions.

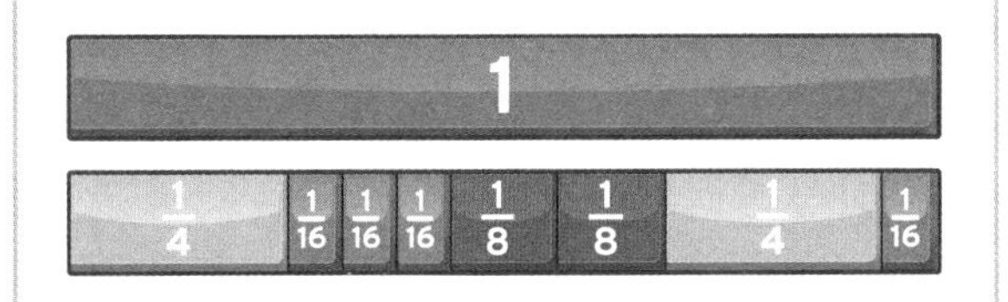

STEP 2 Reorder the fraction pieces.

STEP 3 Rewrite the equation.

STEP 4 Combine fractions.

> PRACTICE

2

STEP 1 Write an equation with fractions.

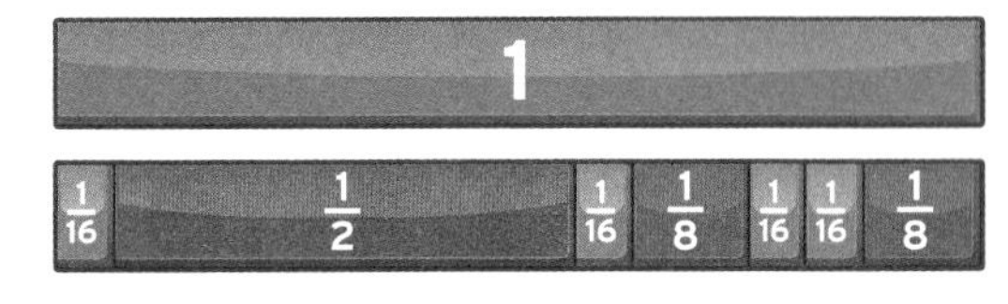

STEP 2 Reorder the fraction pieces.

STEP 3 Rewrite the equation.

STEP 4 Combine fractions.

BLOCK 4

unit fraction *(n)* One of the parts from an equally divided whole; its numerator is always 1.

PRACTICE

3

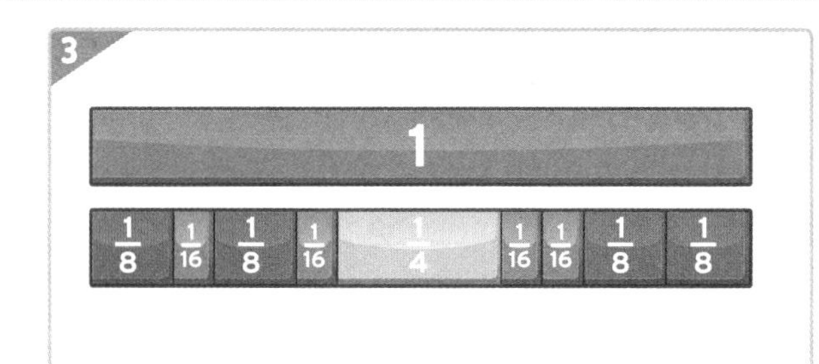

4

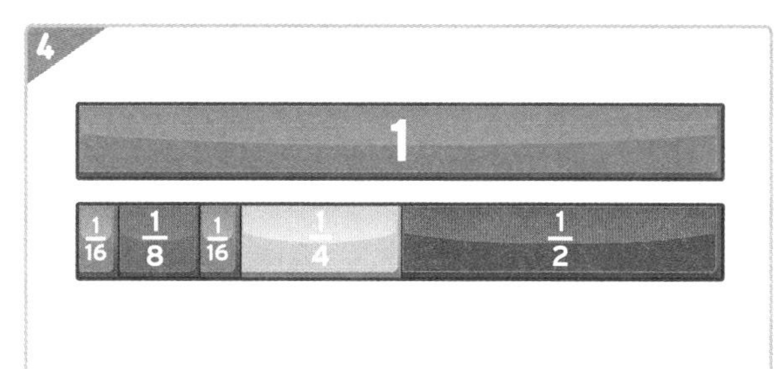

5

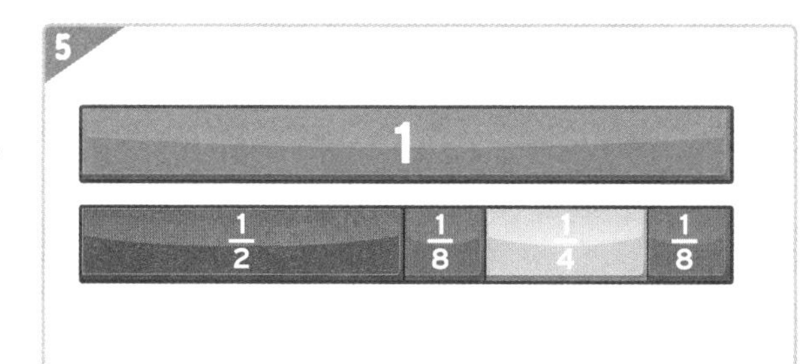

6

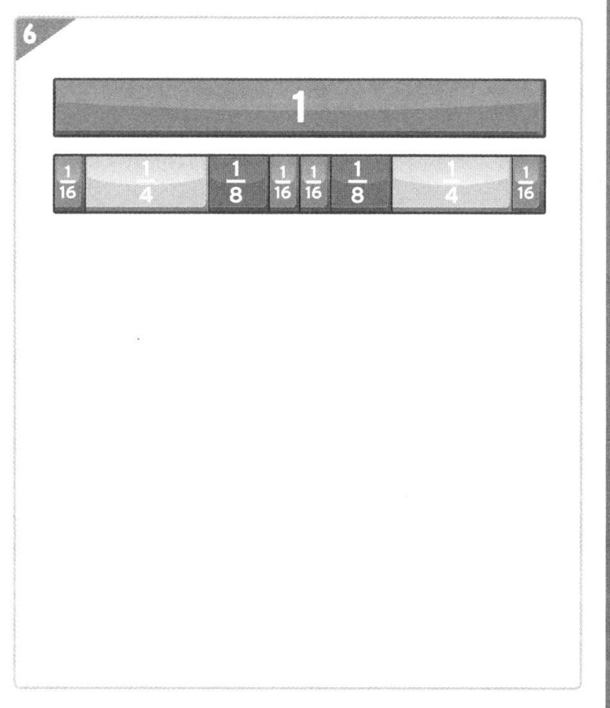

EXIT Ticket

TOPIC 3

TOPIC 2

TOPIC 1

Find the errors and fix them.

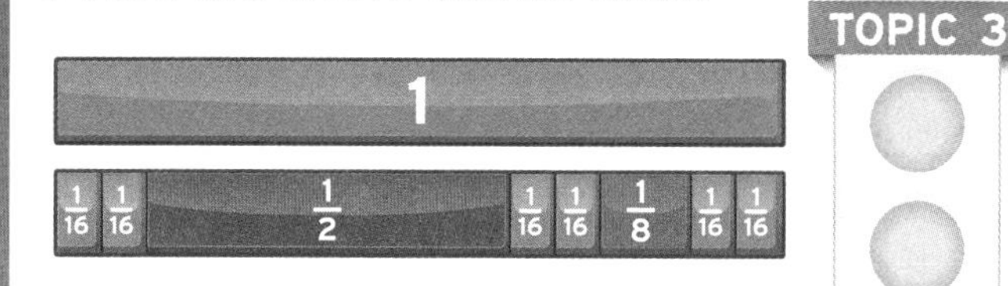

$$\frac{1}{16} + \frac{1}{16} + \frac{1}{2} + \frac{1}{16} + \frac{1}{16} + \frac{1}{8} + \frac{1}{16} = 1$$

$$\frac{1}{2} + \frac{1}{8} + \frac{5}{16} = 1$$

Explain how you found the errors.

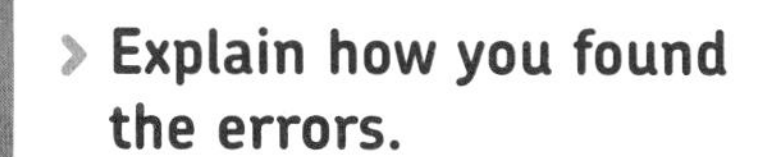

I found the errors by ______________

____

____

____

____

SCORE (0) (1) (2)

Use Models to Compare Fractions

> WORKED EXAMPLE

STEP 1 Compare equivalent fractions.

$\frac{1}{2} = \frac{4}{8}$

STEP 2 Use "less than" to compare fractions.

$\frac{1}{2} < \frac{5}{8}$

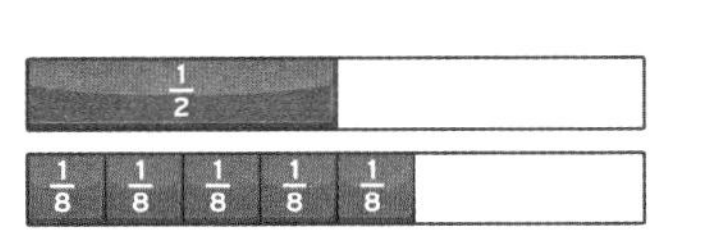

STEP 3 Use "greater than" to compare fractions.

$\frac{3}{4} > \frac{5}{8}$

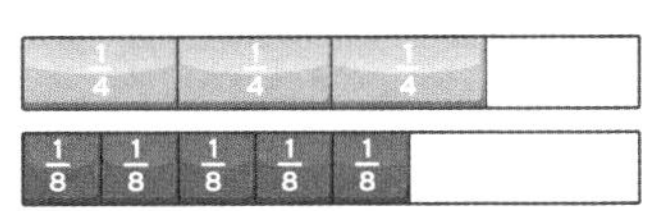

> TRY IT

1

STEP 1 Model the first fraction.

$\frac{1}{4} \square \frac{3}{16}$

STEP 2 Model the second fraction.

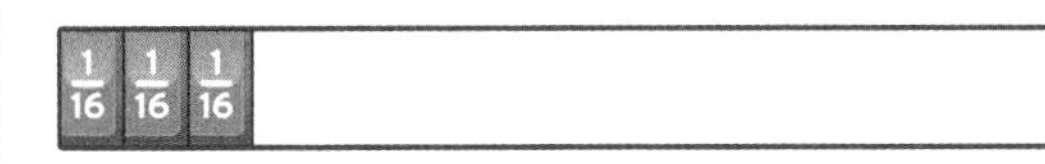

STEP 3 Compare fractions and write an inequality.

$\frac{1}{4} \square \frac{3}{16}$

> PRACTICE

2

STEP 1 Model the first fraction.

$\frac{3}{8} \square \frac{1}{2}$

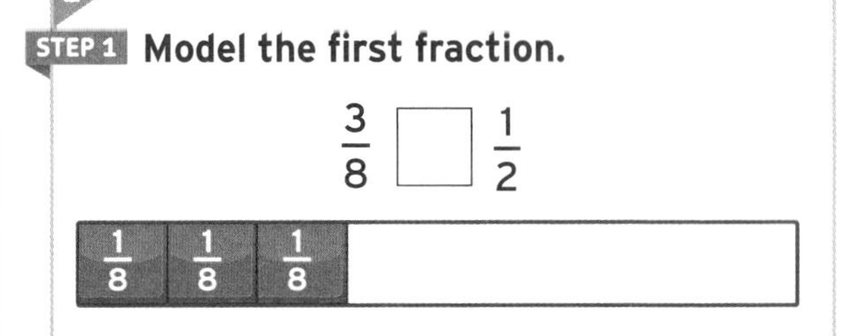

STEP 2 Model the second fraction.

STEP 3 Compare fractions and write an inequality.

$\frac{3}{8} \square \frac{1}{2}$

equivalent *(n)* Two or more fractions that name the same part of a whole.

inequality *(n)* A mathematical sentence that shows that two values are not equal.

PRACTICE

3

$\frac{6}{16}$ □ $\frac{3}{8}$

4

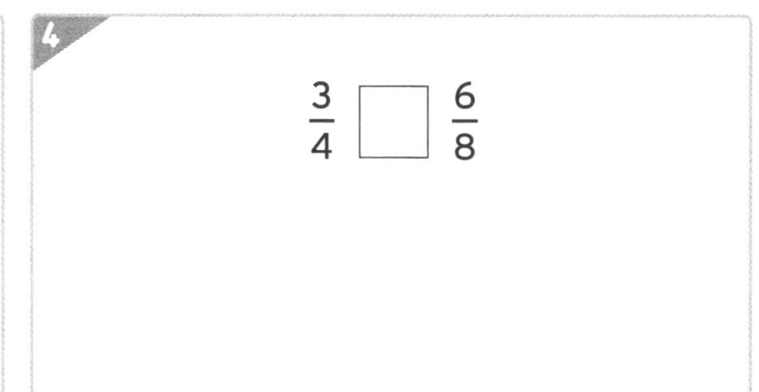

$\frac{3}{4}$ □ $\frac{6}{8}$

5

$\frac{9}{16}$ □ $\frac{3}{8}$

6

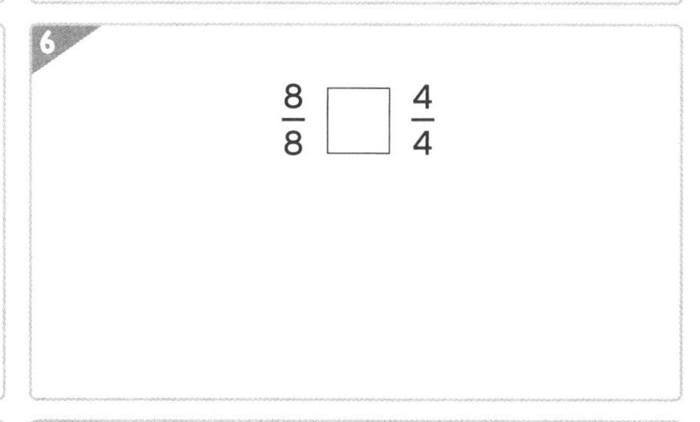

$\frac{8}{8}$ □ $\frac{4}{4}$

7

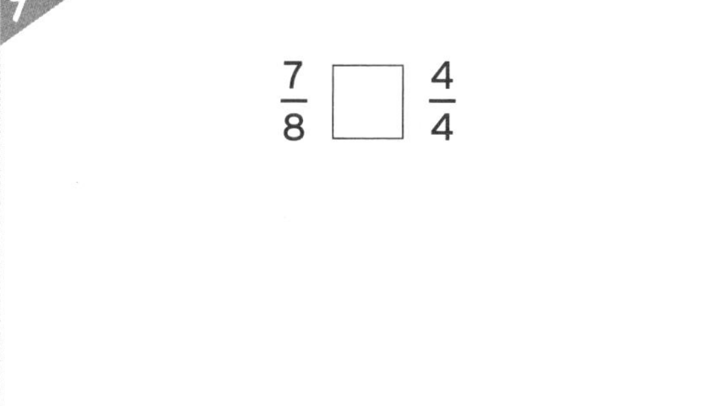

$\frac{7}{8}$ □ $\frac{4}{4}$

8

$\frac{2}{8}$ □ $\frac{1}{2}$

9

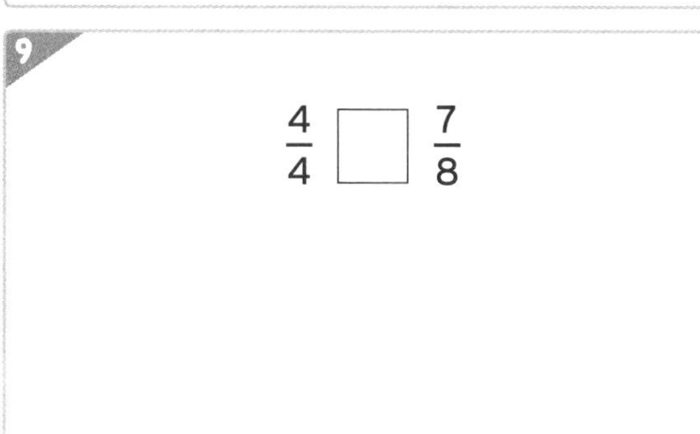

$\frac{4}{4}$ □ $\frac{7}{8}$

10

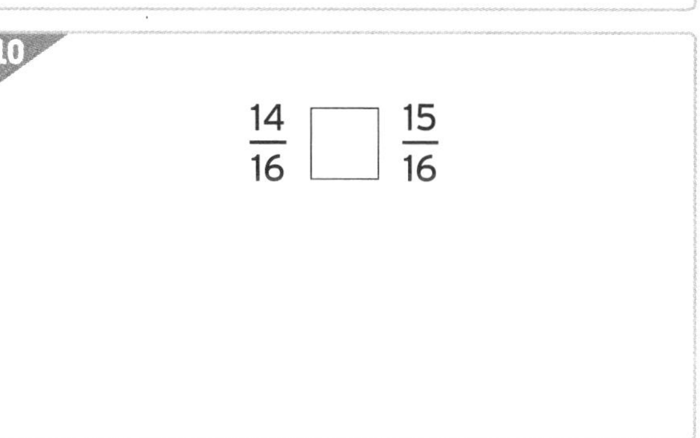

$\frac{14}{16}$ □ $\frac{15}{16}$

EXIT Ticket

BLOCK 4

TOPIC 3

TOPIC 2

TOPIC 1

Solve this problem.

$\frac{4}{8}$ □ $\frac{8}{16}$

Choose two fractions you can compare without using fraction pieces. How did you compare them?

I can compare ____________ *and* _______ *by* ________________

____

____

____

Building the fraction models helps me see which fraction is greater.

SCORE ⓪ ① ②

Develop Number Sense With Fractions

RULES

Fraction Action (Level 1)

What You Need

- *mSpace* pages 154–157
- Fraction Cube (red, $\frac{1}{2}$, $\frac{1}{4}$, $\frac{1}{8}$, $\frac{1}{8}$, $\frac{1}{16}$, $\frac{1}{16}$)
- Fraction Pieces

What to Know

- Both players start with a one-whole fraction piece.
- If the fraction rolled makes the fraction row longer than one whole, record the fraction, but don't place the piece.

How to Win

- The winner is the first player to exactly cover the one-whole fraction piece.

> HOW TO PLAY

STEP 1 **Roll the fraction cube.**

1

STEP 2 **Write the fraction rolled on the recording sheet.**

FRACTION ROLLED	$\frac{1}{4}$		
EQUATION			

STEP 3 **Place the fraction piece that matches the fraction rolled on top of the one-whole piece.**

STEP 4 **When the one-whole fraction piece is completely covered, write an equation to match.**

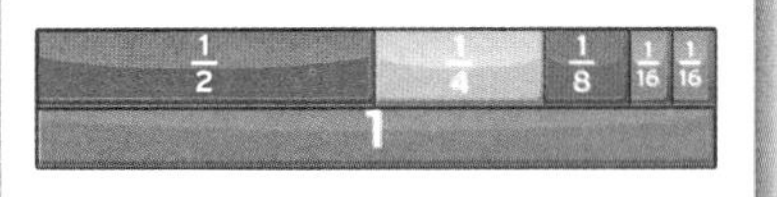

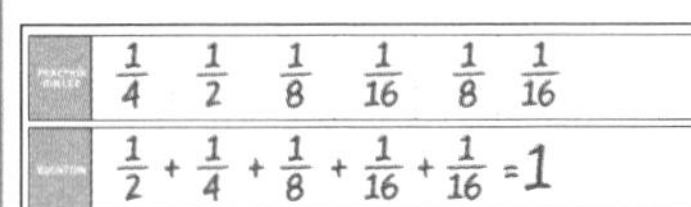

FRACTION ROLLED	$\frac{1}{4}$	$\frac{1}{2}$	$\frac{1}{8}$	$\frac{1}{16}$	$\frac{1}{8}$	$\frac{1}{16}$
EQUATION	$\frac{1}{2}+\frac{1}{4}+\frac{1}{8}+\frac{1}{16}+\frac{1}{16}=1$					

RECORDING SHEET

Fraction Action (Level 1)

> Record the fraction rolled after each turn. When the one-whole fraction piece is completely covered, write the equation that matches.

FRACTION ROLLED										
EQUATION										

FRACTION ROLLED										
EQUATION										

FRACTION ROLLED										
EQUATION										

RECORDING SHEET

Fraction Action (Level 1)

> Record the fraction rolled after each turn. When the one-whole fraction piece is completely covered, write the equation that matches.

FRACTION ROLLED										
EQUATION										

FRACTION ROLLED										
EQUATION										

FRACTION ROLLED										
EQUATION										

> Optional: Use this space to check your work or write equations.

EXIT
Ticket

BLOCK 4

TOPIC 3

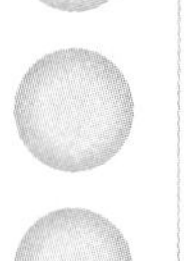

TOPIC 2

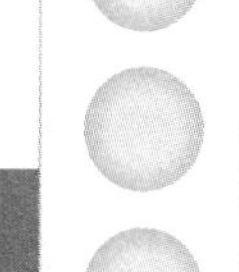

TOPIC 1

> **Answer this question.**

What is the least number of rolls needed to win a game? Explain.

The least number of rolls needed to win a game is _____ because __________

____

____

____

____

____

SCORE (0) (1) (2)

CAREER EXPLORATION

> **Event planners use fractions to arrange tables for a party.**

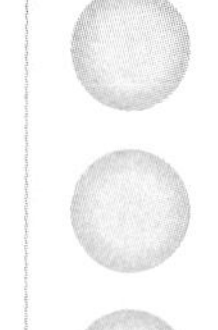

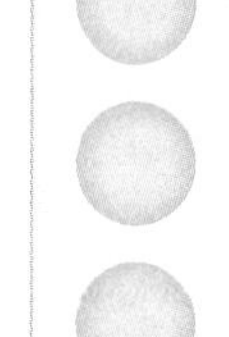

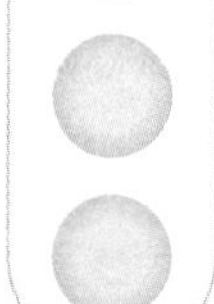

How might an event planner use fractions when deciding what kind of tables to use at a party?

Solve Fraction Problems With Equivalence

> WORKED EXAMPLE

STEP 1 Analyze the problem.

What fraction is *n*, in pounds?

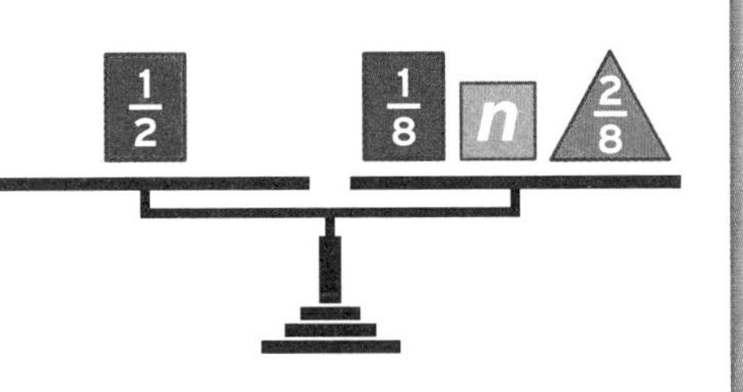

STEP 2 Write an equation for the problem.

$$\frac{1}{2} = \frac{1}{8} + n + \frac{2}{8}$$

STEP 3 Solve the problem.

$$\frac{1}{2} = \frac{1}{8} + n + \frac{2}{8}$$

$$\frac{1}{2} = \frac{3}{8} + n$$

$$n = \frac{1}{8} \text{ lb}$$

STEP 4 Check your work.

> TRY IT

1

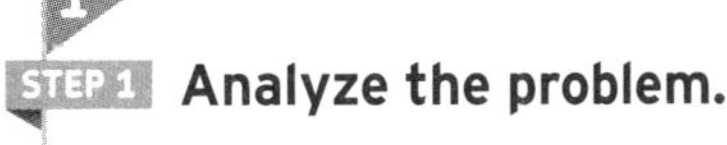

STEP 1 Analyze the problem.

What fraction is *p*, in ounces?

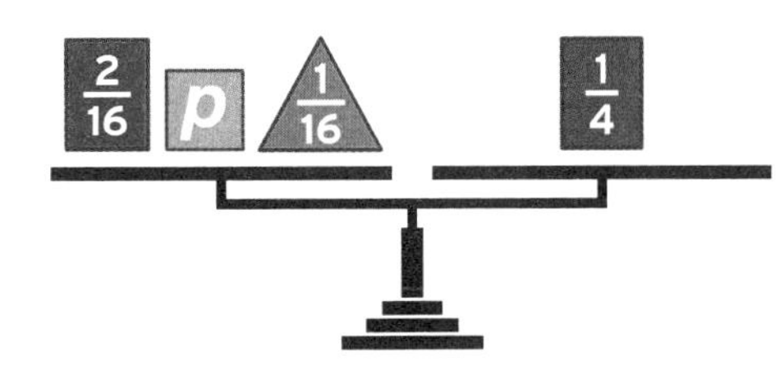

STEP 2 Write an equation for the problem.

STEP 3 Solve the problem.

STEP 4 Check your work.

> PRACTICE

2

STEP 1 Analyze the problem.

What fraction is *n*, in kilograms?

STEP 2 Write an equation for the problem.

STEP 3 Solve the problem.

STEP 4 Check your work.

PRACTICE

3

STEP 1 **Analyze the problem.**

What fraction is n, in pounds?

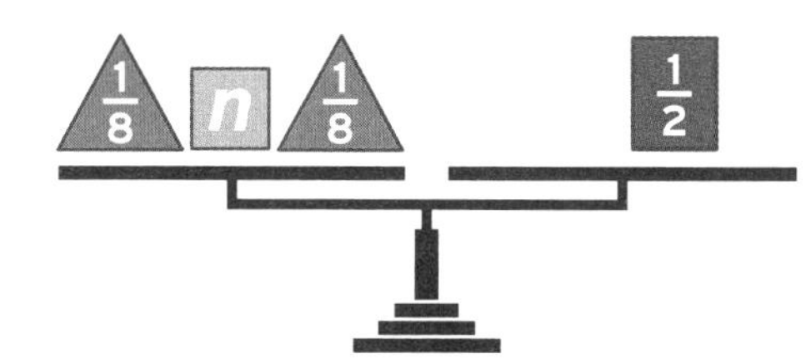

STEP 2 **Write an equation for the problem.**

STEP 3 **Solve the problem.**

STEP 4 **Check your work.**

4

STEP 1 **Analyze the problem.**

What fraction is p, in ounces?

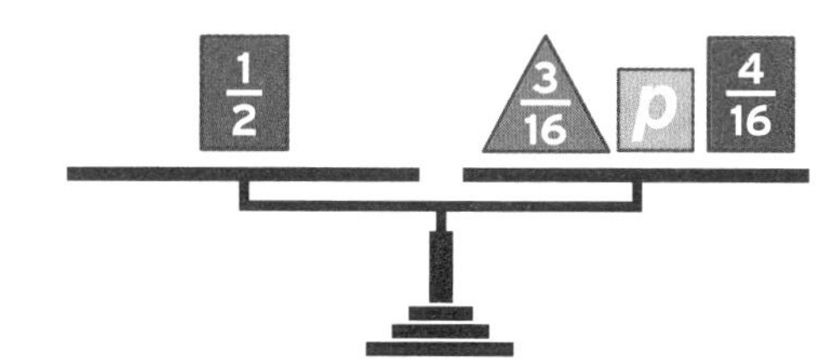

STEP 2 **Write an equation for the problem.**

STEP 3 **Solve the problem.**

STEP 4 **Check your work.**

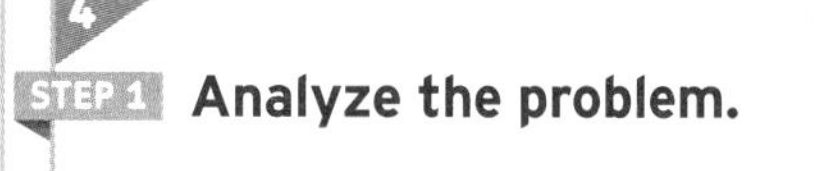

EXIT Ticket

BLOCK 4

TOPIC 3

TOPIC 2

TOPIC 1

Solve this problem.

What fraction is n, in kilograms?

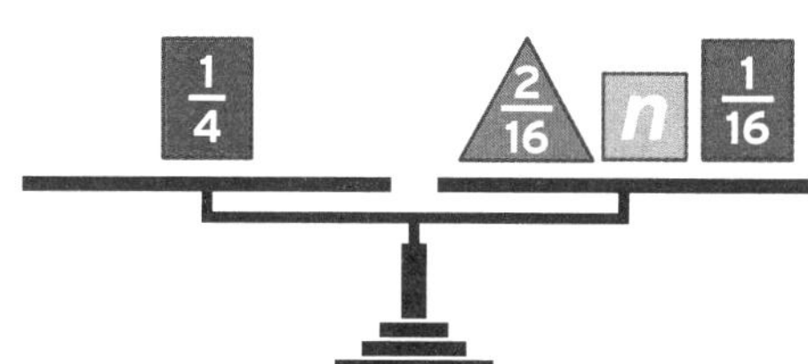

Using fraction pieces helps me solve for the unknown when I work on pan balance problems.

SCORE (0) (1) (2)

Equivalent Fraction Models

LESSON 1

Who's Right?

> Amir and Lola each use fraction pieces to model one whole.

Amir

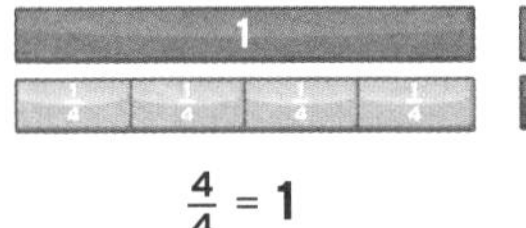

$\frac{4}{4} = 1$

Lola

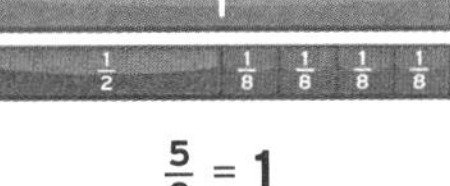

$\frac{5}{8} = 1$

Who's right? ______

> How would you correct the error?

I could correct the error by ______

______

______

______

______

LESSON 2

Tell Me All That You Can

> About $\frac{1}{2}$

- ______
- ______
- ______
- ______
- ______
- ______

> Amy said, "There's a quick way to tell if a fraction is equivalent to $\frac{1}{2}$." Do you agree with Amy?

I agree/disagree with Amy because ______

______

______

LESSON 3

Find the Pattern

> Fill in the blanks with fractions. Each answer is the sum of the fractions in the two boxes below it.

<table>
<tr><td colspan="4">___</td></tr>
<tr><td colspan="2">$\frac{1}{6}$</td><td colspan="2">___</td></tr>
<tr><td>___</td><td>$\frac{1}{12}$</td><td>___</td><td>$\frac{1}{12}$</td></tr>
</table>

> How did you figure out which fraction piece belonged on top?

I figured out which fraction piece belonged on top by ______

______

______

LESSON 4

Which Does Not Belong?

> Circle the fraction that does not belong.

$\frac{8}{12}$ $\frac{6}{12}$ $\frac{2}{3}$ $\frac{4}{6}$

> How do you know which fraction does not belong?

I know which fraction does not belong because ______________________

____

____

LESSON 5

Brain Teaser

> Solve this riddle.

- I am a fraction greater than $\frac{1}{2}$.
- My numerator is 3 less than my denominator.
- If you add $\frac{1}{4}$ to me, you'd have $\frac{7}{8}$.

> Which fraction am I? ____

> What was your first step in solving this riddle?

My first step in solving this riddle was ______________________

____

______________________.

Sum It Up!

> In this Topic, you learned to identify equivalent fractions and use fraction pieces to model them.

How can you show that $\frac{2}{3}$ and $\frac{4}{6}$ are equivalent?

I can make rows of each fraction using fraction pieces. Both rows are the same length.

1			
$\frac{1}{3}$	$\frac{1}{3}$		
$\frac{1}{6}$	$\frac{1}{6}$	$\frac{1}{6}$	$\frac{1}{6}$

Model Fraction Equivalence

WORKED EXAMPLE

STEP 1 Divide one whole into 3 equal parts.

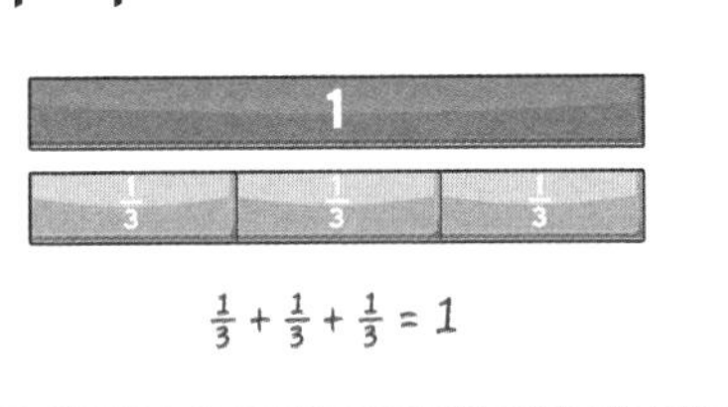

$\frac{1}{3} + \frac{1}{3} + \frac{1}{3} = 1$

STEP 2 Divide one whole into 6 equal parts.

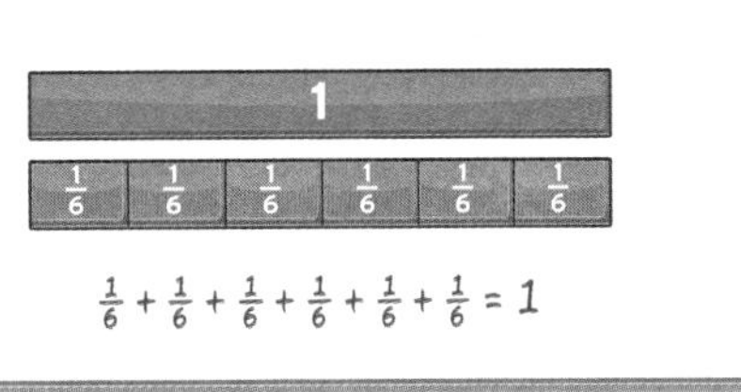

$\frac{1}{6} + \frac{1}{6} + \frac{1}{6} + \frac{1}{6} + \frac{1}{6} + \frac{1}{6} = 1$

STEP 3 Divide one whole into 12 equal parts.

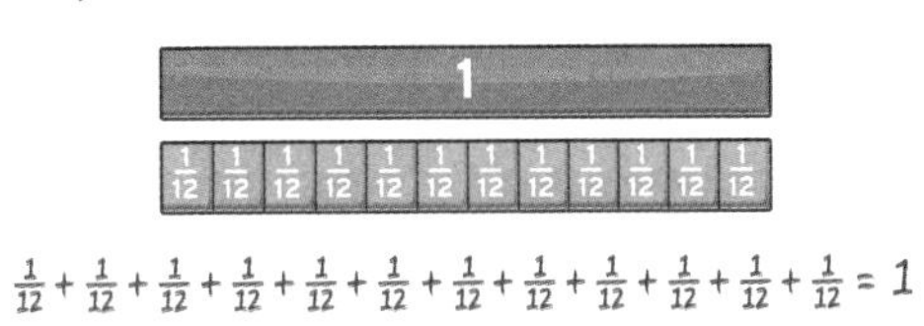

$\frac{1}{12} + \frac{1}{12} + \frac{1}{12} + \frac{1}{12} + \frac{1}{12} + \frac{1}{12} + \frac{1}{12} + \frac{1}{12} + \frac{1}{12} + \frac{1}{12} + \frac{1}{12} + \frac{1}{12} = 1$

TRY IT

1

STEP 1 Show the fraction using fraction pieces.

How many $\frac{1}{6}$ pieces are in $\frac{2}{3}$?

STEP 2 Make an equivalent fraction using different size pieces.

STEP 3 Write equations for each fraction row.

Equation 1 →

____

Equation 2 →

____

STEP 4 Write a pair of equivalent fractions.

$\frac{2}{3} = \frac{\square}{6}$

PRACTICE

2

STEP 1 Show the fraction using fraction pieces.

How many $\frac{1}{3}$ pieces are in $\frac{6}{6}$?

STEP 2 Make an equivalent fraction using different size pieces.

STEP 3 Write equations for each fraction row.

Equation 1 →

____

Equation 2 →

____

STEP 4 Write a pair of equivalent fractions.

$\frac{6}{6} = \frac{\square}{3}$

PRACTICE

3 How many $\frac{1}{6}$ pieces are in $\frac{6}{12}$?

$\frac{6}{12} = \frac{\square}{6}$

4 How many $\frac{1}{12}$ pieces are in $\frac{3}{3}$?

$\frac{3}{3} = \frac{\square}{12}$

5 How many $\frac{1}{12}$ pieces are in $\frac{4}{6}$?

$\frac{4}{6} = \frac{\square}{12}$

6 How many $\frac{1}{3}$ pieces are in $\frac{8}{12}$?

$\frac{8}{12} = \frac{\square}{3}$

7 How many $\frac{1}{6}$ pieces are in $\frac{12}{12}$?

$\frac{12}{12} = \frac{\square}{6}$

8 How many $\frac{1}{12}$ pieces are in $\frac{5}{6}$?

$\frac{5}{6} = \frac{\square}{12}$

EXIT Ticket

TOPIC 3

TOPIC 2

TOPIC 1

Solve this problem.

How many $\frac{1}{12}$ pieces are in $\frac{1}{3}$?

$\frac{1}{3} = \frac{\square}{12}$

Explain how you used your fraction pieces to solve this problem.

I used my fraction pieces to solve this problem by ____________

____

____

____

____

____

SCORE (0) (1) (2)

Use Models to Add Fractions

> WORKED EXAMPLE

STEP 1 Model the addition expression.

$$\frac{1}{3} + \frac{2}{4}$$

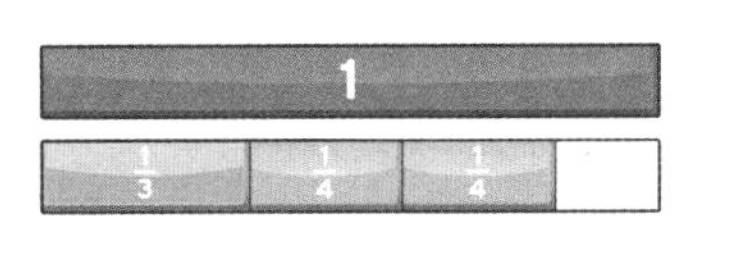

STEP 2 Use fraction pieces to find the sum.

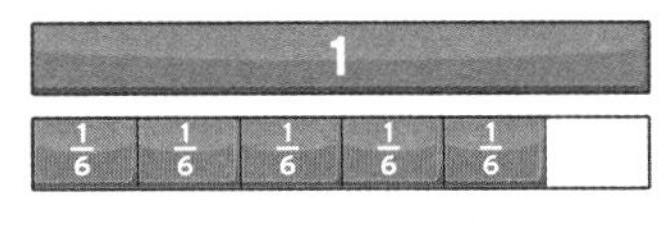

$$\frac{1}{3} + \frac{2}{4} = \frac{5}{6}$$

STEP 3 Use different fraction pieces to find the sum.

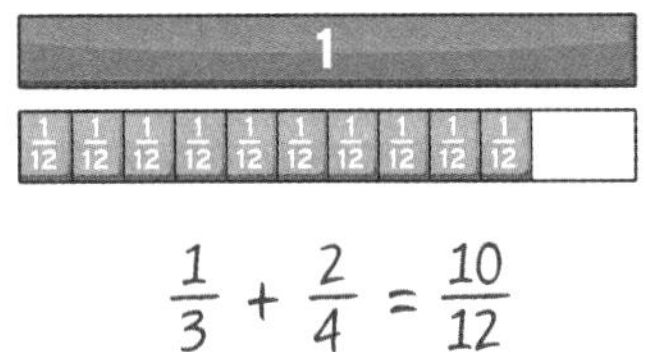

$$\frac{1}{3} + \frac{2}{4} = \frac{10}{12}$$

> TRY IT

1

STEP 1 Model the addition expression.

$$\frac{1}{2} + \frac{2}{8}$$

STEP 2 Use fraction pieces to find the sum.

STEP 3 Use different fraction pieces to find the sum.

> PRACTICE

2

STEP 1 Model the addition expression.

$$\frac{2}{3} + \frac{1}{6}$$

STEP 2 Use fraction pieces to find the sum.

STEP 3 Use different fraction pieces to find the sum.

simplest form *(n)* When 1 is the only whole number that divides both the numerator and denominator evenly.

› PRACTICE

3 $\frac{4}{12} + \frac{1}{6}$

4 $\frac{3}{8} + \frac{4}{16}$

5 $\frac{1}{3} + \frac{1}{2}$

6 $\frac{1}{2} + \frac{1}{4}$

7 $\frac{2}{3} + \frac{2}{6}$

8 $\frac{1}{4} + \frac{1}{3} + \frac{1}{12}$

EXIT Ticket

BLOCK 4

TOPIC 3

TOPIC 2

TOPIC 1

› Find the sum.

Write two equations to show the sum of:

$$\frac{2}{4} + \frac{2}{6}$$

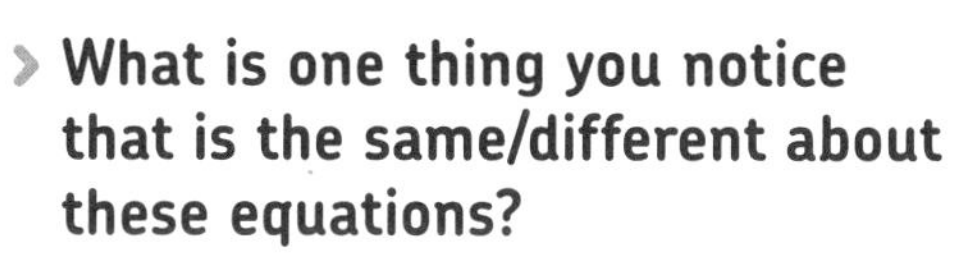

› What is one thing you notice that is the same/different about these equations?

One thing I notice that is the same/different about the equations is ____________

SCORE ⓪ ① ②

Develop Reasoning About Equivalence

RULES

Fraction Action (Level 2)

What You Need

- *mSpace* pages 166–169
- Fraction Cube (red, $\frac{1}{2}$, $\frac{1}{4}$, $\frac{1}{8}$, $\frac{1}{8}$, $\frac{1}{16}$, $\frac{1}{16}$)
- Fraction Pieces

What To Know

- Both players start with a one-whole fraction piece covered with two $\frac{1}{2}$ fraction pieces.
- After each roll, players record their actions.

How to Win

- A game continues until a player removes all the fraction pieces from the one-whole piece.
- The winner is the first player to uncover the one-whole fraction piece.

STEP 1 Roll the fraction cube.

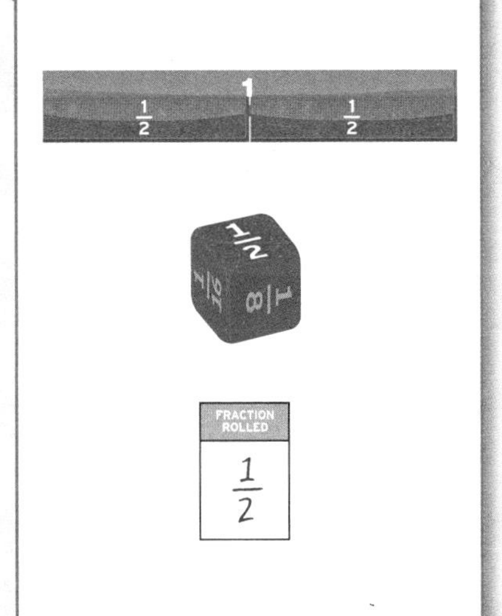

STEP 2 Choose one of the following three actions:

ACTION 1

Remove fraction pieces equivalent to the fraction rolled.

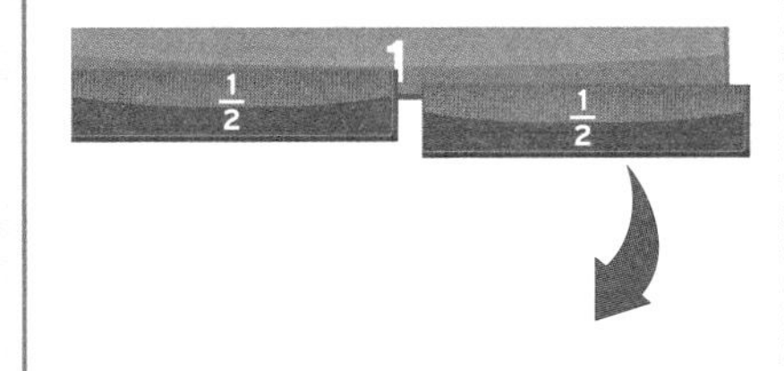

REMOVE PIECES

I removed one $\frac{1}{2}$ piece(s).

ACTION 2

Exchange a fraction piece for equivalent pieces.

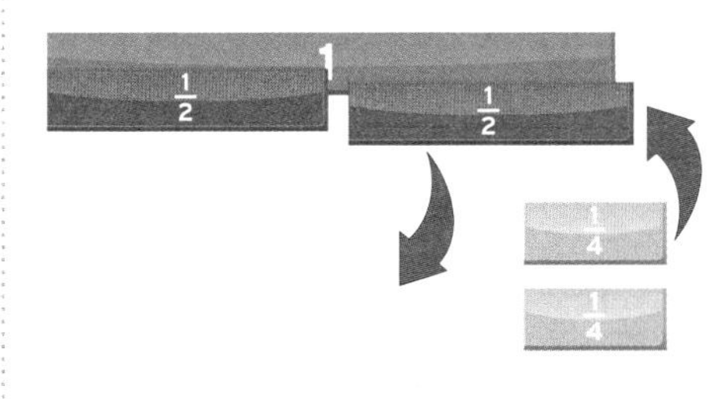

EXCHANGE PIECES

I exchanged one $\frac{1}{2}$ piece for two $\frac{1}{4}$ piece(s).

ACTION 3

If no actions are possible, skip a turn.

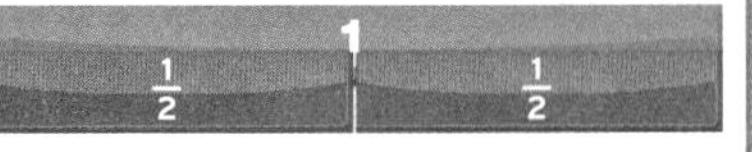

RECORDING SHEET

Fraction Action (Level 2)

› Record your move here after each roll.
Optional: Use the grid paper on page 169 to add fractions.

	CHOOSE ONE ACTION		
FRACTION ROLLED	REMOVE PIECES	EXCHANGE PIECES	SKIP TURN
	I removed ______ $\frac{\square}{\square}$ piece(s).	I exchanged one $\frac{\square}{\square}$ piece for ______ piece(s).	
	I removed ______ $\frac{\square}{\square}$ piece(s).	I exchanged one $\frac{\square}{\square}$ piece for ______ piece(s).	
	I removed ______ $\frac{\square}{\square}$ piece(s).	I exchanged one $\frac{\square}{\square}$ piece for ______ piece(s).	
	I removed ______ $\frac{\square}{\square}$ piece(s).	I exchanged one $\frac{\square}{\square}$ piece for ______ piece(s).	
	I removed ______ $\frac{\square}{\square}$ piece(s).	I exchanged one $\frac{\square}{\square}$ piece for ______ piece(s).	
	I removed ______ $\frac{\square}{\square}$ piece(s).	I exchanged one $\frac{\square}{\square}$ piece for ______ piece(s).	
	I removed ______ $\frac{\square}{\square}$ piece(s).	I exchanged one $\frac{\square}{\square}$ piece for ______ piece(s).	

RECORDING SHEET

Fraction Action (Level 2)

> Record your move here after each roll.
Optional: Use the grid paper on page 169 to add fractions.

	CHOOSE ONE ACTION		
FRACTION ROLLED	REMOVE PIECES	EXCHANGE PIECES	SKIP TURN
	I removed ______ $\frac{\square}{\square}$ piece(s).	I exchanged one $\frac{\square}{\square}$ piece for ______________ piece(s).	
	I removed ______ $\frac{\square}{\square}$ piece(s).	I exchanged one $\frac{\square}{\square}$ piece for ______________ piece(s).	
	I removed ______ $\frac{\square}{\square}$ piece(s).	I exchanged one $\frac{\square}{\square}$ piece for ______________ piece(s).	
	I removed ______ $\frac{\square}{\square}$ piece(s).	I exchanged one $\frac{\square}{\square}$ piece for ______________ piece(s).	
	I removed ______ $\frac{\square}{\square}$ piece(s).	I exchanged one $\frac{\square}{\square}$ piece for ______________ piece(s).	
	I removed ______ $\frac{\square}{\square}$ piece(s).	I exchanged one $\frac{\square}{\square}$ piece for ______________ piece(s).	
	I removed ______ $\frac{\square}{\square}$ piece(s).	I exchanged one $\frac{\square}{\square}$ piece for ______________ piece(s).	

> Optional: Use this space to add fractions or check your work.

EXIT
Ticket

BLOCK 4

> The only piece left on your strip is $\frac{1}{2}$. You rolled a $\frac{1}{4}$. What action will you take and why?

1	
	$\frac{1}{2}$

I will ______________________________

____

____

because ______________________________

____

____

____

SCORE (0) (1) (2)

TOPIC 3

TOPIC 2

TOPIC 1

CAREER EXPLORATION

> Florists design arrangements for special events like weddings.

How could a florist use fractions to choose flowers for a party with a purple and green theme?

Model Fractions Greater Than 1

WORKED EXAMPLE

STEP 1 Model the addition expression.

$\frac{1}{3} + \frac{1}{3} + \frac{1}{4} + \frac{1}{6} + \frac{1}{6}$

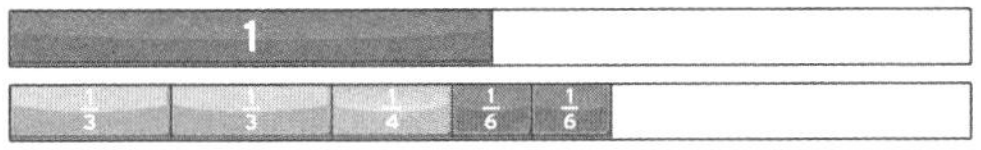

STEP 2 Use fraction pieces to find the sum.

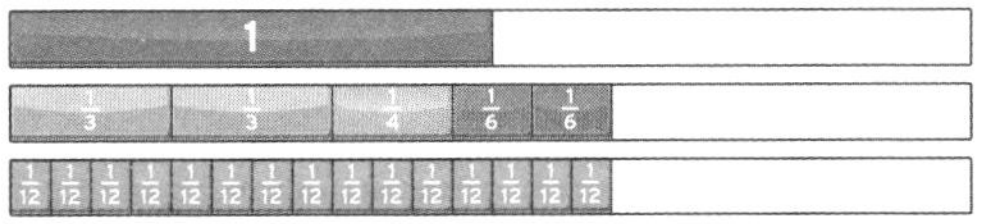

STEP 3 Name the sum.

$\frac{1}{3} + \frac{1}{3} + \frac{1}{4} + \frac{1}{6} + \frac{1}{6} = \frac{15}{12}$

STEP 4 Rename the sum as a mixed number.

$\frac{15}{12} = 1\frac{3}{12}$

TRY IT

1

STEP 1 Model the addition expression.

$\frac{1}{8} + \frac{1}{8} + \frac{1}{8} + \frac{1}{4} + \frac{1}{4} + \frac{1}{2}$

STEP 2 Use fraction pieces to find the sum.

STEP 3 Name the sum.

STEP 4 Rename the sum as a mixed number.

PRACTICE

2

STEP 1 Model the addition expression.

$\frac{1}{2} + \frac{1}{6} + \frac{2}{3}$

STEP 2 Use fraction pieces to find the sum.

STEP 3 Name the sum.

STEP 4 Rename the sum as a mixed number.

mixed number *(n)* A fraction greater than 1 that includes both a whole number part and a fractional part.

PRACTICE

3 $\frac{1}{2} + \frac{3}{4}$

4 $\frac{5}{6} + \frac{3}{4}$

5 $\frac{2}{3} + \frac{1}{4} + \frac{4}{8}$

6 $\frac{11}{12} + \frac{1}{3} + \frac{2}{6}$

7 $\frac{1}{2} + \frac{1}{3} + \frac{1}{4}$

8 $\frac{7}{8} + \frac{4}{16} + \frac{1}{4}$

EXIT Ticket

BLOCK 4

TOPIC 3

TOPIC 2

TOPIC 1

Find the errors and fix them.

$$\frac{5}{6} + \frac{8}{12}$$

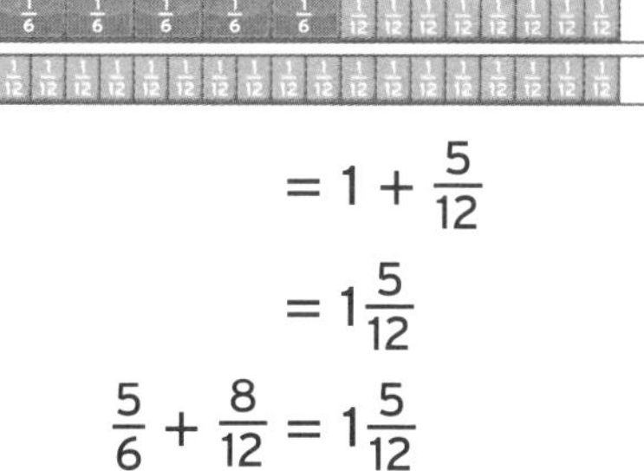

$$= 1 + \frac{5}{12}$$

$$= 1\frac{5}{12}$$

$$\frac{5}{6} + \frac{8}{12} = 1\frac{5}{12}$$

How did you find the errors? Explain your thinking.

I found the errors by ____________

____

____

When I use fraction pieces, I see that $\frac{12}{12}$ is the same as one whole. How many $\frac{1}{12}$ pieces are there after the one whole?

SCORE (0) (1) (2)

Solve Part-Part-Whole Problems

> WORKED EXAMPLE

Read It! Read and identify the problem.

CATERER

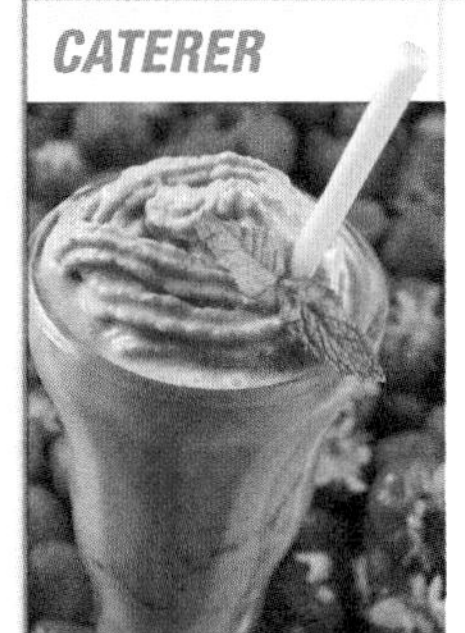

Paul makes 1 cup of smoothie. He mixes $\frac{1}{4}$ cup yogurt, $\frac{7}{12}$ cup strawberries, and banana for the rest. How much banana does Paul use?

PROBLEM TYPE Part-Part-Whole

Show It! Represent the problem.

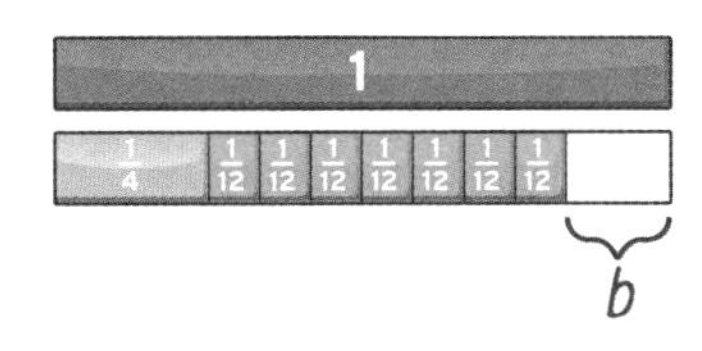

Solve It! Solve the problem.

$$\frac{1}{4} + \frac{7}{12} + b = 1$$
$$\frac{1}{4} + \frac{7}{12} + \frac{2}{12} = 1$$
$$b = \frac{2}{12}$$
$$b = \frac{1}{6} \text{ cup}$$

Check It! Check your work.

> TRY IT

1

Read It! Read and identify the problem.

BAKER

Hayley baked a cheesecake. She used $\frac{5}{8}$ pound cream cheese, $\frac{4}{16}$ pound sugar, and $\frac{6}{8}$ pound peaches. How much did the ingredients weigh altogether?

PROBLEM TYPE ______________________

Show It! Represent the problem.

Solve It! Solve the problem.

Check It! Check your work.

> PRACTICE

2

Read It! Read and identify the problem.

RESTAURANT MANAGER

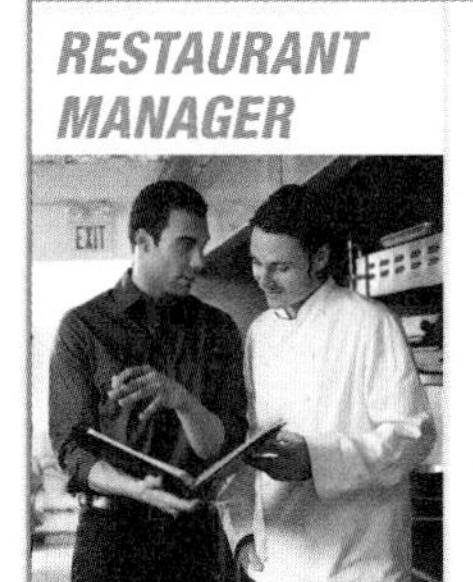

Ahmed spends $\frac{7}{12}$ of his time reviewing accounts, $\frac{1}{4}$ greeting customers, and the rest in the kitchen. What fraction of his time does Ahmed spend in the kitchen?

PROBLEM TYPE ______________________

Show It! Represent the problem.

Solve It! Solve the problem.

Check It! Check your work.

PRACTICE

3

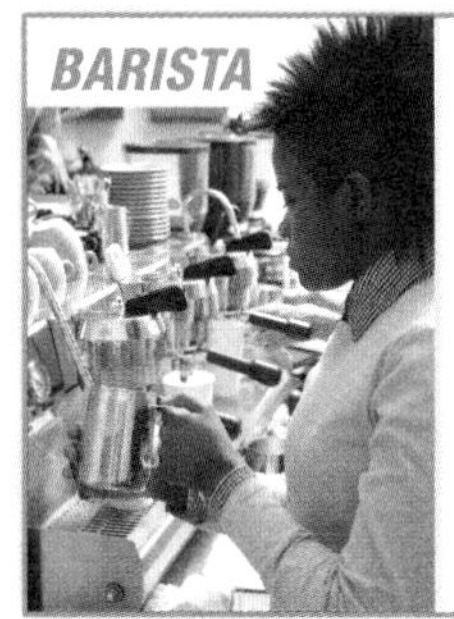

BARISTA

At a café, Jen brewed $\frac{11}{12}$ liter coffee. Jen also made $\frac{2}{6}$ liter tea and $\frac{1}{4}$ liter hot chocolate. What quantity of drinks did Jen make altogether?

PROBLEM TYPE ____________________

4

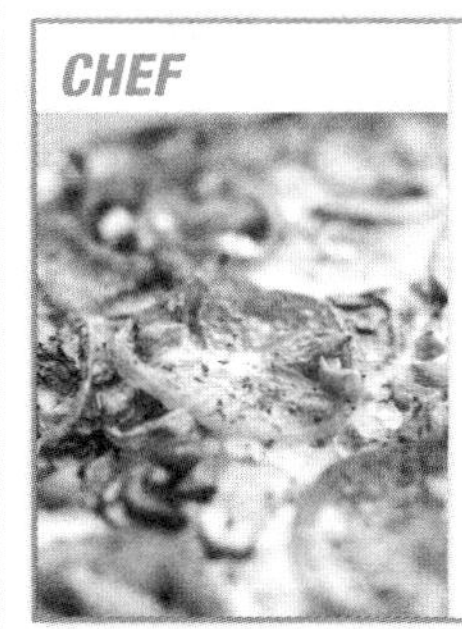

CHEF

A pizza has $\frac{3}{4}$ cup tomato sauce, $\frac{1}{4}$ cup pepperoni slices, $\frac{1}{2}$ cup parmesan cheese, and $\frac{1}{12}$ cup peppers. What quantity of ingredients did the chef use altogether?

PROBLEM TYPE ____________________

EXIT Ticket

BLOCK 4

TOPIC 3

Solve this problem.

At a hotel, $\frac{3}{12}$ of the guests are college athletes, $\frac{1}{2}$ are on vacation, and the rest are staying for business. What fraction of the guests are in town for business?

PROBLEM TYPE ____________________

TOPIC 2

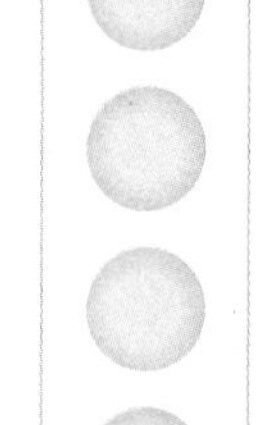

TOPIC 1

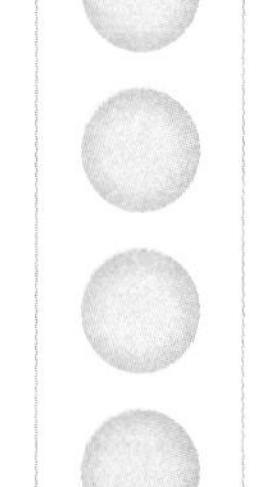

SCORE ⓪ ① ②

DO NOW! Fractions as Division

LESSON 1

Brain Teaser

> In which group would one friend get the most money? ____________

- **Group A:** 2 friends share 24 dollars evenly
- **Group B:** 3 friends share 27 dollars evenly
- **Group C:** 4 friends share 36 dollars evenly

> Write an equation for the group whose friends get the most money:

____

> How could you solve this in a different way?

I would explain how to solve this problem by ____________

____

____

LESSON 2

Find the Pattern

> Find the rule. Then write a fraction in the circle using the rule.

Outside the circle: $\frac{1}{8}$, $\frac{1}{2}$, $\frac{1}{2}+\frac{1}{3}$, $\frac{2}{6}$

Inside the circle: $\frac{1}{3}+\frac{1}{3}$, $\frac{8}{12}$, $\frac{4}{6}$, $\frac{1}{6}+\frac{1}{6}+\frac{1}{6}+\frac{1}{6}$

> Why does the fraction you wrote belong in the circle?

I wrote ____________ in the circle because ____________

____

____

LESSON 3

Build It

> Build as many fractions as you can. Your fractions must:

- be greater than 1
- use only these numbers:

1, 2, 3, 4, 5, 10, 12

> What strategy did you use to build fractions greater than 1?

The strategy I used to build fractions greater than 1 was

____

____

BLOCK 4

LESSON 4

Who's Right?

Sofia and Jacob found two different answers to the same problem.

Sofia	Jacob
$3\overline{)20}$ = 6 R3 −18 2	$3\overline{)20}$ = 6 R2 −18 2

Who's right? ________

How would you help the person who solved the problem incorrectly?

I would help him/her by ________

____

____

____

LESSON 5

Brain Teaser

Solve this riddle.

- I am a fraction greater than $\frac{1}{2}$ and less than $\frac{6}{8}$.
- You can build me with your fraction pieces.

Which fraction could I be?

____

Did you find all of the solutions? How do you know?

I did/did not find all of the the solutions because ________

____

____

Sum It Up!

In this Topic, you learned how fractions can help you solve division problems.

Help me figure out how much I feed each of my fish. I feed 5 goldfish 3 ounces of fish food. Each fish eats the same amount of food. How much food does each fish eat?

By dividing the circles into fifths, I see that $3 \div 5 = \frac{3}{5}$.

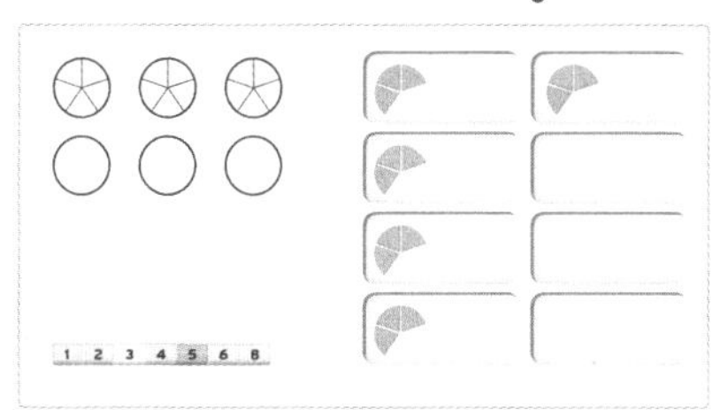

Each fish eats $\frac{3}{5}$ ounce of food.

Model Fractions as Division

WORKED EXAMPLE

STEP 1 **Write the division expression.**

2 pies are shared equally by 3 people. How much of a pie does each person get?

2 ÷ 3

STEP 2 **Divide the wholes into equal parts.**

2 ÷ 3

STEP 3 **Share the parts equally.**

2 ÷ 3

STEP 4 **Write the equations.**

2 ÷ 3

$2 \div 3 = \frac{2}{3}$

$\frac{2}{3} = 2 \div 3$

TRY IT

1

STEP 1 **Write the division expression.**

3 pies are shared equally by 4 people. How much of a pie does each person get?

_____ ÷ _____

STEP 2 **Divide the wholes into equal parts.**

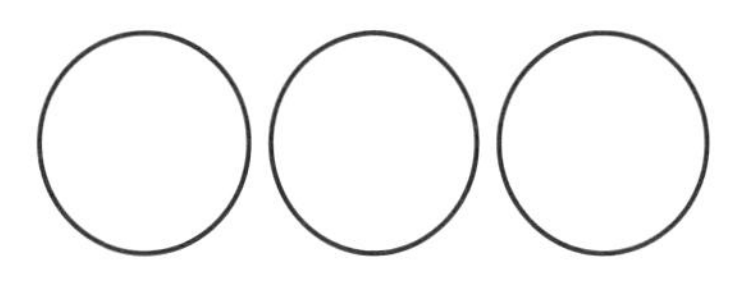

STEP 3 **Share the parts equally.**

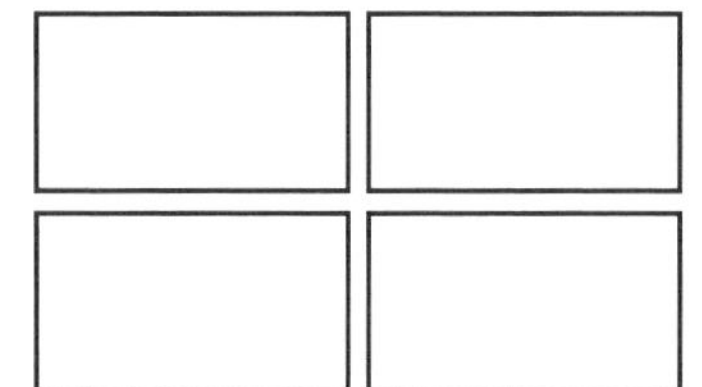

STEP 4 **Write the equations.**

_____ ÷ _____ = _____

_____ = _____ ÷ _____

PRACTICE

2

STEP 1 **Write the division expression.**

6 pies are shared equally by 8 people. How much of a pie does each person get?

_____ ÷ _____

STEP 2 **Divide the wholes into equal parts.**

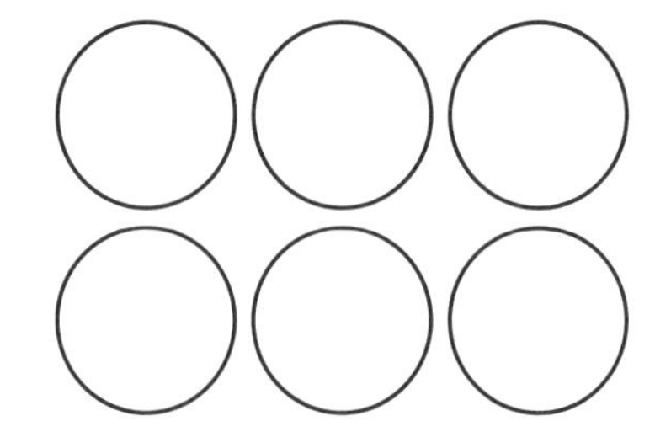

STEP 3 **Share the parts equally.**

STEP 4 **Write the equations.**

_____ ÷ _____ = _____

_____ = _____ ÷ _____

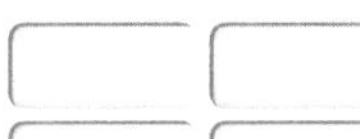

divide *(v)* To split into equal parts or groups.

> PRACTICE

3

4 pies are shared equally by 6 people. How much of a pie does each person get?

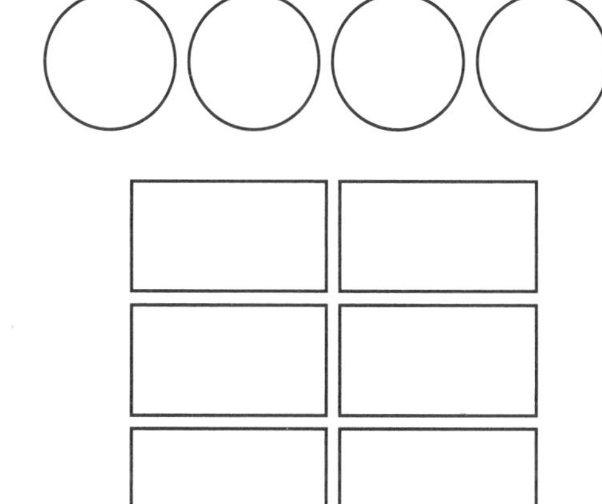

_____ ÷ _____ = _____

_____ = _____ ÷ _____

4

5 pies are shared equally by 8 people. How much of a pie does each person get?

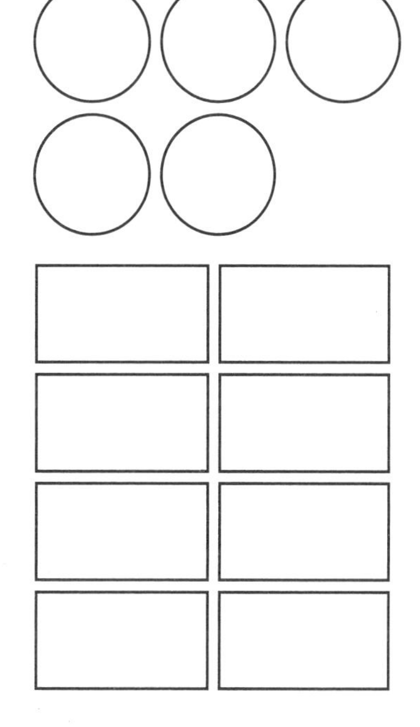

_____ ÷ _____ = _____

_____ = _____ ÷ _____

EXIT Ticket

> **Solve this problem.**

Donna buys 2 pies for 6 people to share. How much of a pie does each person get?

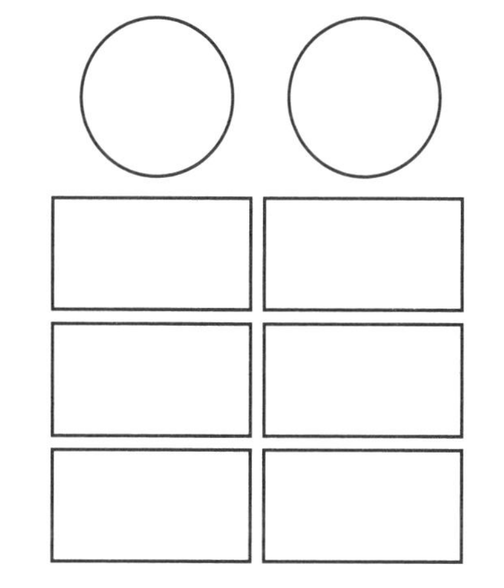

_____ ÷ _____ = _____

_____ = _____ ÷ _____

Answer this question. How do you know that each person will get the same amount of pie?

I know that each person will get the same amount of pie because ____________________

____

____

____

SCORE (0) (1) (2)

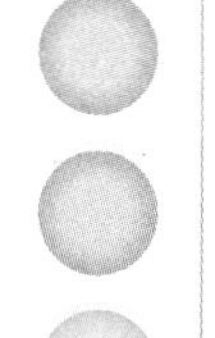

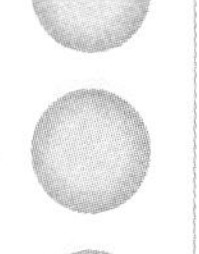

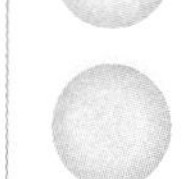

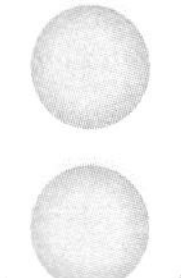

Reinforce Fractions as Division

RULES

Fraction Action (Level 3)

What You Need

- *mSpace* pages 178–181
- Fraction Cube (blue, $\frac{1}{2}$, $\frac{1}{3}$, $\frac{1}{4}$, $\frac{1}{6}$, $\frac{1}{12}$, $\frac{1}{12}$)
- Fraction Pieces

What to Know

- Both players start with a one-whole fraction piece covered with three $\frac{1}{3}$ fraction pieces.
- After each roll, players record their actions.

How to Win

- A game continues until a player removes all of the fraction pieces from the one-whole piece.
- The winner is the first player to uncover the one-whole fraction piece.

> HOW TO PLAY

STEP 1 Roll the fraction cube.

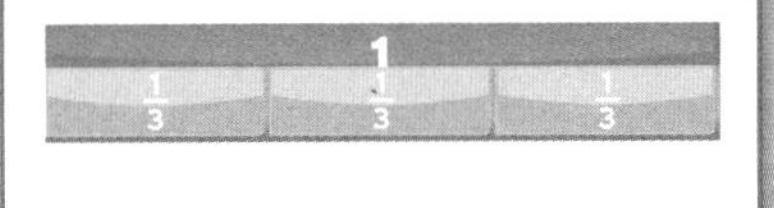

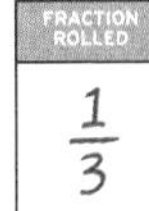

STEP 2 Choose one of the following three actions:

ACTION 1

Remove fraction pieces equivalent to the fraction rolled.

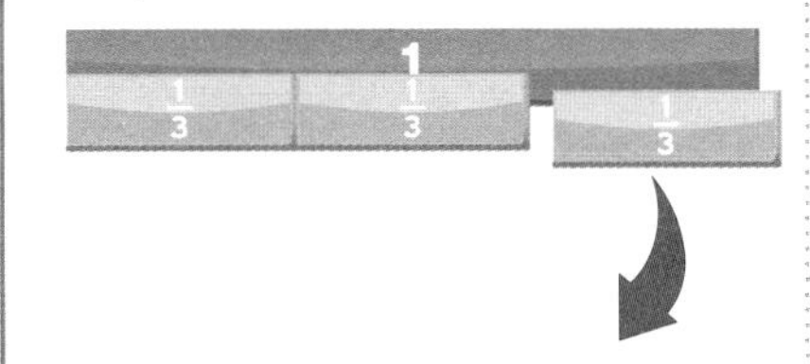

REMOVE PIECES

I removed one $\frac{1}{3}$ piece(s).

ACTION 2

Exchange a fraction piece for equivalent pieces.

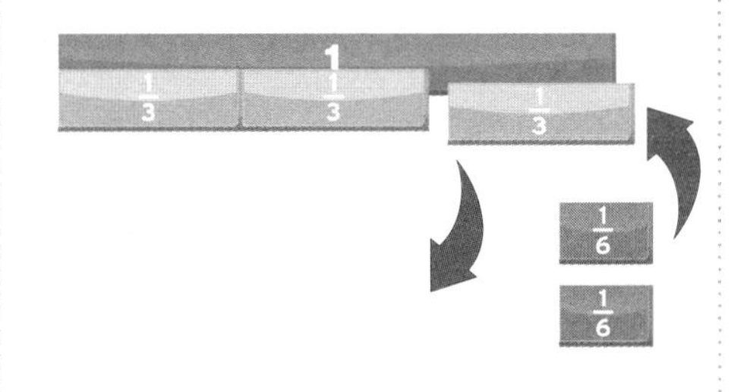

EXCHANGE PIECES

I exchanged one $\frac{1}{3}$ piece for two $\frac{1}{6}$ piece(s).

ACTION 3

If no actions are possible, skip a turn.

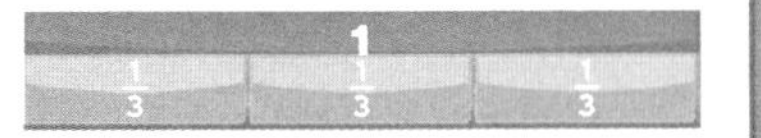

RECORDING SHEET

Fraction Action (Level 3)

› Record your move here after each roll.
Optional: Use the grid paper on page 181 to add fractions.

	CHOOSE ONE ACTION		
FRACTION ROLLED	REMOVE PIECES	EXCHANGE PIECES	SKIP TURN
	I removed ______ $\frac{\square}{\square}$ piece(s).	I exchanged one $\frac{\square}{\square}$ piece for ______________ piece(s).	
	I removed ______ $\frac{\square}{\square}$ piece(s).	I exchanged one $\frac{\square}{\square}$ piece for ______________ piece(s).	
	I removed ______ $\frac{\square}{\square}$ piece(s).	I exchanged one $\frac{\square}{\square}$ piece for ______________ piece(s).	
	I removed ______ $\frac{\square}{\square}$ piece(s).	I exchanged one $\frac{\square}{\square}$ piece for ______________ piece(s).	
	I removed ______ $\frac{\square}{\square}$ piece(s).	I exchanged one $\frac{\square}{\square}$ piece for ______________ piece(s).	
	I removed ______ $\frac{\square}{\square}$ piece(s).	I exchanged one $\frac{\square}{\square}$ piece for ______________ piece(s).	
	I removed ______ $\frac{\square}{\square}$ piece(s).	I exchanged one $\frac{\square}{\square}$ piece for ______________ piece(s).	

RECORDING SHEET

Fraction Action (Level 3)

> Record your move here after each roll.
Optional: Use the grid paper on page 181 to add fractions.

	CHOOSE ONE ACTION		
FRACTION ROLLED	REMOVE PIECES	EXCHANGE PIECES	SKIP TURN
	I removed ______ $\frac{\square}{\square}$ piece(s).	I exchanged one $\frac{\square}{\square}$ piece for ______________ piece(s).	
	I removed ______ $\frac{\square}{\square}$ piece(s).	I exchanged one $\frac{\square}{\square}$ piece for ______________ piece(s).	
	I removed ______ $\frac{\square}{\square}$ piece(s).	I exchanged one $\frac{\square}{\square}$ piece for ______________ piece(s).	
	I removed ______ $\frac{\square}{\square}$ piece(s).	I exchanged one $\frac{\square}{\square}$ piece for ______________ piece(s).	
	I removed ______ $\frac{\square}{\square}$ piece(s).	I exchanged one $\frac{\square}{\square}$ piece for ______________ piece(s).	
	I removed ______ $\frac{\square}{\square}$ piece(s).	I exchanged one $\frac{\square}{\square}$ piece for ______________ piece(s).	
	I removed ______ $\frac{\square}{\square}$ piece(s).	I exchanged one $\frac{\square}{\square}$ piece for ______________ piece(s).	

> Optional: Use this space to add fractions or check your work.

EXIT Ticket

TOPIC 3

> **Answer this question.**

These are your fraction pieces:

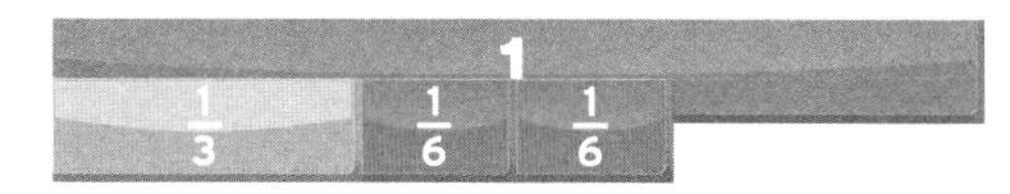

What do you hope your next roll is? Why?

I hope my next roll is ______

because ______

______

______

SCORE (0) (1) (2)

TOPIC 2

CAREER EXPLORATION

> **Chefs use measuring cups to measure ingredient amounts.**

How could a chef measure ingredients if the measuring cup she needs is missing?

TOPIC 1

LESSON 3
CONCEPT

Express Whole Numbers As Fractions

> WORKED EXAMPLE

STEP 1 Use fraction shapes to show whole numbers.

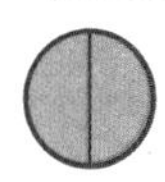
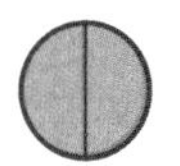
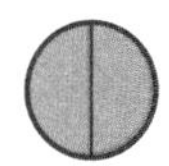
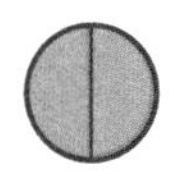

$4 = \frac{8}{2}$

STEP 2 Create a list.

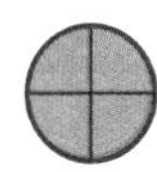
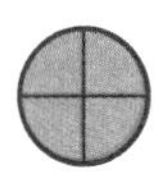
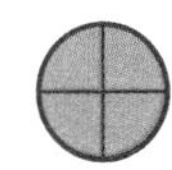
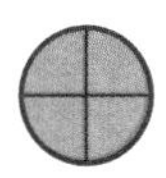

$4 = \frac{8}{2}$ $4 = \frac{16}{4}$ $4 = \frac{24}{6}$

STEP 3 Look for a pattern and define a rule.

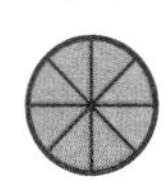
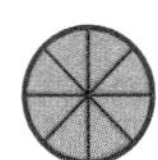

$4 = \frac{8}{2}$ $4 = \frac{16}{4}$ $4 = \frac{24}{6}$

$4 = \frac{12}{3}$ $4 = \frac{20}{5}$ $4 = \frac{32}{8}$

STEP 4 Apply the rule.

$$8 = \frac{\boxed{40}}{5}$$

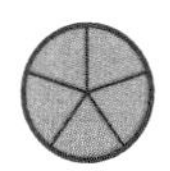
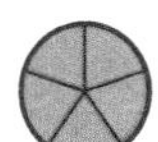

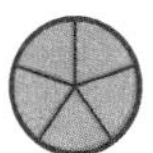
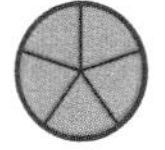
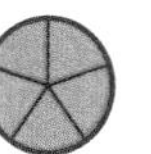
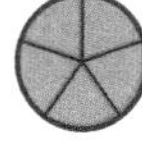

> TRY IT

1

STEP 1 Divide wholes into equal parts.

$$5 = \frac{\square}{6}$$

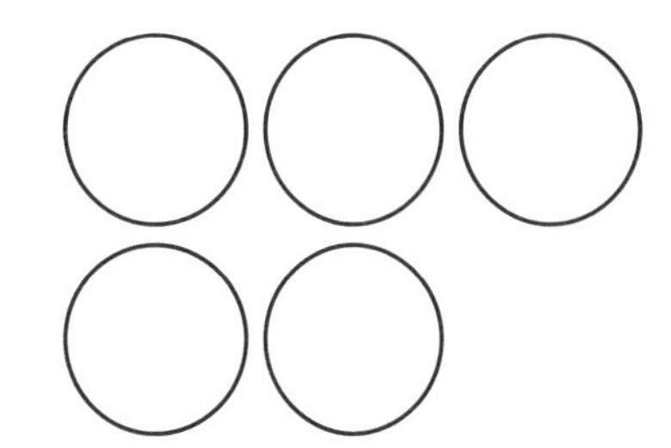

STEP 2 Find the number of parts.

______ × ______ = ______

STEP 3 Complete the equation.

$$5 = \frac{\square}{6}$$

STEP 4 Verify with division.

______ ÷ ______ = ______

> PRACTICE

2

STEP 1 Divide wholes into equal parts.

$$5 = \frac{\square}{2}$$

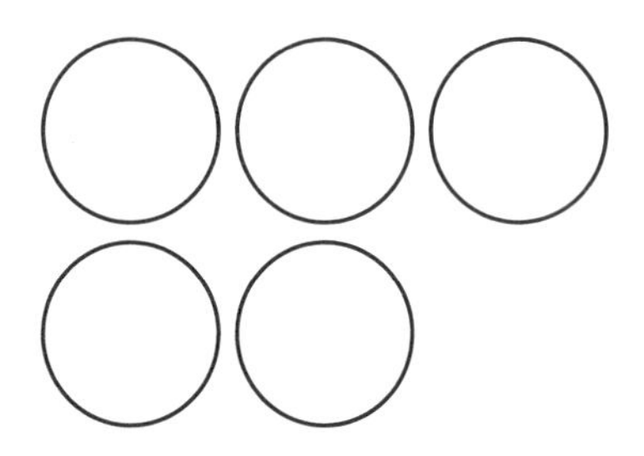

STEP 2 Find the number of parts.

______ × ______ = ______

STEP 3 Complete the equation.

$$5 = \frac{\square}{2}$$

STEP 4 Verify with division.

______ ÷ ______ = ______

PRACTICE

3

$7 = \frac{\square}{4}$

______ × ______ = ______

______ = $\frac{\square}{\square}$

______ ÷ ______ = ______

4

$3 = \frac{\square}{8}$

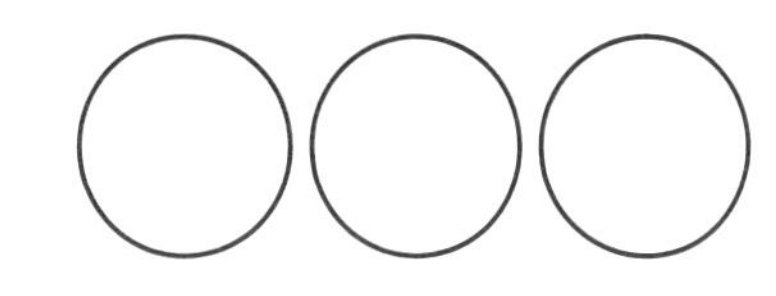

______ × ______ = ______

______ = $\frac{\square}{\square}$

______ ÷ ______ = ______

5

$15 = \frac{\square}{3}$

______ × ______ = ______

______ = $\frac{\square}{\square}$

______ ÷ ______ = ______

6

$25 = \frac{\square}{9}$

______ × ______ = ______

______ = $\frac{\square}{\square}$

______ ÷ ______ = ______

EXIT Ticket

TOPIC 3

TOPIC 2

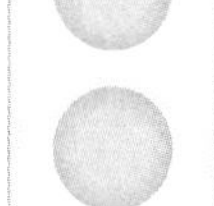
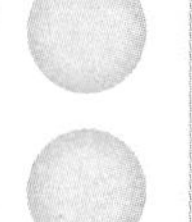
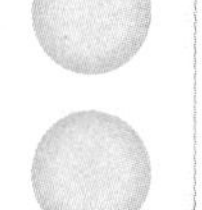

TOPIC 1

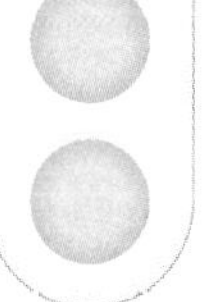

Find the numerator.

$6 = \frac{\square}{8}$

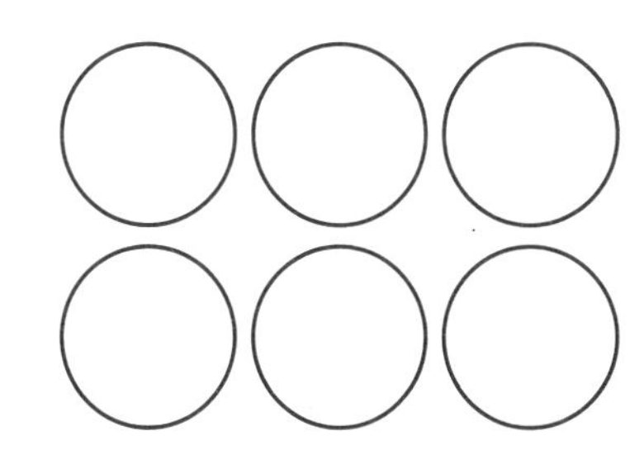

______ × ______ = ______

______ = $\frac{\square}{\square}$

______ ÷ ______ = ______

There are ______ equal parts when 6 circles are divided into eighths.

Represent Remainders as Fractions

> WORKED EXAMPLE

STEP 1 Write the fraction as a division problem.

$\frac{97}{3}$ = 97 ÷ 3

Estimate: 90 ÷ 3 = 30

STEP 2 Use the partial quotient method to divide.

```
      2      32 R1
     30
3 ) 97
   - 90      30 x 3 = 90
      7
    - 6      2 x 3 = 6
      1
```

97 ÷ 3 = 32 R1

STEP 3 Rename the remainder as a fraction.

97 ÷ 3 = $32\frac{1}{3}$

> TRY IT

1

STEP 1 Write the fraction as a division problem.

$\frac{127}{6}$ = ______ ÷ ______

Estimate: ______________

STEP 2 Use the partial quotient method to divide.

6) 127

______ ÷ ______ = ______

STEP 3 Rename the remainder as a fraction.

______ ÷ ______ = ______

> PRACTICE

2

STEP 1 Write the fraction as a division problem.

$\frac{50}{4}$ = ______ ÷ ______

Estimate: ______________

STEP 2 Use the partial quotient method to divide.

4) 50

______ ÷ ______ = ______

STEP 3 Rename the remainder as a fraction.

______ ÷ ______ = ______

mixed number *(n)* A fraction greater than 1 that includes both a whole number part and a fractional part.

> PRACTICE

3

$\frac{130}{8}$ = ______ ÷ ______

Estimate: ____________

______ ÷ ______ = ______

______ ÷ ______ = ______

4

$\frac{104}{9}$ = ______ ÷ ______

Estimate: ____________

______ ÷ ______ = ______

______ ÷ ______ = ______

5

$\frac{671}{10}$ = ______ ÷ ______

Estimate: ____________

______ ÷ ______ = ______

______ ÷ ______ = ______

6

$\frac{352}{12}$ = ______ ÷ ______

Estimate: ____________

______ ÷ ______ = ______

______ ÷ ______ = ______

EXIT **Ticket**

BLOCK 4

> **Find the error and fix it.**

```
    4     14 R3
   10
5) 73
 - 50    10 × 5 = 50
   23
 - 20     4 × 5 = 20
    3
```

$\underline{73} \div \underline{5} = \underline{14\frac{1}{3}}$

The error is that ____________

____

____

____

The quotient should be ______

A division problem can represent a fraction, so a remainder can be written as a fraction.

TOPIC 3

TOPIC 2

TOPIC 1

SCORE (0) (1) (2)

BLOCK 4 > TOPIC 3

LESSON 5

PROBLEM SOLVING

Solve Compare Problems With Fractions

> WORKED EXAMPLE

Read It! **Read and identify the problem.**

CHEF

Kim makes pasta sauce. She uses $\frac{10}{12}$ ounce basil. Then she adds $\frac{4}{6}$ ounce oregano. How much more basil than oregano did Kim use?

PROBLEM TYPE Compare Problem

Show It! **Represent the problem.**

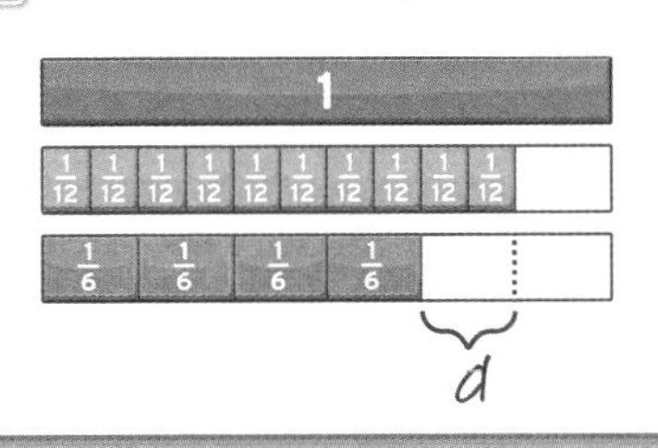

Solve It! **Solve the problem.**

$$d = \frac{10}{12} - \frac{4}{6}$$

$$= \frac{1}{6} \text{ oz}$$

Check It! **Check your work.**

> TRY IT

1

Read It! **Read and identify the problem.**

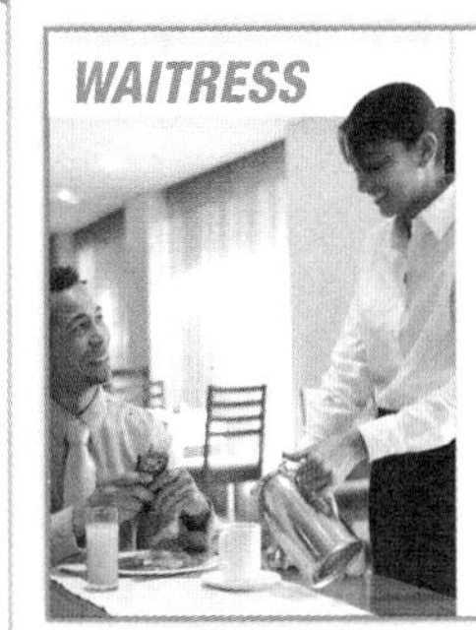

WAITRESS

Lea works at a cafe. Lea served $\frac{5}{6}$ liter tea and $\frac{3}{12}$ liter orange juice. How much more tea than orange juice did Lea serve?

PROBLEM TYPE ______________________

Show It! **Represent the problem.**

Solve It! **Solve the problem.**

Check It! **Check your work.**

> PRACTICE

2

Read It! **Read and identify the problem.**

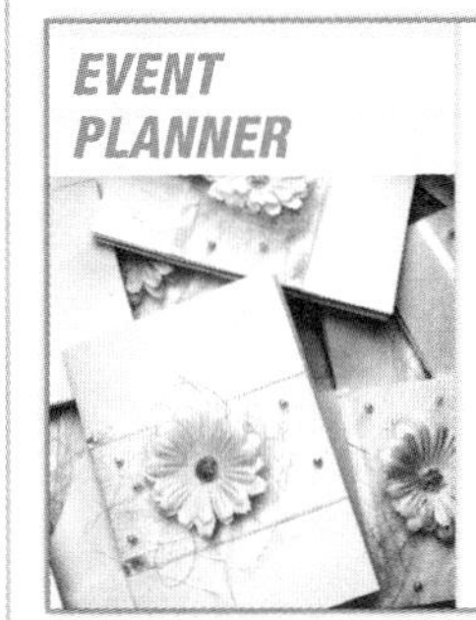

EVENT PLANNER

Heidi bought two equal-sized sets of invitation cards. $\frac{7}{8}$ of the first set were for a wedding. $\frac{11}{16}$ of the second set were for a fundraiser. How many more cards were for the wedding?

PROBLEM TYPE ______________________

Show It! **Represent the problem.**

Solve It! **Solve the problem.**

Check It! **Check your work.**

BLOCK 4

> PRACTICE

3

TOUR GUIDE

Alan is doing a history project. Alan spends $\frac{8}{12}$ of his time on walking tours. Then he does research $\frac{1}{3}$ of the time. How much more of his time does Alan spend on walking tours?

PROBLEM TYPE ______________________

4

BAKER

Dex baked a batch of cupcakes. $\frac{1}{8}$ of the cupcakes were lemon, and the rest were vanilla. How many more cupcakes were vanilla?

PROBLEM TYPE ______________________

EXIT Ticket

BLOCK 4

> **Solve this problem.**

Ming put $\frac{1}{3}$ ounce parmesan cheese and $\frac{9}{12}$ ounce mozzarella cheese on a pizza. How much more mozzarella cheese did she use?

PROBLEM TYPE ______________________

TOPIC 3

TOPIC 2

TOPIC 1

> **How did you check you work?**

I checked my work by ____________

____

____

____

SCORE ⓪ ① ②

PERFORMANCE TASK

BLOCK 4

> YOUR JOB
Chef

> YOUR TASK
Write recipes using fractions for a three-course meal.

> MATERIALS
Fraction Pieces

ANCHOR VIDEO CONNECTION

As the Anchor Video shows, chefs must carefully measure each ingredient. Many of the measurements are in fractions.

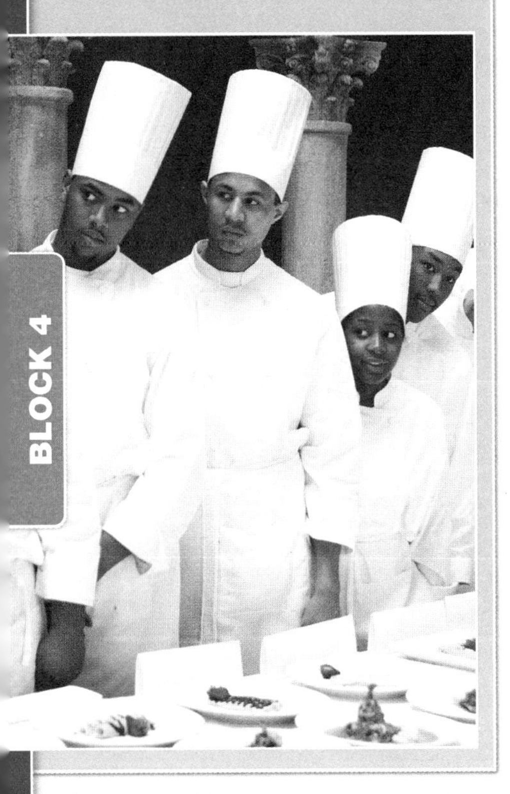

Take the Chef's Challenge

> You have entered a cooking competition. To win, you must prepare the best three-course meal from a list of ingredients.

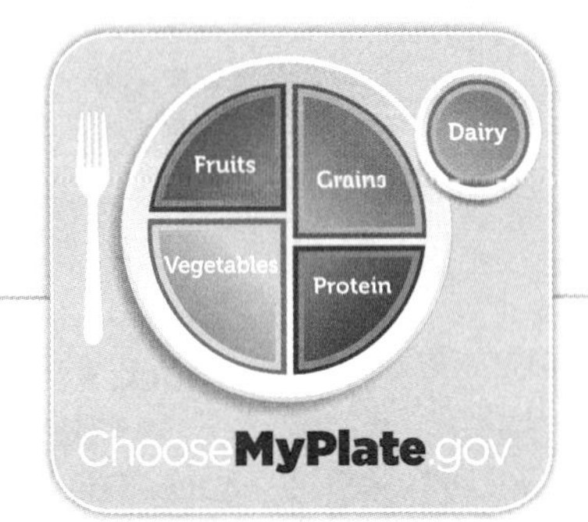

A EXPLORE

Review the list of ingredients. Find groups of ingredients that you think would work well together in an appetizer, main course, and dessert. Take notes to record your ideas.

Food Groups									
Ingredients (cups)									
Protein		Vegetables		Fruits		Dairy		Grains	
red beans	$\frac{1}{2}$	broccoli florets	$\frac{1}{4}$	apple slices	$\frac{5}{12}$	butter	$\frac{1}{2}$	corn chips	$\frac{1}{4}$
ground beef	$\frac{1}{3}$	carrots	$\frac{5}{12}$	banana slices	$\frac{1}{6}$	milk	$\frac{3}{4}$	rice	$\frac{2}{3}$
diced chicken	$\frac{1}{3}$	crushed tomatoes	$\frac{1}{4}$	blueberries	$\frac{1}{6}$	parmesan cheese	$\frac{1}{8}$	granola	$\frac{1}{4}$
sausage slices	$\frac{1}{4}$	peas	$\frac{1}{3}$	strawberries	$\frac{1}{2}$	ricotta cheese	$\frac{3}{4}$	flour	$\frac{1}{2}$
white beans	$\frac{2}{3}$	spinach	$\frac{1}{2}$			yogurt	$\frac{1}{3}$		

B APPLY

Write recipes for three dishes. For each dish, one ingredient and the size are chosen for you. You may use ingredients in any available amount, but include at least two ingredients from each food group.

Appetizer Name: ______

INGREDIENT	SIZE (CUPS)
crushed tomatoes	$\frac{1}{4}$
TOTAL	1

Main Course Name: ______

INGREDIENT	SIZE (CUPS)
red beans	$\frac{1}{2}$
TOTAL	$2\frac{1}{2}$

Dessert Name: ______

INGREDIENT	SIZE (CUPS)
yogurt	$\frac{1}{3}$
TOTAL	$1\frac{1}{2}$

C ANALYZE

EXPLAIN How could $\frac{3}{4}$ cup of milk be split among two or three recipes? Include equations in your answer.

REFLECT Each of your dishes serves two people. Rewrite one recipe so it serves four people.

Evaluate

> **Rate how well you and your partner understood and completed each part of the performance task.**

Rating Scale			
None	Limited	Partial	Thorough
0	1	2	3

A Chose ingredients for three recipes.

Me	0	1	2	3
Partner	0	1	2	3

B Wrote recipes according to the rules.

Me	0	1	2	3
Partner	0	1	2	3

C Answered each question accurately.

Me	0	1	2	3
Partner	0	1	2	3

EXTEND

Write a recipe for some of the ingredients that you did not use.

Reflect on Your Learning Attitudes

Congratulations! You've completed Block 4 of *MATH 180*. Respond to these questions by checking EACH sentence that describes your mindset.

A GETTING FOCUSED

These strategies help you have a clear focus and plan to meet the challenges of learning difficult mathematics.

Before you took the BLOCK 4 *mSkills* assessment, how did you begin?

- ☐ I set a clear and challenging goal for myself to do well on the assessment.
- ☐ I made a plan for how I would study, and I stuck to that plan.
- ☐ I listed the math concepts that the assessment covered, and I focused my attention on learning them.
- ☐ I started to study early and used my time well.
- ☐ I made sure I didn't have any distractions while I was studying.

☐ Other *(please describe)*:

____

____

____

____

____

B DEVELOPING YOUR BRAIN

These strategies help new connections develop in your brain, allowing you to think in new ways and learn new knowledge.

When learning a new concept in BLOCK 4, what did you do?

- ☐ I broke it down into smaller parts or steps.
- ☐ I connected the new information to things I already knew.
- ☐ I used different pathways or senses to learn, such as by drawing pictures or by making diagrams or charts.
- ☐ I repeated and wrote down new math concepts and academic words in order to learn them.
- ☐ I reviewed the worked examples and completed problems in the *mSpace* before I started working on new problems.

☐ Other *(please describe)*:

____

____

____

____

____

____

C KEEPING POSITIVE

Negative emotions can make learning difficult or impossible. These strategies keep your brain ready to learn.

What did you do to keep your mood and motivation positive during BLOCK 4?

- ☐ I reminded myself to think positive instead of negative thoughts.
- ☐ I pictured growing my brain cells and getting smarter.
- ☐ I reminded myself that I can learn from mistakes.
- ☐ I chose to work with positive classmates.
- ☐ I practiced calming strategies like taking deep breaths, remembering a fun time, or thinking of things I enjoy doing.

☐ Other *(please describe)*:

____

____

____

____

____

Score Your Mindset

› **Count up all your checks and write the total here:**

TOTAL CHECKS

If you checked:	*You were in the following zone, which means:*
Less than 3	**Fixed Mindset Zone** You didn't use many brain-wise learning strategies this time. Your mindset may have held you back from doing your best.
3–5	**Mixed Mindset Zone** You used some good strategies but skipped some others. Your mindset may have held you back from doing your best.
6 or more	**Growth Mindset Zone** Overall, your use of learning strategies was in the Growth Zone this time. You used lots of good strategies that will help you grow your brain and get smarter.

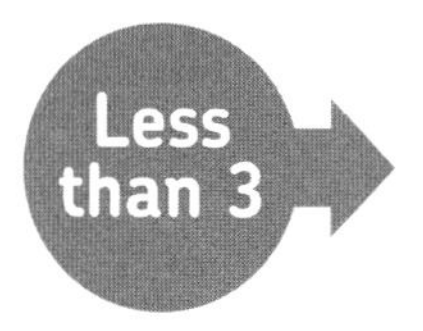

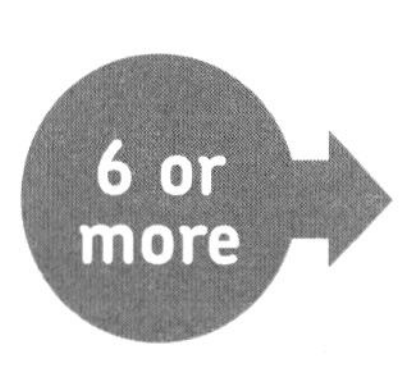

› **What can you do about it?**

- Categories with lots of checks represent your Growth Mindset areas.
- Categories with few checks represent improvement areas.
- Look at each category to see how moving yourself into the Growth Zone can help.

Brain Boosting

› **What will you do to help your brain stay in the Growth Mindset Zone?**

I will work to:

- ☐ Focus my attention
- ☐ Develop new brain connections
- ☐ Keep a positive mood and motivation

"I have not failed. I've just found 10,000 ways that won't work."

Thomas Edison
Successful inventor

What will I do?

Who will help me?

When will I do it?

How will this help me to grow?

CONCEPT BOOK

Table of Contents

Multiplication Facts

› Use this table to help you remember multiplication facts.

×	0	1	2	3	4	5	6	7	8	9	10	11	12
0	0	0	0	0	0	0	0	0	0	0	0	0	0
1	0	1	2	3	4	5	6	7	8	9	10	11	12
2	0	2	4	6	8	10	12	14	16	18	20	22	24
3	0	3	6	9	12	15	18	21	24	27	30	33	36
4	0	4	8	12	16	20	24	28	32	36	40	44	48
5	0	5	10	15	20	25	30	35	40	45	50	55	60
6	0	6	12	18	24	30	36	42	48	54	60	66	72
7	0	7	14	21	28	35	42	49	56	63	70	77	84
8	0	8	16	24	32	40	48	56	64	72	80	88	96
9	0	9	18	27	36	45	54	63	72	81	90	99	108
10	0	10	20	30	40	50	60	70	80	90	100	110	120
11	0	11	22	33	44	55	66	77	88	99	110	121	132
12	0	12	24	36	48	60	72	84	96	108	120	132	144

Symbols

› **Mathematicians use symbols to show relationships between numbers.**

SYMBOL	EXAMPLE	MEANING
$+$	$56.01 + 0.6$	plus or add
$-$	$\frac{3}{4} - \frac{1}{4}$	minus or subtract
$\times$	180×4	times or multiply
$\div$	$14 \div 7$	divide
$\overline{)}$	$7\overline{)14}$	divide
—	$\frac{14}{7}$	divide
$=$	$0.5 = \frac{1}{2}$	is equal to; shows equivalence
$\neq$	$\frac{1}{10} \neq 0.01$	is not equal to

SYMBOL	EXAMPLE	MEANING
$\approx$	$1.978 \approx 2$	is approximately equal to
$<$	$40 < 400$	is less than
$>$	$16 > 1.6$	is greater than
$\ldots$	$0.333333\ldots$	continues without end
$+$	$+4$	positive
$-$	-5	negative
$(\ \ )$	operations: $(3 + 4) - 2$ numbers: $5 - (-2)$	parentheses; shows what to evaluate first
$\{\ \ \}$	$\{0, 1, 2, 3, 4\}$	braces; shows members of a set
n	$14 + n = 34$	variable; represents an unknown quantity

Measurement

> Knowing how measurements relate to one another helps you solve problems.

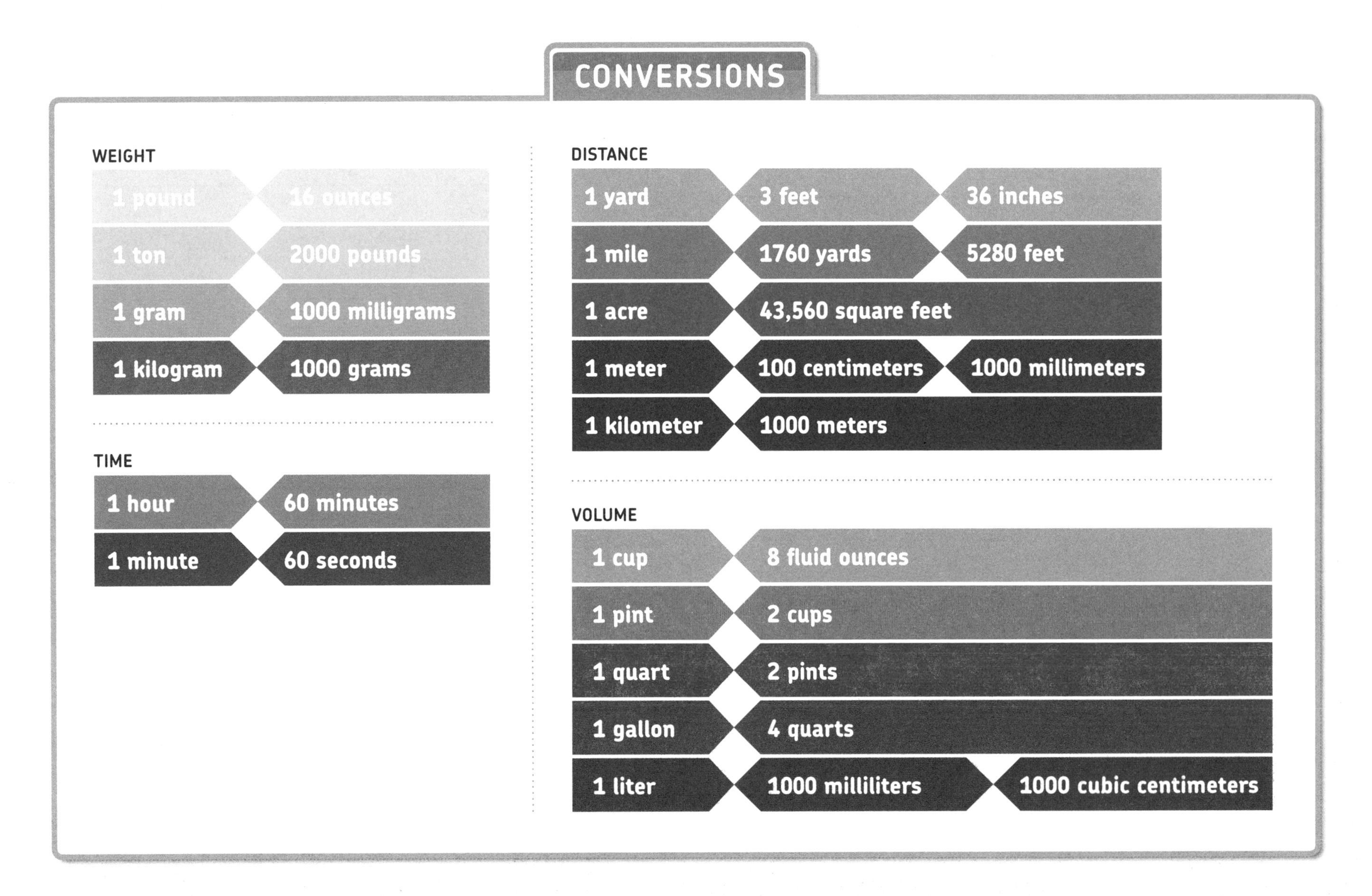

FORMULAS

perimeter

width

length

Perimeter of a rectangle = (2 × length) + (2 × width)

$$P = 2l + 2w$$

area

width

length

Area of a rectangle = length × width

$$A = l \times w$$

volume

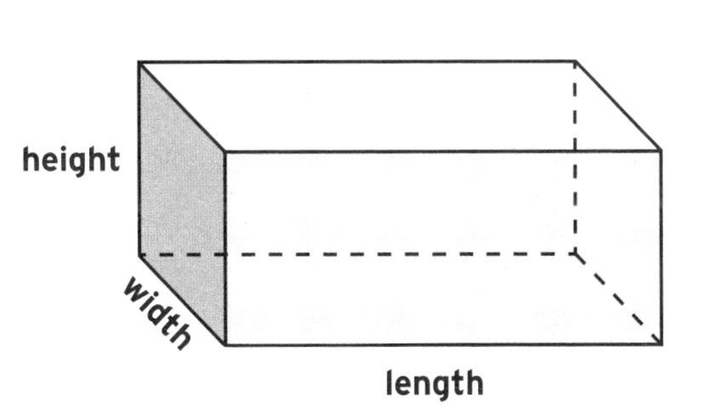

Volume of a rectangular prism = length × width × height

$$V = l \times w \times h$$

Volume of a rectangular prism = Area of the base × height

$$V = A \times h$$

Properties

› In mathematics, a property is a characteristic of a number or operation.

THE ASSOCIATIVE PROPERTY

PROPERTY	MEANING	EXAMPLE
Associative Property of Addition	The way we group three or more addends doesn't change the sum.	$(3 + 4) + 5 = 3 + (4 + 5)$ $7 + 5 = 3 + 9$ $12 = 12$
Associative Property of Multiplication	The way we group three or more factors doesn't change the product.	$(2 \times 3) \times 4 = 2 \times (3 \times 4)$ $6 \times 4 = 2 \times 12$ $24 = 24$

THE COMMUTATIVE PROPERTY

PROPERTY	MEANING	EXAMPLE
Commutative Property of Addition	Changing the order of the addends does not change the sum.	$4 + 3 = 3 + 4$ $7 = 7$
Commutative Property of Multiplication	Changing the order of the factors does not change the product.	$4 \times 3 = 3 \times 4$ $12 = 12$

THE DISTRIBUTIVE PROPERTY

PROPERTY	MEANING	EXAMPLE
Distributive Property of Multiplication	Multiplying a sum by a number is the same as adding the partial products.	$8 \times 24 = 8 \times (20 + 4)$ $= (8 \times 20) + (8 \times 4)$ $= 160 + 32$ $= 192$

THE IDENTITY PROPERTY

PROPERTY	MEANING	EXAMPLE
Additive Identity Property	Adding 0 to a number does not change the number's value.	$4 + 0 = 4$ or $0 + 4 = 4$
Multiplicative Identity Property	Multiplying a number by 1 does not change the number's value.	$7 \times 1 = 7$ or $1 \times 7 = 7$

THE INVERSE PROPERTY

PROPERTY	MEANING	EXAMPLE
Inverse Property of Addition	Adding a number to its opposite results in a sum of 0.	$5 + (-5) = 0$ or $(-5) + 5 = 0$
Inverse Property of Multiplication	Multiplying a number (excluding 0) by its reciprocal results in a product of 1.	$4 \times \frac{1}{4} = 1$ or $(-\frac{1}{4}) \times (-4) = 1$

CONCEPT BOOK

Visual Models

› **Visual models are helpful tools for representing and solving problems.**

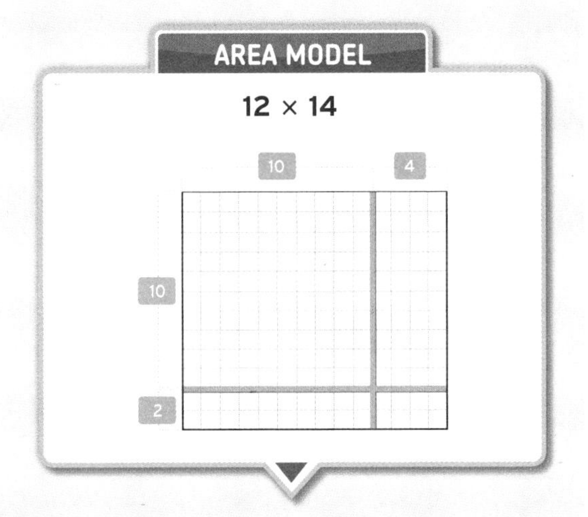

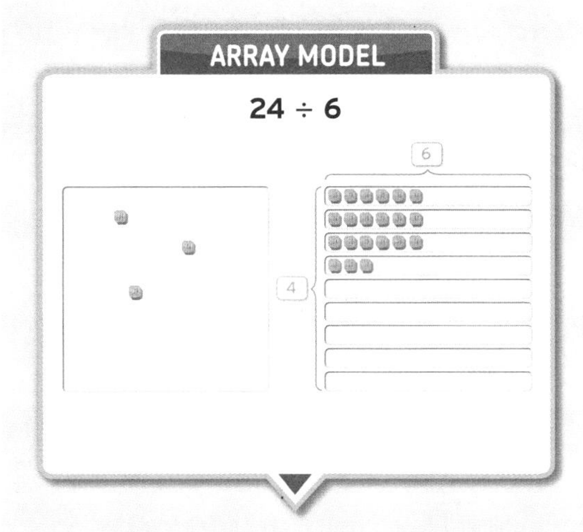

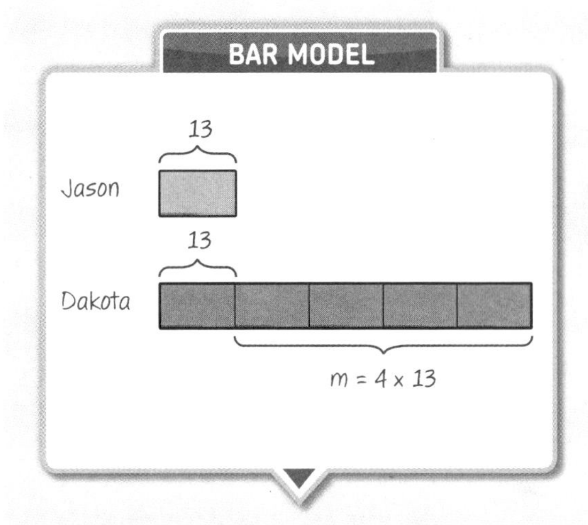

WHAT IS IT?

An **Area Model** is a rectangle made up of equal-sized squares that can be used to find the product of two numbers.

An **Array Model** is used to arrange equal-sized objects in rows to represent equal groups in multiplication and division.

A **Bar Model** is made up of one or more rectangular bars that represent known and unknown quantities and their relationships.

WHY USE IT?

Use an **Area Model** to...

- multiply two factors
- find partial products when you use the Distributive Property to multiply
- use the Commutative Property to multiply

Use an **Array Model** to...

- represent multiplication
- identify factors of a number
- represent division
- represent parts of sets as fractions

Use a **Bar Model** to represent and solve...

- part-part-whole problems
- compare problems
- change problems
- equal groups problems

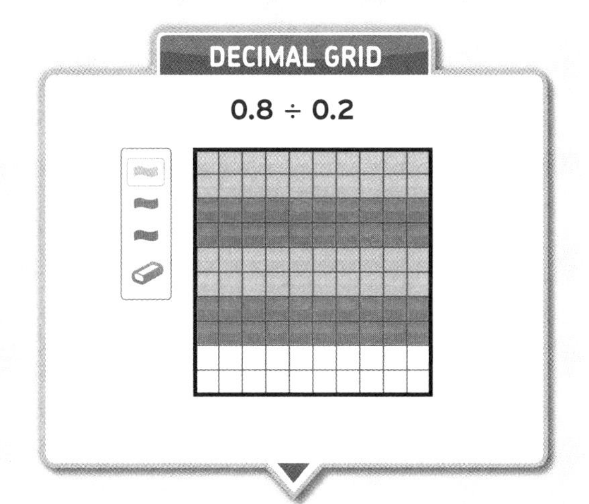

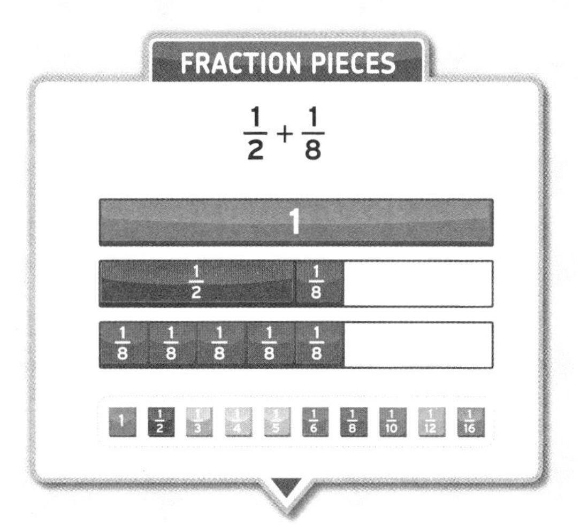

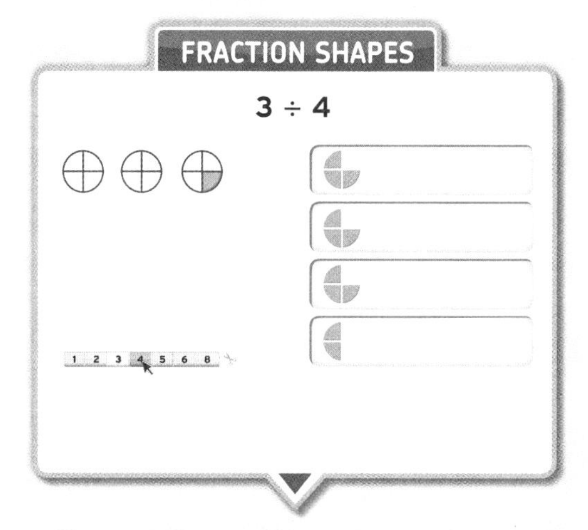

WHAT IS IT?

A **Decimal Grid**, which represents one whole, is a 10 by 10 square that is divided into 100 squares. It is used to represent decimals.

Fraction Pieces are models that represent unit fractions and can be combined to form greater fractions.

Fraction Shapes are circular fraction models that are used to represent sharing situations.

WHY USE IT?

Use a **Decimal Grid** to...

- represent decimals
- name fractions with denominators of 10 and 100 as decimals
- compare fractions and decimals
- apply place value to decimals

Use **Fraction Pieces** to...

- represent fractions
- compose fractions and wholes with unit fractions
- compare and order fractions
- solve problems with equivalent fractions
- add and subtract fractions

Use **Fraction Shapes** to...

- represent fractions as division
- represent fractions in multiplication and division problems

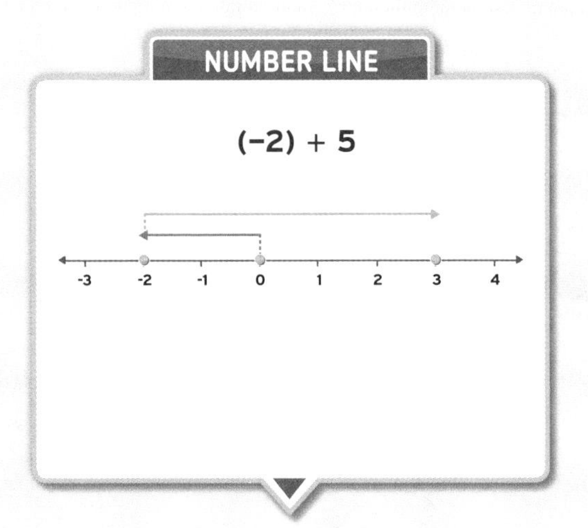

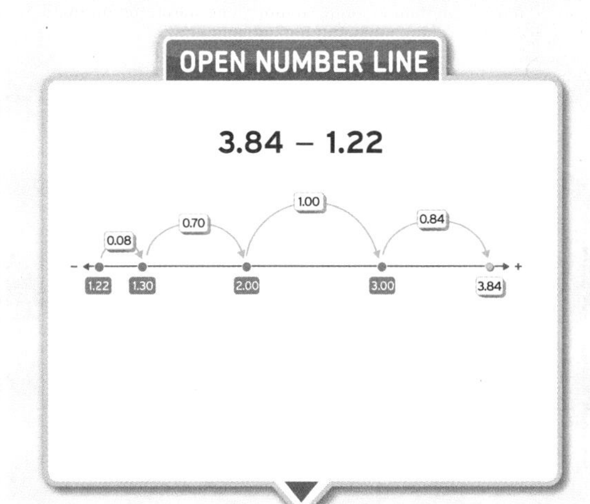

WHAT IS IT?

A **Number Line** is a horizontal or vertical line labeled with tick marks at equal intervals. It is used to show relationships among numbers.

An **Open Number Line** is a horizontal or vertical line without tick marks that represents number relationships.

WHY USE IT?

Use a **Number Line** to...

- locate any number, including whole numbers, fractions, decimals, integers, and rational numbers
- add numbers
- subtract to find the distance between numbers
- compare and order numbers
- name decimals between decimals

Use an **Open Number Line** to...

- plot any number, including whole numbers, fractions, decimals, integers, and rational numbers
- add numbers
- subtract to find the distance between numbers

Problem-Solving Routine

› **Use this routine to help you analyze and solve word problems.**

STEPS	WHAT TO DO	EXAMPLE
Read It! **Read and identify the problem.**	▪ Read and understand the problem. ▪ Figure out what the problem is asking you to do. ▪ Identify the problem type. Is it a part-part-whole, change, compare, or equal groups problem?	**APP DESIGNER** Jason created 13 cell phone apps. Dakota created 5 times as many. How many more cell phone apps did Dakota create? PROBLEM TYPE *Compare Problem*
Show It! **Represent the problem.**	▪ Use a visual model to represent the problem. ▪ Remember to label all the quantities.	Jason: 13 Dakota: 13 $m = 4 \times 13$
Solve It! **Solve the problem.**	▪ Write equations to represent the solution. ▪ Solve the problem.	4×13 $10 + 3$ $4 \times 13 = (4 \times 10) + (4 \times 3)$ $= 40 + 12$ $m = 52$
Check It! **Check your work.**	▪ Check the steps and your work for reasonableness. ▪ You may want to estimate the solution or work backwards. ▪ Ask yourself, "Does my answer make sense?"	Estimate: $4 \times 10 = 40$ My answer is reasonable because 52 is close to 40.

Problem Types

> Remember the four problem types when using the Bar Model.

PROBLEM TYPE	HOW TO TELL	EXAMPLE
Equal Groups Problems	▪ Look for multiple groups of equal size. ▪ The unknown in the problem can be the group size, the number of groups, or the total number in each group.	Mia designed a bookshelf with 6 shelves. Each shelf weighs 12 pounds. The frame weighs 38 pounds. What does the bookshelf weigh? *equal groups* 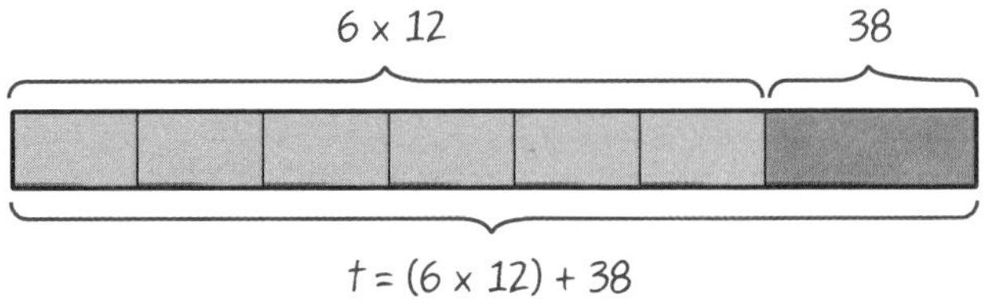 6 x 12 38 $t = (6 \times 12) + 38$
Compare Problems	▪ Look for unequal quantities that are being compared. ▪ The unknown in the problem can be one of the unequal quantities or the difference between them.	Jason created 13 cell phone apps. Dakota created 5 times as many. How many more cell phone apps did Dakota create? 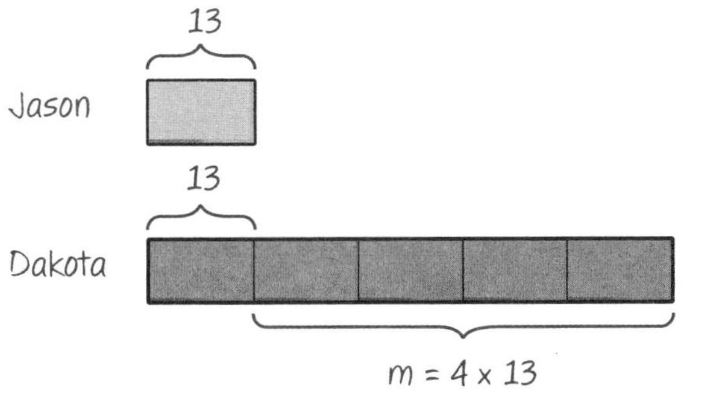 *first quantity* *second quantity* Jason: 13 Dakota: 13 $m = 4 \times 13$

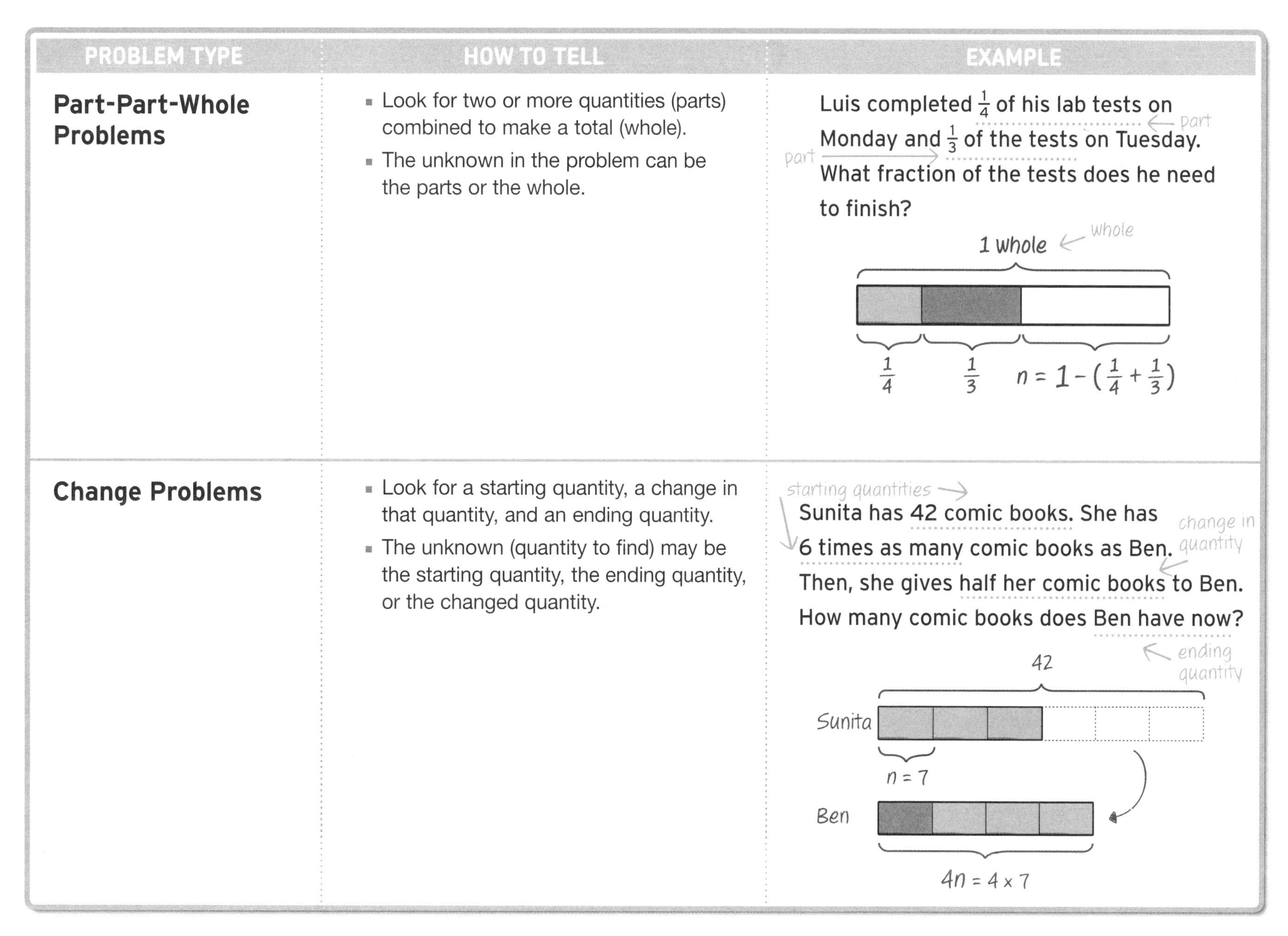

PROBLEM TYPE	HOW TO TELL	EXAMPLE
Part-Part-Whole Problems	▪ Look for two or more quantities (parts) combined to make a total (whole). ▪ The unknown in the problem can be the parts or the whole.	Luis completed $\frac{1}{4}$ of his lab tests on Monday and $\frac{1}{3}$ of the tests on Tuesday. What fraction of the tests does he need to finish? part; part; 1 whole; whole $\frac{1}{4}$ $\frac{1}{3}$ $n = 1 - (\frac{1}{4} + \frac{1}{3})$
Change Problems	▪ Look for a starting quantity, a change in that quantity, and an ending quantity. ▪ The unknown (quantity to find) may be the starting quantity, the ending quantity, or the changed quantity.	Sunita has 42 comic books. She has 6 times as many comic books as Ben. Then, she gives half her comic books to Ben. How many comic books does Ben have now? starting quantities; change in quantity; ending quantity 42; Sunita; $n = 7$; Ben; $4n = 4 \times 7$

Talking About Math

› **Use clear mathematical language to talk about math problems and concepts.**

ANALYZE

- This problem is asking me to ______.
- The quantities in this problem are ______. They are related because ______.
- I already know that ______.

REASON

- I agree/disagree with ______ that ______ because ______.
- My idea builds upon ______'s because ______.
- When is ______ always/sometimes/ never true?

CONTEXTUALIZE

- A real-life example of ______ is ______.
- I used ______ to represent ______ because ______.
- How could you represent ______ with numbers?

EVALUATE

- One tool I can use to help me is ______ because ______.
- What is another strategy for ______?
- When I compare my result with my prediction, I find that ______.

IDENTIFY

- The value can/can't be ______ because ______ .
- I can find ______ by ______ because ______.
- What is the relationship between/among ______?

I figured out what the problem is asking me to do by drawing a bar model that shows that Jason created 13 apps and Dakota created 5 times as many.

INFER

- I tried ______ and found out ______. Then I tried ______.
  - I figured out what the problem is asking me to do by ______.
  - What's another way to ______?

JUSTIFY

- I used the strategy of ______ because ______.
- Another example of ______ is ______.
- Does ______ still work if you ______?

I can represent the problem by shading alternate colors on a decimal grid because I can show there are 4 groups of 0.2 in 0.8.

REPRESENT

- I can represent the problem by ______ because ______.
- I can conclude that ______ because I know ______.
- The result makes sense because ______.

DEFINE

- I know the value ______ is appropriate for this situation because ______.
- The term/symbol ______ means ______.
- Can you explain how to ______?

GENERALIZE

- If ______, then the result will be ______ because ______.
- I notice that ______ will/won't always work because ______.
- ______ is a reasonable answer because ______.

If you multiply two unit fractions, then the product will be less than both fractions because the denominator will be greater, resulting in a smaller fraction.

MATH TERMS

Glossary of Math Terms

A

MATH TERM	MEANING	EXAMPLE
add *(verb)*	To combine two or more numbers to find their *sum*. (see *addition*, *add to*)	4 + 8 = 12
add to *(verb)*	To increase a number by another number. (see *add*)	37 + 4 = 41
addend *(noun)*	The number you combine with another number in an addition *expression*. (see *addition*)	(4)+(8)= 12 addends
addition *(noun)*	The *operation* of combining two or more numbers. (see *add*)	4 + 8 = 12
Additive Identity Property *(noun)*	Adding *zero* to a number does not change the number's *value*. (see *add, property*)	4 + 0 = 4 or 0 + 4 = 4
additive inverse *(noun)*	The number you *add* to another number to get a *sum* of *zero*. (see *inverse operation*, *opposite of a number*)	−4 +(4)= 0 additive inverse of -4
algebra *(noun)*	A branch of math that uses symbols, usually letters, to represent *unknown* numbers. (see *symbol*, *variable*)	3 + *a* = 4 *a* = 1
algebraic expression *(noun)*	An *expression* that uses variables to represent *unknown* quantities. (see *quantity*, *variable*)	8*p* *x* + 3 2 (*a* − *b*)

MATH TERM	MEANING	EXAMPLE
area *(noun)*	The measure of the amount of space inside a flat figure; area is measured in square units; the *formula* for the area of a rectangle is $A = l \times w$, where l and w represent the length and the width. (see *volume*)	A = 5 × 7 The area of the rectangle is 35 square units. 7 5
array *(noun)*	An arrangement of objects or numbers in rows and columns; can be used to represent *multiplication* or *division*.	6 × 4 = 24 24 ÷ 6 = 4 6 4 4 × 3 = 12 12 ÷ 4 = 3
Associative Property of Addition *(noun)*	The way we group three or more addends doesn't change the *sum*. (see *addend*, *property*)	(3 + 4) + 5 = 3 + (4 + 5) 7 + 5 = 3 + 9 12 = 12
Associative Property of Multiplication *(noun)*	The way we group three or more factors doesn't change the *product*. (see *factor*, *property*)	(2 × 3) × 4 = 2 × (3 × 4) 6 × 4 = 2 × 12 24 = 24

B

MATH TERM	MEANING	EXAMPLE
benchmark numbers *(noun)*	Familiar numbers that you use to make comparisons and estimates. (see *estimate*, *one-half*, *zero*)	$\frac{1}{3}$ $\frac{1}{3}$ $\frac{1}{3}$ $\frac{1}{3}$ 1 $\frac{1}{6}$ $\frac{1}{6}$ $\frac{1}{6}$ $\frac{1}{6}$ $\frac{1}{6}$ $\frac{4}{3}$ > (1) $\frac{5}{6}$ < (1) benchmark

C

MATH TERM	MEANING	EXAMPLE
common denominator *(noun)*	The *denominator* of two or more fractions that have the same denominator. (see *fraction*)	$\frac{5}{8}$ $\frac{7}{8}$ common denominator

MATH TERM	MEANING	EXAMPLE
common factor (noun)	A *factor* of two or more numbers that have the same factor. (see *factors of a number*, *greatest common factor*)	factors of 8: 1, 2, 4, 8 factors of 12: 1, 2, 3, 4, 6, 12 common factors of 8 and 12: 1, 2, 4
common numerator (noun)	The *numerator* of two or more fractions that have the same numerator. (see *fraction*)	common numerator $\frac{3}{4}$ $\frac{3}{16}$
Commutative Property of Addition (noun)	Changing the order of the addends does not change the *sum*. (see *addend*, *property*)	4 + 3 = 3 + 4 7 = 7
Commutative Property of Multiplication (noun)	Changing the order of the factors does not change the *product*. (see *factor*, *property*)	4 × 3 = 3 × 4 12 = 12
decimal number (noun)	A number with digits arranged by *place value*; we usually refer to numbers as decimals only if there is a *decimal point* followed by digits. (see *digit*)	2654.387 decimal number
decimal point (noun)	A *symbol* (dot or period) used to separate the *whole number* part from the fractional part in a *decimal number*.	0.8 decimal point
denominator (noun)	Tells the total number of *equal* parts in the *whole* in a *fraction*; the number below the *fraction bar* in a fraction.	$\frac{3}{4}$ denominator

MATH TERM	MEANING	EXAMPLE
difference (noun)	The result of *subtraction*; the amount left over when an amount is subtracted from another amount.	5 − 1 = 4 difference
digit (noun)	One of the symbols 0, 1, 2, 3, 4, 5, 6, 7, 8, and 9 when written in a number; its *value* is determined by its place in a number. (see *symbol*, *place value*)	12,563 five-digit number
Distributive Property (noun)	Multiplying a *sum* by a number is the same as adding the *partial products*. (see *multiply*)	8 × 24 = 8 × (20 + 4) = (8 × 20) + (8 × 4) = 160 + 32 = 192
divide (verb)	To split into *equal* parts or groups. (see *division*, *equal groups*)	6)24 = 4 24 ÷ 6 = 4 $\frac{24}{6}$ = 4 6, 4
dividend (noun)	The number that is divided into *equal* parts or groups; the number you *divide*. (see *equal groups*)	dividend: 24 ÷ 6 = 4 6)24 = 4 dividend dividend: $\frac{24}{6}$ = 4
divisible (adjective)	Able to *divide* a *dividend* with no *remainder*.	12 ÷ 3 = 4 divisible by 3 14 ÷ 3 = 4 R2 not divisible by 3
division (noun)	The *operation* of creating *equal* parts from a number or creating *equal groups* in a set. (see *divide*)	6)24 = 4 24 ÷ 6 = 4 $\frac{24}{6}$ = 4 6, 4

MATH TERMS

Glossary of Math Terms

MATH TERM	MEANING	EXAMPLE
divisor *(noun)*	The number you *divide* by. (see *divide*)	$24 \div 6 = 4$ (6 circled: divisor); $6\overline{)24}$ = 4 (6 circled: divisor); $\frac{24}{6} = 4$ (6 circled: divisor)
E		
equal *(adjective)*	Having the same amount. (see *equation*, *equivalent*, *inequality*)	$11 + 7 = 18$ 60 seconds = 1 minute 1 dollar = 100 cents
equal groups *(noun)*	Collections that each have the same number of items. (see *divide*, *division*, *multiply*, *multiplication*)	3 equal groups of 6
equation *(noun)*	A mathematical sentence in which the values on both sides of the *equal* sign are the same (equal). (see *equivalent*, *evaluate*, *expression, value*)	$3 + 7 = 10$ $20 = 5 \times 4$
equivalent *(adjective)*	Having the same meaning or having the same amount. (see *equal*, *equation*, *equivalent fractions*)	5×4 is equivalent to 5 groups of 4 5×4 is equivalent to $10 + 10$ 5×4 is equivalent to 2×10
equivalent fractions *(noun)*	Two or more fractions that name the same part of a *whole*. (see *equal*, *equivalent*)	$\frac{3}{4} = \frac{6}{8}$
estimate *(noun)*	A number that is an approximate calculation based on numbers that are easier to work with; is close to the exact answer. (see *estimation*)	$10.12 + 9.22$ $10 + 9 = 19$ (19 circled: estimate)

MATH TERM	MEANING	EXAMPLE
estimate *(verb)*	To approximate a calculation using numbers that are easier to work with. (see *estimation*)	$10.12 + 9.22$ $10 + 9 = 19$ (19 circled: estimate)
estimation *(noun)*	The process of approximating a calculation by using numbers that are easier to work with; the result of estimation is close to the exact answer. (see *estimate*)	$10.12 + 9.22$ is close to $10 + 9$
evaluate *(verb)*	To find the *value* of. (see *equation*, *expression*)	If $x = 20$, then evaluate $100 \div x$ $100 \div 20 = 5$
even number *(noun)*	Any integer that is *divisible* by 2; not an *odd number*. (see *integers*)	even numbers: ... -4, -2, 0, 2, 4, 6, 8, 10 ...
expanded form *(noun)*	A number written as the *sum* of the values of each *digit* based on its *place value*. (see *value*)	$135 = 100 + 30 + 5$ $3.14 = 3 + 0.1 + 0.04$
expression *(noun)*	A grouping of numbers and/or variables and *operation* symbols; does not have an *equal* sign or is on one side of an equal sign. (see *equation*, *evaluate*, *symbol*, *variable*)	$2n + 4 = 4 \times 10$ (each side circled: expression)

F

MATH TERM	MEANING	EXAMPLE
factor *(noun)*	The number you *multiply* to find a *product.* (see *factors of a number*)	4 × 5 = 20 (factors)
factors of a number *(noun)*	The numbers that *divide* exactly, with no *remainder*, into a number. (see *factor*, *common factor*, *greatest common factor*, *multiple*)	18 = 1 × 18 18 = 2 × 9 18 = 3 × 6 factors of 18: 1, 2, 3, 6, 9, 18
formula *(noun)*	A general rule that shows a relationship among variables in which the *value* of one *variable* is dependent on the value of other variables. (see *area*, *volume*)	8, 3 Area = length × width
fraction *(noun)*	A number that names parts of a *whole* or parts of a set. (see *fraction bar*, *denominator*, *numerator*)	$\frac{1}{4}$ of a whole (1); $\frac{1}{4}$ of a set
fraction bar *(noun)*	The line that separates the *numerator* from the *denominator* of a *fraction*.	$\frac{3}{4}$ fraction bar
function table *(noun)*	A table that shows the relationship of one set of numbers to another set of numbers; one set is the input and the other is the output; the rule provides the way to determine an output for any input.	(table below) Output = Input × 8

INPUT	EQUATIONS	OUTPUT
1		8
2		16
3		24
4		32
5	5 x 8 = 40	40
10	10 x 8 = 80	80
12	12 x 8 = 96	96

G

MATH TERM	MEANING	EXAMPLE
greater than *(adjective)*	Has a *value* farther to the right on a *number line*; is a larger *quantity*; the *symbol* that expresses that one quantity is greater than another quantity is >, where the open side of the symbol faces the greater quantity. (see *less than*)	0 1 2 3 4 5 6 7 8 9 10 10 > 8 10 is greater than 8
greatest common factor *(noun)*	The largest *common factor* of two or more numbers; the greatest common factor is also called the GCF. (see *factors of a number*)	factors of 8: 1, 2, 4, 8 factors of 12: 1, 2, 3, 4, 6, 12 greatest common factor

H

MATH TERM	MEANING	EXAMPLE
hundreds place *(noun)*	The third place to the left of the *decimal point*, which shows how many hundreds are in a number; the digit's *value* in that place is the *digit* times 100. (see *place value*)	2654.387 hundreds place
hundredths place *(noun)*	The second place to the right of the decimal point which shows how many hundredths are in a number; the digit's *value* in that place is the digit times $\frac{1}{100}$. (see *digit, place value*)	2654.387 hundredths place

I

MATH TERM	MEANING	EXAMPLE
inequality *(noun)*	A mathematical sentence that shows that two values are not *equal*. The symbols > (*greater than*), < (*less than*), ≠ (not equal to), and ≈ (approximately equal to) can be placed between the two numbers to show their relationships. (see *symbol*, *value*)	$1 + 4 < 6$ $910 > 901$ $14 + 36 \neq 40$ $0.97 \approx 1$

MATH TERMS

Glossary of Math Terms

MATH TERM	MEANING	EXAMPLE
integers *(noun)*	Whole numbers, their opposites, and *zero*. (see *opposite of a number*, *positive number*, *negative number*, *whole number*)	... −5, −4, −3, −2, −1, 0, 1, 2, 3, 4, 5, ...
inverse operation *(noun)*	An *operation* that reverses the effect of another operation. (see *additive inverse*, *multiplicative inverse*, *Inverse Property of Addition*, *Inverse Property of Multiplication*, *opposite of a number*)	Addition and subtraction are inverse operations $3 + 4 = 7$ $7 - 4 = 3$ Multiplication and division are inverse operations $3 \times 4 = 12$ $12 \div 4 = 3$
Inverse Property of Addition *(noun)*	Adding a number to its opposite results in a *sum* of *zero*. (see *add*, *inverse operation*, *opposite of a number*, *property*)	$5 + (-5) = 0$ and $(-5) + 5 = 0$
Inverse Property of Multiplication *(noun)*	Multiplying a number (excluding 0) by its reciprocal results in a *product* of 1. (see *inverse operation*, *multiplicative inverse*, *reciprocal of a number*, *property*)	$4 \times \frac{1}{4} = 1$ or $(-\frac{1}{4}) \times (-4) = 1$
L		
less than *(adjective)*	Has a *value* farther to the left on a *number line*; is a smaller *quantity*; the *symbol* that expresses that one quantity is less than another is <, where the small part of the symbol points to the smaller quantity. (see *greater than*)	0 1 2 3 4 5 6 7 8 9 10 $8 < 10$ 8 is less than 10

MATH TERM	MEANING	EXAMPLE
M		
mixed number *(noun)*	A *fraction* greater than 1 that includes both a *whole number* part and a fractional part. (see *greater than*)	mixed number $= 1\frac{57}{100}$
model *(noun)*	A mathematical *representation* of a mathematical or real-world situation; usually in the form of an *equation* or drawing.	6 x 12 38 $t = (6 \times 12) + 38$
multiple *(noun)*	A *product* of a given number and a *whole number.* (see *factors of a number*, *multiple of 10*)	multiple of 5: 5, 10, 15, 20, 25, ...
multiple of 10 *(noun)*	A number that has a *factor* of 10. (see *multiple*)	multiple of 10: 10, 20, 30, 40, 50, ...
multiplication *(noun)*	The *operation* of determining the total number of objects in *equal groups.* (see *multiply*)	$3 \times 6 = 18$ 3 equal groups of 6 is 18
Multiplicative Identity Property *(noun)*	Multiplying a number by 1 does not change the number's *value*. (see *multiply*, *property*)	$4 \times 1 = 4$ or $1 \times 4 = 4$

MATH TERM	MEANING	EXAMPLE
multiplicative inverse *(noun)*	The number you *multiply* by another number to get a *product* of 1. (see *inverse operation*, *Inverse Property of Multiplication*, *reciprocal of a number*)	inverse of 6: $6 \times \frac{1}{6} = \frac{6}{6} = 1$ inverse of $\frac{3}{4}$: $\frac{3}{4} \times \frac{4}{3} = \frac{12}{12} = 1$
multiply *(verb)*	To determine the total number of objects in *equal groups*. (see *multiplication*)	5 groups of 2: $5 \times 2 = 10$ 3 groups of $\frac{1}{2}$: $3 \times \frac{1}{2} = \frac{3}{2}$

N

MATH TERM	MEANING	EXAMPLE
negative *(adjective)*	On the left side of *zero* on a *number line*; the opposite of. (see *negative number*, *opposite of a number*, *positive*)	negative −9 −8 −7 −6 −5 −4 −3 −2 −1 0 1 2 3
negative number *(noun)*	Number to the left of *zero* on the *number line*; a number *less than* zero. (see *integers*, *negative*, *positive number*)	−9 −8 −7 −6 −5 −4 −3 −2 −1 0 1 2 3 negative numbers
number line *(noun)*	A line on which every point names one number and every number has a unique location.	−9 −8 −7 −6 −5 −4 −3 −2 −1 0 1 2 3
numerator *(noun)*	Tells how many *equal* parts of the *whole* a *fraction* is describing; the number above the *fraction bar* in a fraction.	numerator $\frac{3}{4}$

O

MATH TERM	MEANING	EXAMPLE
odd number *(noun)*	Any integer that is not *divisible* by 2; not an *even number*. (see *integers*)	odd numbers: ... −5, −3, −1, 1, 3, 5, 7, ...
one-eighth *(noun)*	One part out of one *whole* that has been divided into eight *equal* parts; written as $\frac{1}{8}$. (see *divide*, *unit fraction*)	$\frac{1}{8}$
one-fourth *(noun)*	One part out of one *whole* that has been divided into four *equal* parts; written as $\frac{1}{4}$. (see *unit fraction*)	
one-half *(noun)*	One part out of one *whole* that has been divided into two *equal* parts; written as $\frac{1}{2}$. (see *benchmark numbers*, *divide*, *unit fraction*)	$\frac{1}{2}$
one-hundredth *(noun)*	One part out of one *whole* that has been divided into one hundred *equal* parts; written as $\frac{1}{100}$ or 0.01. (see *decimal number*, *hundredths place*, *unit fraction*)	one-hundredth
one-sixteenth *(noun)*	One part out of one *whole* that has been divided into sixteen *equal* parts; written as $\frac{1}{16}$. (see *divide*, *unit fraction*)	$\frac{1}{16}$

MATH TERM	MEANING	EXAMPLE
one-sixth *(noun)*	One part out of one *whole* that has been divided into six *equal* parts; written as $\frac{1}{6}$. (see *divide, unit fraction*)	
one-tenth *(noun)*	One part out of one *whole* that has been divided into ten *equal* parts; written as $\frac{1}{10}$ or 0.1. (see *decimal number*, *divide, tenths place*, *unit fraction*)	one-tenth
one-third *(noun)*	One part out of one *whole* that has been divided into three *equal* parts; written as $\frac{1}{3}$. (see *divide, unit fraction*)	
one-twelfth *(noun)*	One part out of one *whole* that has been divided into twelve *equal* parts; written as $\frac{1}{12}$. (see *divide, unit fraction*)	
ones place *(noun)*	The first place to the left of the *decimal point*, which shows how many ones are in a number; the digit's *value* in that place is the *digit* times 1. (see *place value*)	2654.387 ones place
operation *(noun)*	A mathematical process; defined by a rule, performed on one or more numbers to get a resulting number; the most common operations are *addition*, *subtraction*, *multiplication*, and *division*.	$24 \div 6 = 4$ $10.12 + 9.22 = 19.34$ operation
opposite of a number *(noun)*	The number that when added to another number gives a *sum* of *zero*; on a *number line*, the number that is the same distance from 0 as another number but in the opposite direction from zero. (see *additive inverse*, *inverse operation*, *Inverse Property of Addition*, *negative*)	opposite of 4 $4 + (-4) = 0$ opposite of −4
order of operations *(noun)*	A rule that specifies which order to perform the operations in an *expression* with more than one *operation*: 1. parentheses 2. *multiply/divide* left to right 3. *add/subtract* left to right	$2 \times (5 - 2) + 3$ $2 \times 3 + 3$ $6 + 3 = 9$
P		
partial products *(noun)*	Numbers you *add* when you break one of the factors into a *sum* of its parts to calculate a *product*. (see *Distributive Property*, *factor*)	8×16 $8 \times (10 + 6)$ $(8 \times 10) + (8 \times 6)$ $80 + 48 = 128$ partial products
partial quotients *(noun)*	Numbers you *add* to calculate a *quotient*.	partial quotients 2, 10; 12 R3 $6\overline{)75}$ −60 15 −12 3
pattern *(noun)*	An ordered set of numbers or objects arranged in a way that follows a rule.	53, 34, 9, 21, 18, 4, 6, 102, 1 pattern: multiples of 2

MATH TERM	MEANING	EXAMPLE
place value *(noun)*	The *value* of a *digit* in a number; for example, in 2654, 5 represents 5 tens or 50, because 5 is in the tens place. (see also *hundreds place*, *hundredths place*, *ones place*, *ten-thousandths place*, *tenths place*, *thousandths place*, *thousands place*)	2654 2 thousands or 2000 6 hundreds or 600 5 tens or 50 4 ones or 4 place value
positive *(adjective)*	On the right side of zero on a *number line.*	positive −5 −4 −3 −2 −1 0 1 2 3 4 5
positive number *(noun)*	A number to the right of *zero* on the *number line*; a number *greater than* zero. (see *integers*, *positive*, *negative number*)	−5 −4 −3 −2 −1 0 1 2 3 4 5 positive numbers
prime number *(noun)*	A *whole number greater than* 1 that has only two *factors*: 1 and the number itself.	prime: 2, 3, 5, 7, 11, 13, 17...
product *(noun)*	The result of *multiplication*.	4 × 5 = 20 product
property *(noun)*	A characteristic of a number, *operation*, or equality. (see *Additive Identity Property*, *Associative Property of Addition*, *Associative Property of Multiplication*, *Commutative Property of Addition*, *Commutative Property of Multiplication*, *Distributive Property*, *Inverse Property of Addition*, *Inverse Property of Multiplication*, *Multiplicative Identity Property*)	Distributive Property: 8 × 24 8 × (20 + 4) (8 × 20) + (8 × 4) 160 + 32

MATH TERM	MEANING	EXAMPLE
proportion *(noun)*	An *equation* that compares two ratios. (see *ratio*)	4 : 8 = 1 : 2 $\frac{4}{8} = \frac{1}{2}$ 4 to 8 = 1 to 2
Q		
quantity *(noun)*	An amount that can be counted or measured; not a label.	There are 54 students in Room 54. quantity label
quotient *(noun)*	The result of *division*.	24 ÷ 6 = 4 (quotient) $6\overline{)24}$ = 4 (quotient) $\frac{24}{6} = 4$ (quotient)
R		
ratio *(noun)*	A *representation* comparing two quantities; specifically a part to a part of the same *whole*, a part to a whole, or a whole to a part. (see *proportion*, *quantity*)	4 : 8 $\frac{4}{8}$ 4 to 8
rational number *(noun)*	Numbers that can be expressed as the *quotient* of two *integers*, where the *divisor* does not *equal* zero. (see *repeating decimal number*, *integers, zero)*	rational number 12 −6 −3.56 $\frac{5}{4}$ $12\overline{)120}$ = 10; −120; 0
reciprocal of a number *(noun)*	The number that you *multiply* another number by that gives a result of one. (see *inverse operation*, *multiplicative inverse*)	reciprocal of 6 $6 \times \frac{1}{6} = \frac{6}{6}$ or 1 $\frac{4}{3} \times \frac{3}{4} = \frac{12}{12}$ or 1 reciprocal of $\frac{4}{3}$
remainder *(noun)*	The *whole number* left over after *division*. (see *divisible*)	2 10 12 R3 $6\overline{)75}$ −60 15 −12 3 remainder 75 ÷ 6 = 12 R3

MATH TERMS

Glossary of Math Terms

MATH TERM	MEANING	EXAMPLE
repeating decimal number *(noun)*	A *decimal number* in which decimal digits repeat forever; generally shortened to a few repetitions of the repeating digits or represented with a line above the repeating digits. (see *digit*, *rational number*)	$\frac{1}{11} = 0.09090909...$ or $0.\overline{09}$ $\frac{1}{3} = 0.33333333...$ or $0.\overline{33}$
representation *(noun)*	The mathematical form used; different representations can reveal different information about a math problem. (see *model*, *symbolic form*)	representations of the number 1.6: 1 + 0.6 one and six-tenths
S		
simplest form *(adjective)*	When the only *whole number* that divides both the *numerator* and *denominator* of a *fraction* evenly is 1. (see *divide*)	$\frac{2}{4} \div \frac{2}{2} = \frac{1}{2}$ simplest form
subtract *(verb)*	To take away one amount from another or to find the *difference* between two numbers. (see *subtraction*)	9 − 7 = 2
subtraction *(noun)*	The *operation* of finding the *difference* between two numbers. (see *subtract*)	9 − 7 = 2
sum *(noun)*	The result of *addition*.	4 + 8 = 12 sum
symbol *(noun)*	A *representation* used to replace a word or phrase; symbols can be used to simplify a complex problem. (see *symbolic form*)	Common math symbols = is equal to > is greater than < is less than + plus − minus × times, multiplication ÷ division
symbolic form *(noun)*	A *representation* of a mathematical statement using symbols. (see *symbol*)	symbolic form: 5 + 3 = 8 word form: five plus three equals eight
T		
ten-thousandths place *(noun)*	The fourth place to the right of the *decimal point*, which shows how many ten-thousandths are in a number; the digit's *value* in that place is the *digit* times $\frac{1}{10,000}$. (see *place value*)	2654.3879 ten-thousandths place
tens place *(noun)*	The second place to the left of the *decimal point*, which shows how many tens are in a number; the digit's *value* in that place is the *digit* times 10. (see *place value*)	2654.3879 tens place
tenths place *(noun)*	The first place to the right of the *decimal point*, which shows how many tenths are in a number; the digit's *value* in that place is the *digit* times $\frac{1}{10}$. (see *place value*)	2654.3879 tenths place

MATH TERM	MEANING	EXAMPLE
thousands place *(noun)*	The fourth place to the left of the *decimal point*, which shows how many thousands are in a number; the digit's *value* in that place is the *digit* times 1000. (see *place value*)	2654.3879 thousands place
thousandths place *(noun)*	The third place to the right of the *decimal point*, which shows how many one-thousandths are in a number; the digit's *value* in that place is the *digit* times $\frac{1}{1000}$. (see *place value*)	2654.3879 thousandths place
U		
unit fraction *(noun)*	One of the parts from an equally divided *whole*; its *numerator* is always 1. (see *divide*, *fraction*, *one-eighth*, *one-fourth*, *one-half*, *one-sixteenth*, *one-sixth*, *one-third*, *one-twelfth*)	$\frac{1}{4}$ unit fraction
unknown *(noun)*	The *value* you solve for in a problem. (see *algebra*, *variable*)	$4 \times 7 = \square$ unknown unknown $n + 8 = 12$ $\frac{3}{4} = \frac{\square}{8}$ unknown
V		
value *(noun)*	A number or *quantity*; often used for the result of an *operation* or the solution for an *equation*; or the amount that a *digit* represents in a multi digit number. (see *place value*)	The value of 5 in 2593 is 500.

MATH TERM	MEANING	EXAMPLE
variable *(noun)*	A *symbol* in an *expression* that represents a *value* that may change or be *unknown*. (see *algebra*)	$n + 8 = 12$ variable
Venn diagram *(noun)*	A visual *model* used to represent relationships between sets of numbers; sets are shown in either intersecting or non-intersecting circles; if intersecting, the intersection represents numbers that are members of all intersecting sets.	CIRCLE A Numbers divisible by 6: 12, 24, 36; both: 42, 84; CIRCLE B Numbers divisible by 7: 7, 14, 28
volume *(noun)*	The measure of the amount of space inside a solid figure; volume is measured in cubic units; the *formula* for volume of a rectangular prism is $V = l \times w \times h$, where *l*, *w*, and *h* represent length, width, and height. (see *area*)	$V = l \times w \times h$
W		
whole *(noun)*	The total amount; the size of a whole, along with the number of parts, determines the size of the parts. (see *fraction*)	1 whole; $\frac{1}{2}$
whole number *(noun)*	The counting numbers and *zero*; {0, 1, 2, 3,…}.	0, 1, 2, 3,...
Z		
zero *(noun)*	A *whole number* that represents no size or *quantity*; an integer between –1 and 1 on a *number line*. (see *benchmark numbers*, *integers*)	–5 –4 –3 –2 –1 0 1 2 3 4 5; zero

CREDITS

Cover (top to bottom): © Takito/Shutterstock, © Julian Love, © Dieter Lier/Thinkstock, © Igor Gratzer/Shutterstock, © Digital Vision/Thinkstock, © pagadesign/Getty Images, © Ingram Publishing/Thinkstock, © Cienpies Design/Thinkstock, Courtesy Global Soap Project, © Subbotina/Dreamstime, © Valerijs Kostreckis/Thinkstock, © alekup/Shutterstock; **Back cover** (top to bottom): Sean Fine/courtesy of Shine Global, inset: courtesy of Shine Global; © Julian Love, Courtesy Global Soap Project, © Marc Mauceri/First Run Features; p. 2 (top to bottom): Sean Fine/courtesy of Shine Global, © Julian Love, Courtesy Global Soap Project, © Marc Mauceri/First Run Features, inset: courtesy of Shine Global; p. 3 (top to bottom): © Photodisc/Thinkstock, NASA/JPL-Caltech, © Cameron Spencer/Getty Images, © Chris Cutro/The Miami Herald 2008, Mike Waszkiewicz/National Science Foundation; p. 4 l: Sean Fine/courtesy of Shine Global, r: © Julian Love, inset: courtesy of Shine Global; p. 5 l: Courtesy Global Soap Project, r: © Marc Mauceri/First Run Features; p. 5B cr: Ken Karp © Scholastic Inc.; p. 5D tl: © Archivio Mondadori via Getty Images, tr: Ken Karp © Scholastic Inc.; p. 5E cl: © MPF Photography/Fotolia, bl: Ken Karp © Scholastic Inc., br: © Ethan Miller/Getty Images for Clear Channel; p. 5F br: Ken Karp © Scholastic Inc.; p. 5G cl: National Wildlife Federation, t: Ken Karp © Scholastic Inc., b: © Kevin Winter/Getty Images; p. 5H t: © Ben Rose/WireImage/Getty Images, cr: Ken Karp © Scholastic Inc.; p. 6: Sean Fine/courtesy of Shine Global, inset: courtesy of Shine Global; p. 7 tr: © Ingram Publishing/Thinkstock, cl: © Comstock Images/Thinkstock, cr: © Tony Avelar/Bloomberg via Getty Images, inset: © Oleksiy Mark/Thinkstock, bl: © Bernd Lauter/MediaBakery, inset: © Aleksandar Bunevski/Thinkstock, br: © Cienpies Design/Thinkstock; p. 9: Ken Karp © Scholastic Inc.; p. 11 tr: Sean Fine/courtesy of Shine Global; p. 11 br: Ken Karp © Scholastic Inc.; p. 16 tr: Ken Karp © Scholastic Inc.; p. 19 br: © Vladgrin/Thinkstock; p. 21 br: Ken Karp © Scholastic Inc.; p. 23: Ken Karp © Scholastic Inc.; p. 30 cr: Ken Karp © Scholastic Inc.; p. 33 br: © Franck Reporter/iStockphoto; p. 34 l: © Chad Baker/Thinkstock, c: © Vstock LLC/Thinkstock, r: © Comstock/Thinkstock; p. 35 l: © Ojo Images/MediaBakery, t: Ken Karp © Scholastic Inc., c: © Federico Caputo/Thinkstock; p. 37: Ken Karp © Scholastic Inc.; p. 39 br: Ken Karp © Scholastic Inc.; p. 40 tr: Ken Karp © Scholastic Inc.; p. 43 br: © Mythja/Thinkstock; p. 48 l: © Digital Vision/Thinkstock, c: © Lilyana Vynogradova/Thinkstock, inset: © Pogonici/Thinkstock, r: © Jupiterimages/Getty Images/Thinkstock; p. 49 t: Ken Karp © Scholastic Inc., c: © Wavebreakmedia Ltd/Thinkstock; p. 50 bl: courtesy of Shine Global, l: © Cobalt 88/Shutterstock, cl: © Ingus Evertovskis/Fotolia, c: © Pagadesign/iStockphoto, cr: © Hemera/Thinkstock, r: © Alexander Shirokov/Thinkstock; p. 51B tr: © Sean Rowland/Covered Images/ZUMAPRESS via Newscom; p. 52: © Julian Love; p. 53 t: © pagadesign/Getty Images, cr: © Digital Vision/Thinkstock , br: © Altay Kaya/Shutterstock, inset: Courtesy FlashMint.com, bc: © Miljan Mladenovic/iStockphoto, b: © Buena Vista Images/Getty Images, bl: © Nisian Hughes/Getty Images, cl: © Ciaran Griffin/Thinkstock, c: © malerapaso/iStockphoto; p. 55: Ken Karp © Scholastic Inc. p. 57 tr: © Julian Love; p. 58 tr: Ken Karp © Scholastic Inc.; p. 61 br: © Takito/Shutterstock; p. 65 br: Ken Karp © Scholastic Inc.; p. 66 l: © LeicaFoto/iStockphoto, c: © Heather Weston/MediaBakery, r: © Ignacio Salaverria Garzon/iStockphoto; p. 67 l: © Steven Errico/Getty Images, t: Ken Karp © Scholastic Inc., c: © Sören

Stache/dpa/Corbis; p. 69: Ken Karp © Scholastic Inc.; p. 73 br: Ken Karp © Scholastic Inc.; p. 74 tr: Ken Karp © Scholastic Inc.; p. 77 bl: © ronstik/Shutterstock; p. 80 l: © Aurinko/Dreamstime, c: © Digital Vision/Getty Images, r: © Marje Cannon/iStockphoto; p. 81 l: © Adisa/Fotolia, c: © illustrart/Alamy, br: Ken Karp © Scholastic Inc.; p. 83: Ken Karp © Scholastic Inc.; p. 88 tr: Ken Karp © Scholastic Inc.; p. 91 br: © Miguel Villagran/Getty Images; p. 94 l: © MediaBakery, c: © Steve Prezant/Corbis/MediaBakery, r: © Dennis Macdonald/Getty Images; p. 95 l: © Edie Layland/Fotolia, c: © Dave Bartruff/Corbis, br: Ken Karp © Scholastic Inc.; p. 96 bl: © Julian Love; p. 97B tr: © Matthew Stockman/Getty Images; p. 98: Courtesy Global Soap Project; p. 99 cl: © Cienpies Design/Thinkstock, t: © Comstock Images/Thinkstock, tr: © Saniphoto/Dreamstime, cr: © Miquel Llonch/Thinkstock, br: © Ryan McVay/Thinkstock, bl: © Godong/MediaBakery, cl: © Comstock Images/Thinkstock, cr: © Blair Bunting/Thinkstock; p. 101: Ken Karp © Scholastic Inc.; p. 103 tr: Courtesy Global Soap Project; p. 107 br: Ken Karp © Scholastic Inc.; p. 108 tr: Ken Karp © Scholastic Inc.; p. 111 br: © Ron Chapple Stock/Thinkstock; p. 112 l: © Steve Debenport/iStockphoto, c: © Hemera Technologies/Getty Images/Thinkstock, r: © Nick White/Thinkstock; p. 113 l: © Darrin Klimek/Thinkstock, c: © Brand X Pictures/Thinkstock, br: Ken Karp © Scholastic Inc.; p. 115: Ken Karp © Scholastic Inc.; p. 119 br: Ken Karp © Scholastic Inc.; p. 122 tr: Ken Karp © Scholastic Inc.; p. 125 br: © Okea/Thinkstock; p. 129: Ken Karp © Scholastic Inc.; p. 136 tr: Ken Karp © Scholastic Inc.; p. 139 br: © Thomas Samson/AFP/Getty Images; p. 140 l: © Brand X Pictures/Thinkstock, c: © Story Stock/Thinkstock, r: © Ingram Publishing/Thinkstock; p. 141 l: © Spwidoff/Thinkstock, c: © Colin Gray/MediaBakery, br: Ken Karp © Scholastic Inc.; p. 142 bl: Courtesy Global Soap Project, cr: © Dreamzdesigner/Dreamstime; p. 143B tr: © Jonathan Daniel/Allsport/Getty Images; p. 144: © Marc Mauceri/First Run Features p. 145 tr (clockwise): © Dieter Lier/Thinkstock, © Tony Gervis/MediaBakery, Michael Brake/Thinkstock, © Andrew Wood/Thinkstock, Medioimages/Photodisc/Thinkstock, br: © Wavebreak Media Ltd/Dreamstime, bc: © Wavebreak Media/Thinkstock, b: © Ron Sachs/CNP/Corbis, bl: © Ron Edmonds/AP Images, cl: © Dmitry Iatsenko/Thinkstock, c: © Pocketcanoe/Thinkstock; p. 147: Ken Karp © Scholastic Inc.; p. 149 tr: © Marc Mauceri/First Run Features, br: Ken Karp © Scholastic Inc.; p. 153 br: Ken Karp © Scholastic Inc.; p. 154 tr: Ken Karp © Scholastic Inc.; p. 157 bl: © Dr. Wilfried Bahnmüller/Glowimages, br: © Keith Levit/Thinkstock; p. 159 br: Ken Karp © Scholastic Inc.; p. 161: Ken Karp © Scholastic Inc.; p. 166 tr: Ken Karp © Scholastic Inc.; p. 169 br: © Marcel Mooij/Thinkstock; p. 171 br: Ken Karp © Scholastic Inc.; p. 172 l: © Olga Lyubkina/Thinkstock, c: © David Cole/Thinkstock, r: © Jupiterimages/Thinkstock; p. 173 l: © Michael Mahovlich/MediaBakery, c: © Stockbyte/Thinkstock; p. 175: Ken Karp © Scholastic Inc.; p. 178 tr: Ken Karp © Scholastic Inc.; p. 181 br: © Dex Images/MediaBakery; p. 185 br: Ken Karp © Scholastic Inc.; p. 186 l: © iStockphoto/Thinkstock, c: © Alistair Berg/MediaBakery; p. 186 r: © iStockphoto/Thinkstock; p. 187 l: © Mika/MediaBakery, c: © Adam Gault/MediaBakery, t: Ken Karp © Scholastic Inc.; p. 188 bl: © Marc Mauceri/First Run Features, tr: USDA.gov; p. 189B tr: Bachrach/Library of Congress; p. 201 tr: © LeicaFoto/iStockphoto; pp. 204–205: Ken Karp © Scholastic Inc.

This book is dedicated to our very own princess, Sydney.

You inspire us every day.
May all your dreams come true.
Love always,
Mom and Dad

JOIN OUR DIGITAL BOOK CLUB